ADVANCED LEVEL

AS

BIOLOGY

For A

NE LOWRIE

Specif

N

Editor MIKE HISCOCK

Heinemann

Heinemann Educational Publishers
Halley Court, Jordan Hill, Oxford, OX2 8EJ
Part of Harcourt Education

Heinemann is the registered trademark of
Harcourt Education Limited

First published 2000

ISBN 0 435 58083 3

04
10 9 8 7 6

Development editor Paddy Gannon

Edited by Ruth Holmes

Designed and typeset by Cambridge Publishing Management

Original Illustrations © Heinemann Educational Publishers 2000

Illustrated by Chartwell Illustrators, Tom Cross, Roger Courthold, Tim Oliver, Oxford Designers & Illustrators and Martin Woodward

Printed and bound in Great Britain by Bath Colour Press

Acknowledgements
The authors and publishers wish to thank Gill Halton, St John Rigby College for setting up the plant tissue culture technique shown on p145.

Photo acknowledgements
The authors and publishers would like to thank the following for permission to use photographs:
Cover photo by Science Photo Library.

(L = left; R = right; T = top; B = bottom; M = middle)

p4 L Eye of Science/SPL; **p4 M** Biophoto Associates; **p4 R** Andrew Syred/SPL; **p5** Hattie Young/SPL; **p6** J. X. Revy/SPL; **p12** FLPA; **p13 T, B** Biophoto Associates; **p15** imb-jena; **p22** John Burbidge/SPL; **p23** Biophoto Associates; **p24** Biophoto Associates/SPL; **p25** Biophoto Associates/SPL; **p30** Biophoto Associates; **p32 T** Maximilin Stock/SPL; **p32 B** Lacteeze; **p33 T, B** Biophoto Associates; **p34 L** Biophoto Associates; **p34 R** Carl Schmidt-luchs/SPL; **pp36–7** Peter Gould; **p41 TL** SPL; **p41 TR, BL, BR** Biophoto Associates; **p42** Sinclair Stammers/SPL; **p43 T, B** Biophoto Associates; **p46** Biophoto Associates; **p47 T** P. Motta & T. Naguro/SPL; **p47 B** Quest/SPL; **p48** Secchi-lecaque-rousel-uclaf/CNRI/SPL; **p49** Biophoto Associates; **p50 L** G. Brad Lewis/SPL; **p50 R** Dr Kari Lounatamaa/SPL; **p51 L, R** Biophoto Associates; **p55 T** CNRI/SPL; **p55 L** Dr Linda Stannard, uct/SPL; **p55 R** CNRI/SPL; **p63** Andrew Lambert; **p66 T** Alfred Pasieka/SPL; **p66 B** imb-jena; **p67** imb-jena; **p73** Claude Nuridsany & Marie Pernnou/SPL; **p75** Sinclair Stammers/SPL; **p83** Dr P. Marazzi/SPL; **p96** NHPA; **p100** SPL; **p116 T** L. Willatt/SPL; **p116 B** Biophoto Associates/SPL; **p117** CNRI/SPL; **p120** A. Barrington Brown/SPL; **p123** Klaus Guldbrandsen/SPL; **p132 T** Eric Grave/SPL; **p132 B** Wellcome Trust Medical Photo Library; **p136** Biophoto Associates/SPL; **p138** Biophoto Associates; **p138 all** Biophoto Associates; **p140 T** Biophoto Associates; **p140 M** Dr Gopl Murti/SPL; **p141** Nancy Kedersha/Immunogen/SPL; **p144** Weiss, Jerrican/SPL; **p145 all** Roger Scruton; **p148 L** Andy Walker, Midland Fertility Services/SPL; **p148 R** Biophoto Associates; **p151 L** Science Photo Library; **p151 TR, BR** Bruce Coleman; **p152 all** Biophoto Associates; **p162** Hank Morgan/SPL; **p166** The iCycler iQ Real-Time PCR Detection System from Bio-Rad Laboratories Ltd; **p180** Associated Press; **p189 M** Volker Steger/SPL; **p189 B** Department of Clinical Radiology/SPL; **p195** T. Hill; **p204 both** Action-Plus; **p207** SPL; **p211** Philip Harris; **p212 L** Andrew Syred/SPL; **p212 R** J.C. Revy/SPL; **p213** J.C. Revy/SPL; **p214 T** Holt Studios; **p214 B** Simon Fraser/SPL; **p215 T** Dr Jeremy Burgess/SPL; **p215 B** Biophoto Associates; **p217** Philip Harris; **p222** Peter Gould; **p224 both** Biophoto Associates; **p224 T** Holt studios; **p224 B** Oxford Scientific Films.

The publishers have made every effort to trace copyright holders, but if they have inadvertently overlooked any, they will be pleased to make the necessary arrangements at the first opportunity.

Picture research by Jennifer Johnson

Tel: 01865 888058 www.heinemann.co.uk

Contents

Module 2 Genes and Genetic Engineering

Module 3 Physiology and Transport

Introduction

To the student

This book has been written for the new AS Biology specification. Progress in biology has been very fast in recent years and wherever possible the authors have used up-to-date examples to help you recognise the importance of scientific progress to everyday life.

The book is split into three main sections or modules, which link to the three main themes of AS Biology. Each module is split into units which cover a main topic area, and each double page covers one key concept of this main topic. At the beginning of each module there is also a concept map which shows you links between different units and different modules.

At the start of each double page there is a summary of the content covered, and how it links to other topics you may have studied in GCSE or another part of the book. On each page there are diagrams linked to the written text, which help to explain the ideas. At some points in the text you will find words in **bold type.** These are important words that you will meet if you read articles in scientific publications or on the Internet. You can find out what these words mean in the Glossary at the end of the book. At the end of each double page or couple of double pages there are key ideas which you can use as a check list. On some of the pages there are questions for you to answer about the information on the pages. You should do these as you work through each double page, as they will help you find out if you have understood what is being explained. The answers to these questions are at the end of the book.

There are also questions at the end of each unit. These are short answer 'examination style' questions about the content of the unit. The answers to these are at the end of the book. At the end of each module there are more short answer 'examination style' questions which expect you to link information from different units together. The answers to these questions are in the Resource Pack which goes with this textbook. There are also extra questions and additional activities in the Resource Pack.

To the teacher

This book is written for Advanced Subsidiary (AS) Biology and matches AQA Specification B (5416). The book has been written so that each double page covers one particular section of the specification. Concept maps at the start of each module show links between different topics. A Resource Pack to complement this textbook gives additional activities and indicates activities which might contribute to key skills.

Module 1

Core Principles

This module is about the organisation of living things and some of the processes they carry out to stay alive.

Unit 1 of the module starts by exploring how living organisms control all the thousands of reactions that occur inside cells and bodies. Unit 2 then looks at the way in which humans obtain the food molecules they need to supply raw materials for all these chemical reactions. As a contrast, the last part of this unit looks at how fungi carry out the same process of obtaining food.

Units 3 and 4 are all about organising the structures and chemicals that make up a living organism. Cellular organisation is studied in unit 3 and molecular organisation in unit 4.

Units 5 and 6 look at supplying cells with sufficient raw materials so they can carry out all of the chemical activities efficiently. The different ways molecules can move in and out of cells is explored in unit 5. Building on this, unit 6 considers some of the different ways animals and plants obtain oxygen and carry it around their bodies so that all cells receive enough to use in respiration, the chemical reaction that releases energy from food.

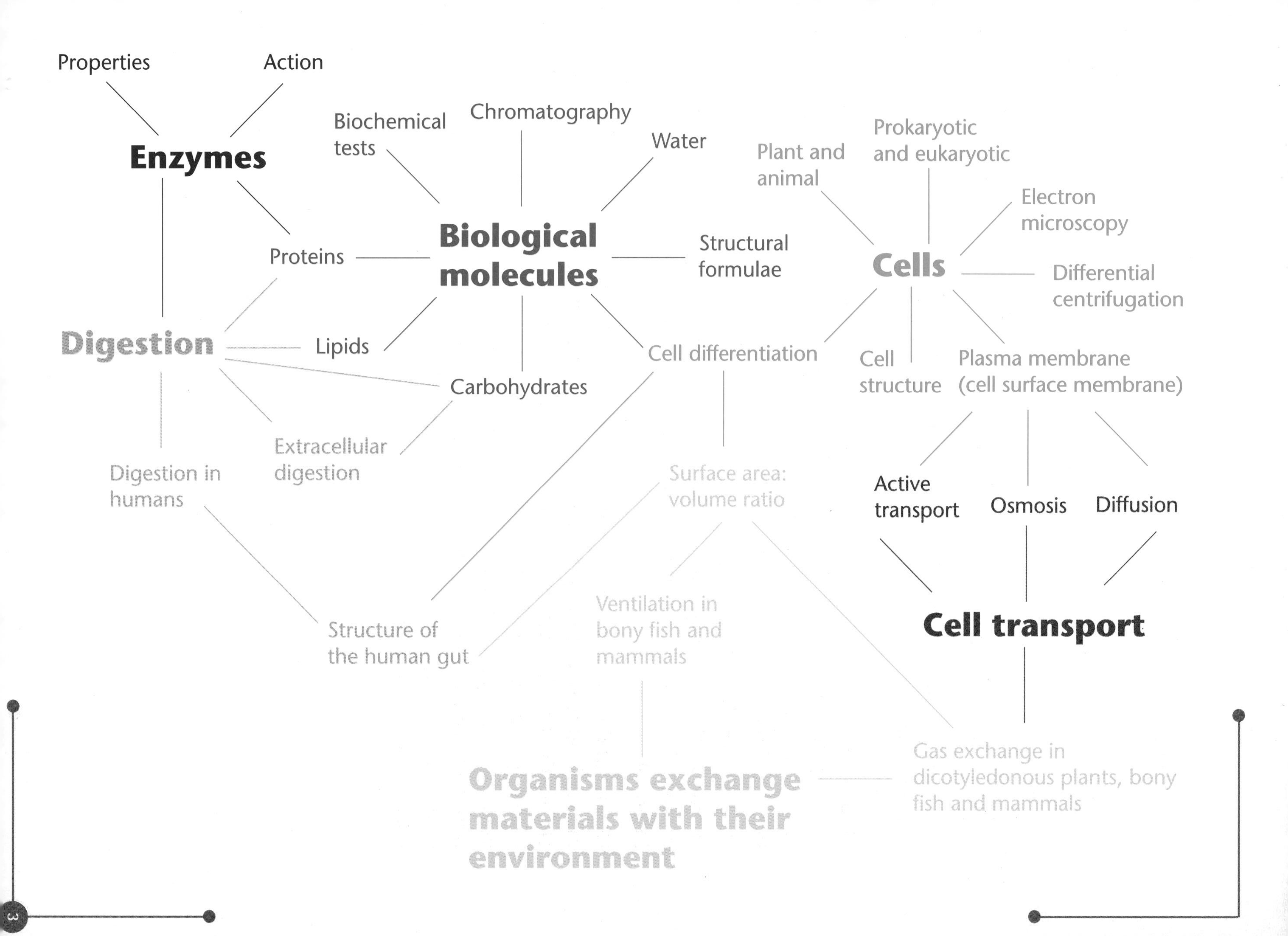
Properties
Action
Enzymes
Biochemical tests
Chromatography
Water
Proteins
Biological molecules
Structural formulae
Digestion
Lipids
Carbohydrates
Cell differentiation
Plant and animal
Prokaryotic and eukaryotic
Electron microscopy
Cells
Differential centrifugation
Cell structure
Plasma membrane (cell surface membrane)
Extracellular digestion
Digestion in humans
Surface area: volume ratio
Active transport
Osmosis
Diffusion
Structure of the human gut
Ventilation in bony fish and mammals
Cell transport
Organisms exchange materials with their environment
Gas exchange in dicotyledonous plants, bony fish and mammals

1 Similar yet different

Biology is the study of living organisms, which include plants, animals and microorganisms. There are many different organisms living on Earth.

Made up of cells

The organisms shown in figure 1 are very different, but they all have one thing in common – they are made up of cells. The **cell** is the building block from which all living organisms are made. Some organisms, such as bacteria, are **unicellular**, which means that they have only one cell. In a unicellular organism, all the life processes take place in its one cell. Animals and plants are **multicellular**, which means that they have many cells.

Figure 1 *(a) This amoeba (×60) is feeding off another amoeba. It carries out all the processes of life in just one cell. Plants such as the bee orchid (b) and animals such as the house dust mite (c) (×100) are multicellular.*

Being organised

Large multicellular organisms have many cells, and they also have many different types of cell. Each type of cell carries out a different function in the organism. This is sometimes known as **division of labour**. Cells that are similar in shape and have a common function are often collected together and attached to each other. They form a **tissue**. Different tissues are grouped together to make an **organ**. These organs work in groups called **organ systems**.

Humans are made up of several organ systems, including the respiratory system, the cardiovascular system and the digestive system. Each organ system is made up of organs, for example, the heart is an organ that forms part of the cardiovascular system. The heart has walls made up of cardiac muscle, a tissue made up of cardiac muscle cells. Each cardiac muscle cell looks alike and has the same function.

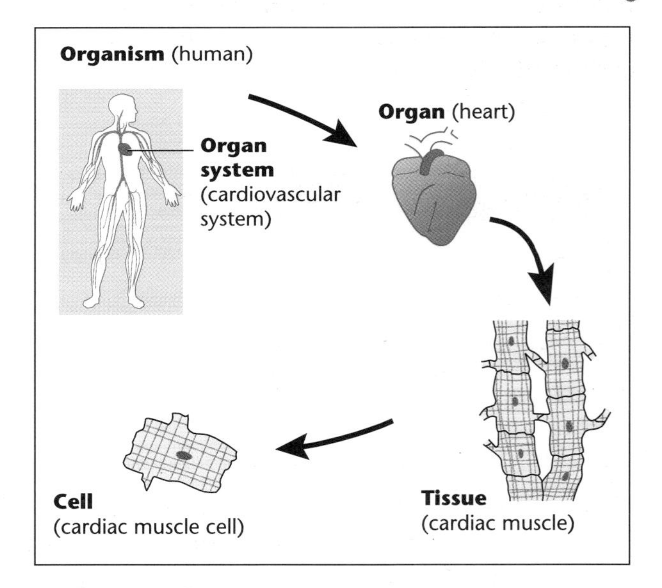

Figure 2 *The levels of organisation in a human – the whole body, organ systems, organs, tissues and cells.*

Life in a cell

The cell is the structural unit, that is, the basic building block, of living organisms. Modern research has shown that the cell is also the functional unit of living organisms. This means that each cell carries out all the physical and chemical reactions needed to keep an organism alive.

Cells themselves are made of chemicals. Like cells, these chemicals are organised. The basic unit of a chemical is an **atom**, and groups of atoms may be joined to form **molecules**. Some of the molecules in living cells are very large. Also present in living cells are **ions** – these are atoms or groups of atoms that are positively or negatively charged.

The reactions of life – metabolism

The sum of all the chemical reactions in a living organism is known as **metabolism**. There are two types of metabolic reaction:

- Reactions that break large molecules down into smaller ones are **catabolic reactions**.
- Reactions that join smaller molecules together to build larger ones are **anabolic reactions**.

Therefore metabolism is the sum of all the catabolic and anabolic reactions that take place in an organism. Catabolic reactions release energy and anabolic reactions use energy.

An important catabolic reaction that you have studied at GCSE is **respiration**. Look at figure 3. Glucose and oxygen react to form carbon dioxide and water. This reaction releases energy.

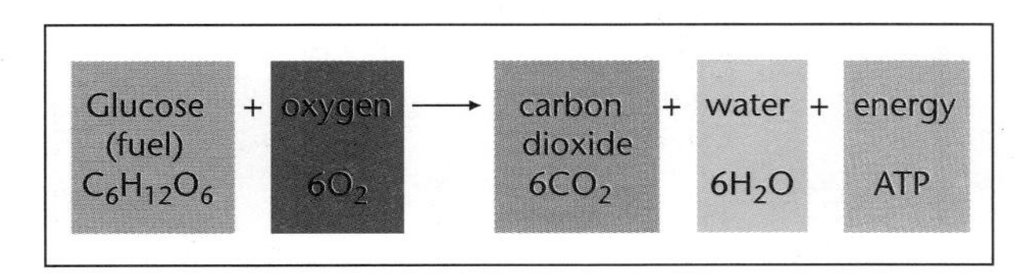

Figure 3 *Respiration is the reaction in your cells that provides the energy for all your life processes.*

Some of the energy released by respiration is used by the body to make other chemicals that the body needs. For example, muscle tissues are made up of protein molecules. The body has to manufacture these proteins in order to grow muscles and repair them. It does this using amino acids from digested foods and energy released by respiration.

Molecules known as **enzymes** are needed for metabolic reactions to take place. Enzymes are **biological catalysts** – they speed up chemical reactions. Without enzymes the reactions that take place in an organism would be too slow for life to continue.

Figure 4 *Bodybuilding shows an example of an anabolic reaction. A bodybuilder's muscles contain protein molecules. These molecules were made in the body by reactions that join amino acids together.*

1 **From where do cells get glucose and oxygen for respiration?**

2 **What happens to the carbon dioxide produced in respiration?**

3 **Some athletes take drugs called anabolic steroids to enhance their performance. What do you think is the effect of these drugs on the body?**

Key ideas 4–5

The cell is the structural and functional unit of living things.

The cells of large multicellular organisms are specialised, and are organised into tissues, organs and organ systems.

Metabolism is all the reactions of life.

2 Helping reactions occur

Most metabolic reactions in the body depend on a set of globular (sphere-shaped) proteins called **enzymes**. Enzymes have two main functions:

1. They act as highly specific **catalysts**. A catalyst speeds up a reaction without itself being used up during the reaction. Enzymes speed up particular reactions in the cell.
2. They provide a way of controlling reactions, as the amount of enzyme available determines how quickly a reaction can proceed.

Specific shapes

Look at figure 1. An enzyme has a specific three-dimensional shape, and an area on its surface called the **active site**. The substance that the enzyme acts on, or helps to react, is called the **substrate**. The substrate fits into the active site – they have shapes that fit together. We say they have **complementary shapes**. The active site of each different enzyme has its own particular three-dimensional shape, so only a substrate with a complementary shape will fit it. The substrate forms a temporary bond with the active site, and this is called **binding** to the active site. Binding to the active site makes the substrate react more quickly.

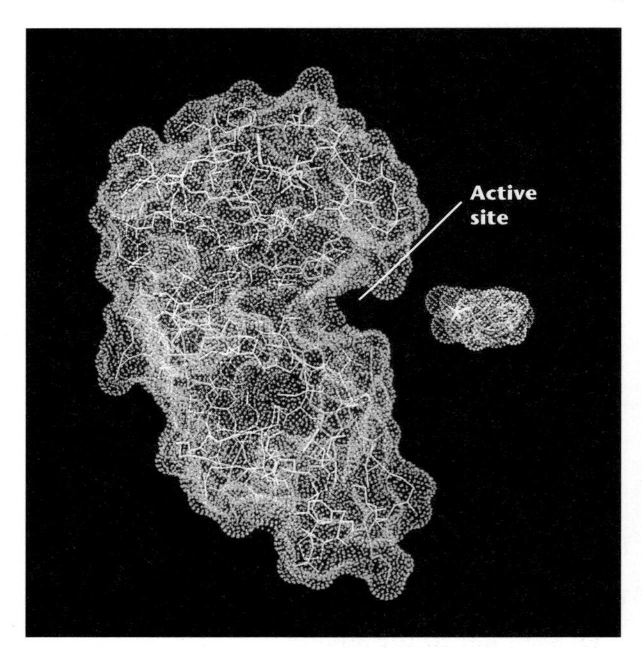

Figure 1 *In this computer-generated model, the enzyme is coloured blue. The smaller substrate fits into the enzyme's active site.*

Most enzymes catalyse (speed up) only one reaction, or one group of reactions. We say that enzymes are **specific**. Figure 2 shows the breakdown of starch to maltose, catalysed by the enzyme amylase. Starch is the substrate for amylase. The substance produced at the end of the reaction is called the **product**. There may be more than one substrate, or more than one product.

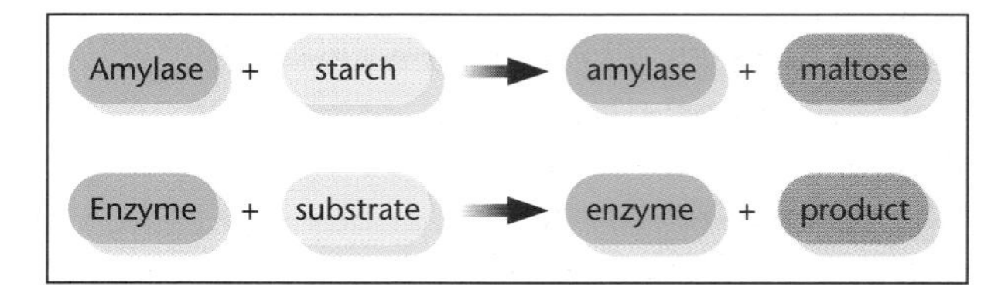

Figure 2 *Amylase catalyses the breakdown of starch.*

Amylase will only speed up the breakdown of starch to maltose – it does not act on any other substrate. Amylase is specific to this particular reaction. Every reaction in the body is catalysed by its own specific enzyme.

1 Name the substrate and the product in the following reaction: Maltase catalyses the breakdown of maltose to glucose.

Lock and key

Enzyme molecules, like all other particles in the cell, are constantly moving about, colliding with other molecules. When an enzyme molecule collides with its substrate molecule, the substrate **binds** to the enzyme's active site. Together they form an **enzyme–substrate complex**. The substrate reacts within this complex to form the product. The product leaves the active site. The enzyme is not used up or changed in the reaction, but is free to react again with any other substrate molecules it collides with.

This description of how enzymes catalyse reactions is called the **lock and key mechanism**. The enzyme is the 'lock' and the substrate is the 'key'.

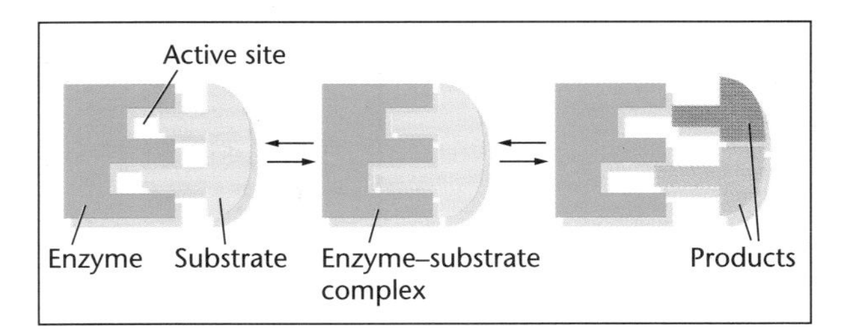

Figure 3 *The lock and key mechanism of enzyme action. In this diagram the enzyme breaks a large molecule into smaller ones. The same enzyme will also catalyse the reverse reaction – it will join the smaller molecules together again.*

2 Explain why an enzyme and its substrate are able to form an enzyme–substrate complex, but an enzyme cannot form a complex with another molecule.

Induced to fit

An enzyme–substrate complex can only be formed if the enzyme's active site and the substrate have complementary shapes. The enzyme and substrate in figure 3 have complementary shapes. Recent research suggests that the active site and the substrate are only fully complementary when the substrate is bound to the active site.

In figure 4 you can see that the enzyme's active site is similar to the shape of the substrate, but not fully complementary to it. As the substrate binds to the enzyme, the enzyme changes shape so that the active site is now fully complementary to the substrate's shape. The substrate can now bind to the active site and react to form the product. This description of how enzymes catalyse reactions is known as the **induced fit hypothesis**.

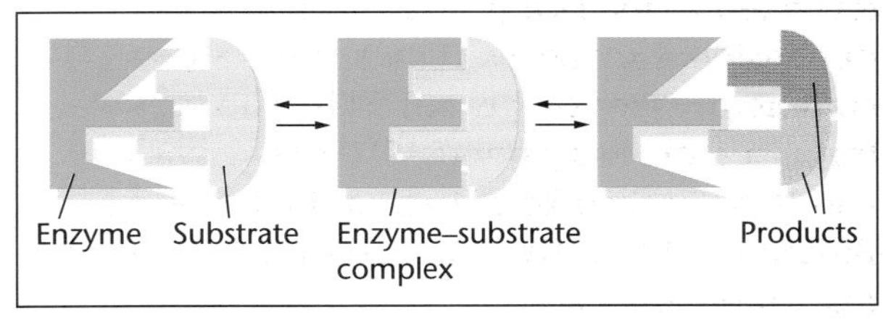

Figure 4 *The induced fit hypothesis of enzyme action. When the substrate binds to the enzyme's active site, it 'induces' a change of shape so that the substrate and enzyme become fully complementary.*

3 Draw a lock and key diagram to show the formation of a large molecule from two smaller molecules.

Key ideas 6–7

Biological processes are controlled by the action of enzymes, which are biological catalysts.

Enzymes act on specific substrates, and their active site shape is complementary to the shape of the substrate.

The enzyme and substrate form an enzyme–substrate complex.

3 Ready for action

For a reaction to occur, the reacting substances must collide with each other, and there must be enough energy available. The energy needed to make a reaction happen is known as the **activation energy** *(E)*. This energy is needed to overcome an **'energy barrier'**.

Getting ready for action

Not all collisions will result in a reaction. A reaction will only take place if the reacting substances collide with sufficient energy to overcome the energy barrier. For the collision energy to be high enough, the substances must be moving fast enough and in the right direction when they collide. The speed of a reaction can be increased by increasing the number of collisions of sufficient energy.

One way of providing energy to overcome the 'barrier' is to heat the reaction mixture. The more heat there is, the faster the molecules will move. This movement energy is called **kinetic energy**. Increasing the kinetic energy of the reacting molecules makes them more likely to collide. However, even at human body temperature, 37 °C, most substrate molecules do not collide with enough energy to overcome the energy barrier. If the body temperature was much higher, chemicals such as proteins in the body would be damaged. Enzymes allow the chemical reactions inside the body to take place at 37 °C. How do they do this?

Enzymes lower the activation energy needed for the reaction, making it easier for the reaction to occur. The formation of the enzyme–substrate complex reduces the activation energy of the reaction.

Look at figure 1. Without an enzyme, an activation energy of E is needed for the substrate to react. When an enzyme is present, you can see that a smaller activation energy E_1 is needed.

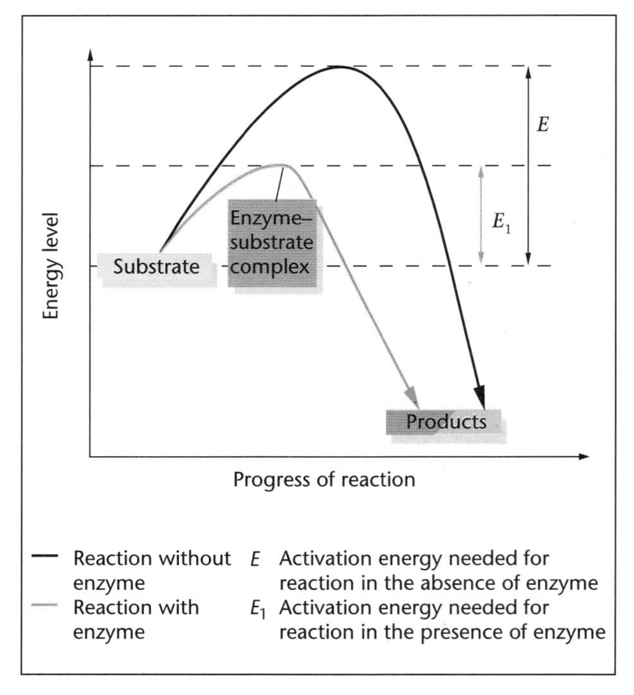

Figure 1 *This graph shows that the activation energy of a reaction is smaller in the presence of an enzyme.*

Shape matters

Enzymes are proteins, and how an enzyme functions is determined by its three-dimensional structure. It is the shape of the active site that makes an enzyme specific. Figure 2(a) shows a greatly simplified active site. It is held together by different bonds, for example **hydrogen bonds** and **ionic bonds**. An enzyme's three-dimensional shape is called its **tertiary structure** (see pages 66–7).

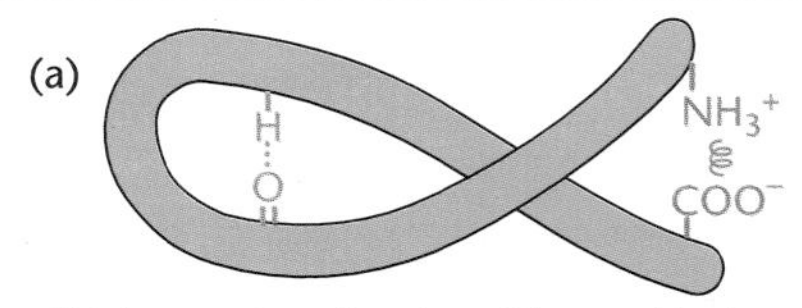

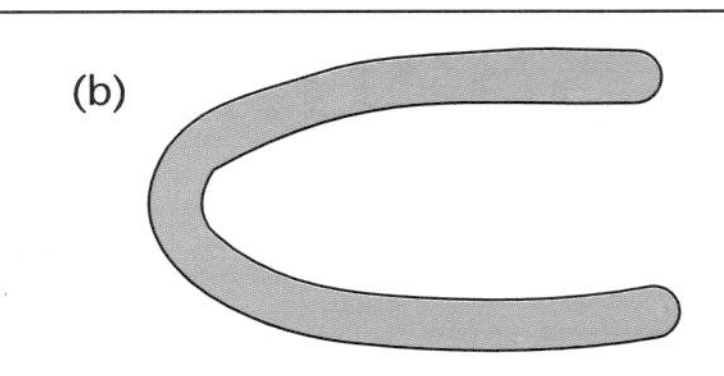

Figure 2 *(a) Hydrogen bonds and ionic bonds help hold an enzyme together in its specific three-dimensional shape. (b) A denatured enzyme – hydrogen bonds and ionic bonds have been broken, and the enzyme loses its shape.*

In figure 2(b), you can see that if the bonds break, the shape of the active site changes. The enzyme can no longer act as a catalyst. The enzyme is said to be **denatured**. Two factors that can affect an enzyme's shape, and therefore how it functions, are temperature and pH.

Q

1 Suggest why changing the shape of an enzyme may affect its efficiency as a catalyst.

Lending a hand

Some enzymes will only function in the presence of a non-protein substance called a **cofactor**. A cofactor can help the chemical reaction to occur by acting as a source of energy. Look at figure 3. You can see that a cofactor, coloured pink, is bound to the active site of the enzyme. There are three sorts of cofactor:

- Inorganic ions such as metal ions can act as cofactors. The ions may combine with either the enzyme or the substrate to reduce the activation energy. These ions are called **activators**. Activators are thought to make the enzyme–substrate complex form more easily. For example, the action of amylase on starch is quicker in the presence of chloride ions.
- A cofactor can be a small organic molecule called a **coenzyme**. This binds temporarily to the enzyme's active site and takes part in the reaction. It can also act as a link between two different reactions.
- Some enzymes have a coenzyme permanently covalently bonded to them, which helps the enzyme to function as a catalyst. In this case the coenzyme is known as a **prosthetic group**.

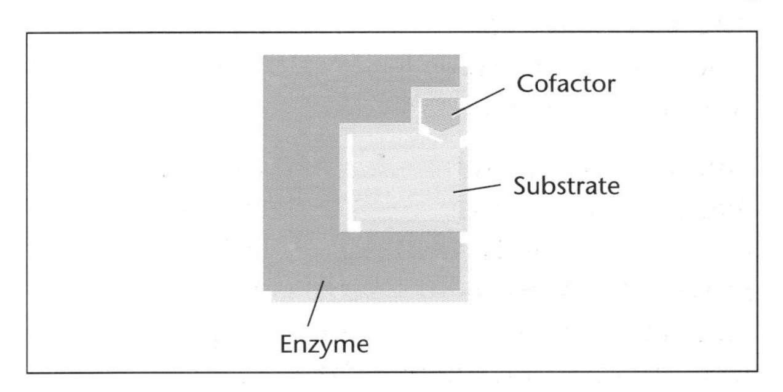

Figure 3 *The cofactor (pink) can bind to the active site of the enzyme along with the substrate.*

Q

2 An enzyme was extracted from liver cells. The enzyme's ability to catalyse a reaction was tested first in the presence of zinc ions and then in the absence of zinc ions. In the presence of zinc ions, the reaction occurred faster. Suggest an explanation for this.

Key ideas 8–9

Enzymes catalyse reactions by reducing the activation energy needed for the reaction. This allows the reactions of life to proceed sufficiently quickly at body temperature.

Some enzymes will only function in the presence of a cofactor.

4 Shaping up

Enzymes are affected by changes in temperature and pH. The wrong temperature or pH can alter the shape of the enzyme, making it ineffective. The temperature at which an enzyme works best is known as its **optimum temperature.** The pH at which an enzyme works best is called its **optimum pH.** Excessive heat, strongly acidic and strongly alkaline conditions can denature an enzyme.

Speeding up reactions

The effect of temperature on an enzyme-catalysed reaction is shown in figure 1. At low temperature, point **A**, the enzyme and substrate are moving slowly – they do not have much kinetic energy. They move so slowly that few collisions occur and the reaction is very slow.

Increasing the temperature gives the substrate and enzyme molecules more kinetic energy. There is more chance of the enzyme and substrate colliding. As the number of collisions increases, the number of enzyme–substrate complexes that form will also increase. This is what determines the **rate of reaction**, or how quickly the product is produced. As the temperature increases between **A** and **B**, the rate of reaction increases.

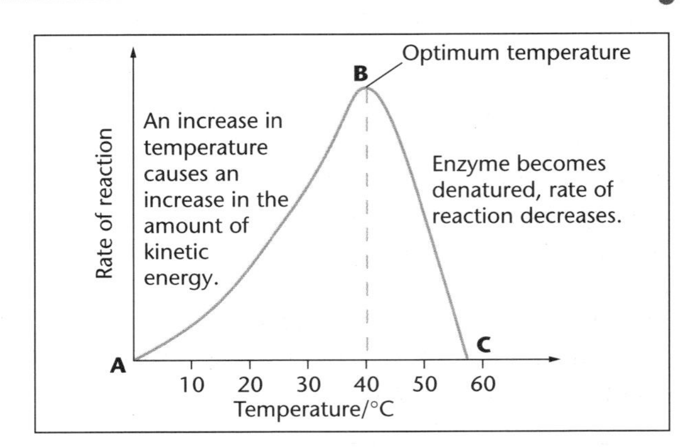

Figure 1 *The effect of temperature on the rate of an enzyme-controlled reaction. Below the optimum temperature, as the temperature increases, the rate of reaction rises* slowly. *At temperatures above the optimum temperature, as the temperature rises, the rate of reaction falls* rapidly.

Slowing down again

At a high temperature, the substrate and enzyme have a lot of kinetic energy. Kinetic energy causes the enzyme molecule to vibrate. If the enzyme vibrates too much, the hydrogen bonds will break, causing the enzyme's shape to change. The enzyme becomes denatured. This is what is happening between **B** and **C** on figure 1. As the temperature increases, the rate of reaction falls because more and more of the enzyme is being denatured. Because the enzyme is denatured, enzyme–substrate complexes cannot form and no product is made.

B is the point at which the rate of reaction is at a maximum. This is the temperature at which the product is being produced at the highest rate. This temperature is known as the enzyme's **optimum temperature**. Most enzymes have an optimum temperature between 40 and 50 °C.

1 Suggest why most enzymes have an optimum temperature between 40 and 50 °C.

2 Use your knowledge of how enzymes function to explain why:

a the rate of reaction increases between points A and B in figure 1

b the graph rises gradually, reaches a peak and then falls quickly.

3 In figure 1, what is the enzyme's optimum temperature?

Shape shifting

Most enzymes have an optimum pH close to 7, which is the pH found within most cells. Enzymes that work outside cells, **extracellular enzymes**, can have very different pH requirements.

pH is a measure of the concentration of hydrogen ions (H^+), or the number of hydrogen ions in a certain volume. The concentration of hydrogen ions affects hydrogen bonds and ionic bonds. A change in these bonds will lead to a change in the enzyme's specific three-dimensional shape. Look at figure 2. When an enzyme's shape changes, the enzyme becomes denatured.

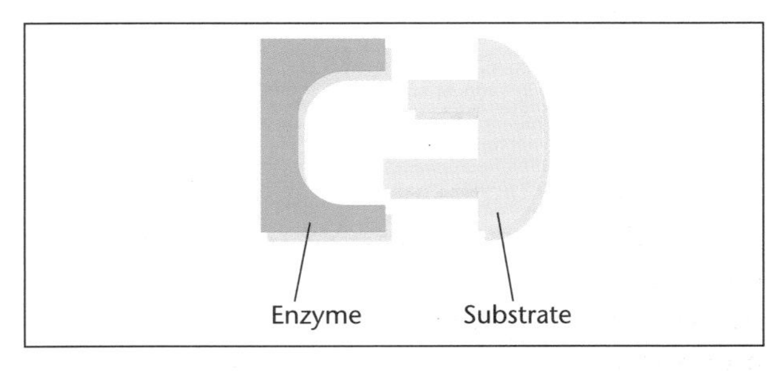

Figure 2 *A change in pH can alter the shape of the active site, and the substrate can no longer bind to it. The enzyme is denatured.*

4 Explain why an enzyme stops working when its shape changes.

The effect of pH on an enzyme-catalysed reaction is shown in figure 3. Look at point **A**. The pH is low (acidic conditions). This affects the number of hydrogen bonds and ionic bonds in the enzyme. The enzyme's shape changes, and the enzyme becomes denatured.

Now look at point **C**. The pH is high (alkaline conditions). This also affects the number of hydrogen bonds and ionic bonds. Again the enzyme becomes denatured.

The graph shows that as the pH rises between **A** and **B**, the rate of reaction increases. Between **B** and **C**, as the pH falls, the rate of reaction decreases. **B** shows the point where the rate of reaction is at a maximum. This is the pH at which the product is being made at the highest rate. This pH is known as the enzyme's **optimum pH**.

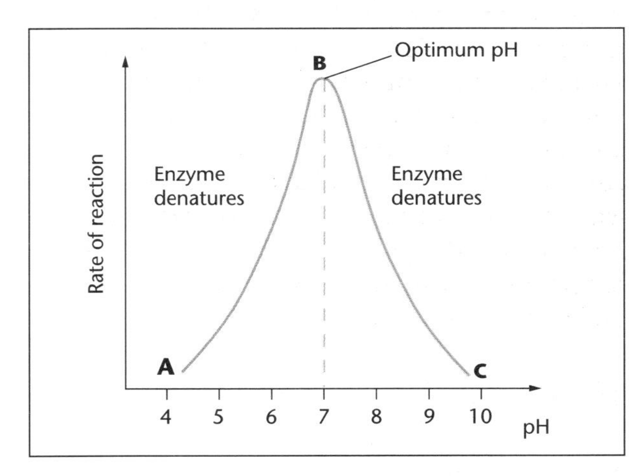

Figure 3 *The graph shows the effect of pH on the rate of an enzyme-controlled reaction.*

5 Using figure 3 and your knowledge of how enzymes function, explain why:

a the rate of reaction increases between points A and B

b the rate of reaction decreases between points B and C

c the graph rises, reaches a peak and then falls again.

6 From the graph, what is the enzyme's optimum pH?

5 Living at the edge

Most organisms have a range of temperature and an optimum pH at which they can live. The conditions need to be suitable for the enzymes that catalyse reactions within the organism's cells. The enzymes of most organisms are denatured by extremes in temperature and pH. Very few living organisms can survive in extremes of cold, heat or pH. A few can, and most of them are microorganisms.

Scientists have realised that the enzymes that allow these microorganisms to survive harsh conditions could have industrial applications. For example, enzymes from a heat-tolerant bacterium are used in 'biological' washing powders as they work at high temperatures in the washing machine.

Some like it cold

Cold environments are more common than hot ones. In the oceans the average temperature range is 1–3 °C, and there are vast areas of the Arctic and Antarctic that are permanently frozen. All these areas support living organisms. 'Cold-loving' organisms are called **psychrophiles**. They can grow at 0 °C, and some can even grow at temperatures as low as –10 °C. They often cannot live above about +25 °C.

Microorganisms are not the only organisms that can survive extreme cold. Look at figure 1. The colouring of snow can be caused by a variety of organisms, such as red algae and green algae.

Food manufacturers are interested in studying psychrophiles to combat food spoilage. Food technologists believe that they can use enzymes from such organisms to avoid spoilage in processed foods.

Figure 1 *Red algae can survive in extreme cold.*

Some like it hot

'Heat-loving' organisms are called **thermophiles**. Thermophiles can grow and reproduce in temperatures higher than 45 °C. Some can thrive in temperatures above 80 °C. An extreme example is *Pyrodictium*, found on geothermally heated areas of the sea bed. *Pyrodictium* has a temperature range for growth of 82–110 °C and an optimum temperature of 105 °C.

Sulpholobus acidocaldarius is a thermophilic microorganism that lives in hot springs. Figure 2 shows a pool in Yellowstone Park, USA. You can see the yellow *Sulpholobus* growing around the edge of the hot spring.

Figure 2 *Acidothermophilic bacteria live in geothermal pools.*

Some like it acidic

Most natural environments on Earth have a pH range of 5–9. **Acidophiles**, 'acid-loving' organisms, thrive in environments where the pH is lower than 5.

Hot springs are not only hot, they are also naturally acidic environments. The species of *Sulpholobus* that live there have an optimum pH for growth of pH 2–3. Not only are they thermophiles, they are also acidophiles. *Sulpholobus* get their energy by oxidising sulphur granules present around the hot springs. This produces sulphuric acid, which makes the pH even lower.

Surprisingly, acidophiles cannot tolerate high acidity in their cells. They survive by keeping the acid out. The molecules that provide this protection are of interest to scientists because they are able to function in extremely acidic conditions. The animal feed industry is already using enzymes as food additives. Enzymes that are acid tolerant are used to make grains more digestible.

Some like it alkaline

Organisms that thrive in environments with a pH above 9 are called **alkalophiles**. Alkalophiles live in soils that contain large amounts of carbonate, or in soda lakes. Figure 3 shows a population of flamingos feeding on Lake Nakuru, a soda lake in the East African Rift Valley. The pH of Lake Nakuru is about pH 10. The flamingos feed on *Spirulina*, a microorganism that grows in the lake.

Scientists are researching the enzymes from alkalophiles. They may have a use in laundry detergents, which tend to be very alkaline.

Figure 3 *Flamingos feeding on Lake Nakuru, Kenya.*

Key ideas 10–13

The properties of enzymes are related to their specific three-dimensional shape (their tertiary structure).

Enzymes work best at an optimum temperature and an optimum pH, at which they give a maximum rate of reaction.

Conditions too different from the optimum temperature and optimum pH can cause the enzyme's shape to change and the enzyme to be denatured.

6 Reaching a maximum

Reactions take place at different speeds or **rates**. You have seen that it is possible to change the rate of an enzyme-controlled reaction by changing the temperature or pH. The rate of an enzyme-controlled reaction also depends on the amount of enzyme and the amount of substrate available. Increasing the amount of either substrate or enzyme increases the number of collisions, and this increases the rate of reaction.

Adding more substrate

Study figure 1, which shows the effect of changing the amount of substrate on the rate of an enzyme-controlled reaction.

At point **A**, the amount of substrate is low. This means few enzyme–substrate complexes will form and little product will be produced. The rate of reaction is low. As the amount of substrate increases between **A** and **B**, the rate of reaction increases as there are more collisions.

As the amount of substrate increases between **B** and **C**, there is no further increase in the rate of reaction. The amount of substrate is now high, and the active sites on all the enzyme molecules are occupied. Product cannot be formed any more quickly than this until more active sites are available, so to increase the rate further, the amount of enzyme must be increased.

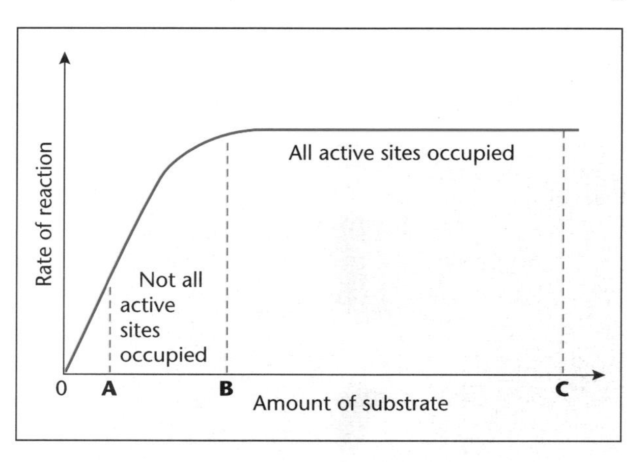

Figure 1 *The effect of changing the amount of substrate on the rate of an enzyme-controlled reaction. As the amount of substrate increases from 0 to* ***B****, the rate of reaction increases. As the amount of substrate increases from* ***B*** *to* ***C****, the rate of reaction does not increase any further.*

1 Use figure 1 and your knowledge of how enzymes function to explain why:
- **a the rate increases between points A and B**
- **b the rate remains the same between points B and C.**

Increasing the amount of enzyme can also cause the rate of reaction to increase.

2 Draw a graph to show the effect of increasing the amount of enzyme on the rate of an enzyme-controlled reaction while the amount of substrate is kept the same.

Diagnostic enzymes

Some enzymes can be used as **diagnostic enzymes**, to detect the amount of certain chemicals present in body fluids, which can help in the diagnosis of disease. Diagnostic enzymes are often used in **biosensors**. These are tools used for finding out about the body. Two common biosensors that are used in daily life are the breathalyser used to detect ethanol (alcohol), and plastic strips called Clinistix™ used to detect glucose in urine. These biosensors show the amount of ethanol or glucose present. Ethanol and glucose are substrates for enzymes on the biosensors.

Blocking reactions – competitive inhibition

Some substances can prevent enzyme–substrate complexes being formed, or slow down their formation. This is called **inhibition**, and these substances are known as **inhibitors**.

Some inhibitors have molecules that are closely related to the 'true' substrate. Look at figure 2. Trypsin, coloured blue, is a digestive enzyme that helps break down proteins. It is a **protease** enzyme. The inhibitor binds to trypsin at the active site, preventing the formation of an enzyme–substrate complex.

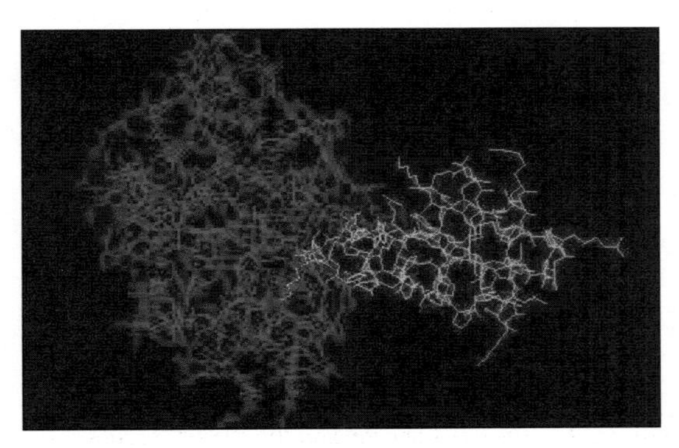

Figure 2 *Competitive inhibitors have a shape similar to that of the substrate. They compete with the substrate for the enzyme's active site.*

When the inhibitor and the substrate are both present, they 'compete' for the active site of the enzyme, and this slows down the rate of reaction. This is called **competitive inhibition**. An inhibitor like this that competes with the substrate for the enzyme's active site is called a **competitive inhibitor**. The effect of competitive inhibition can be reversed by increasing the amount of substrate available, or by reducing the amount of inhibitor. Figure 3 shows the effect of increasing the amount of substrate in the presence of a competitive inhibitor.

At point **A**, the rate of reaction is low because the inhibitor is present. The substrate and inhibitor are competing for the enzyme's active site.

At point **B**, the presence of the inhibitor has not affected the rate of reaction. Increasing the amount of substrate has reduced the amount of competition between the inhibitor and the substrate. With large amounts of substrate, enzyme molecules are more likely to collide with and bind to substrate molecules than inhibitor molecules. More enzyme–substrate complexes can be formed.

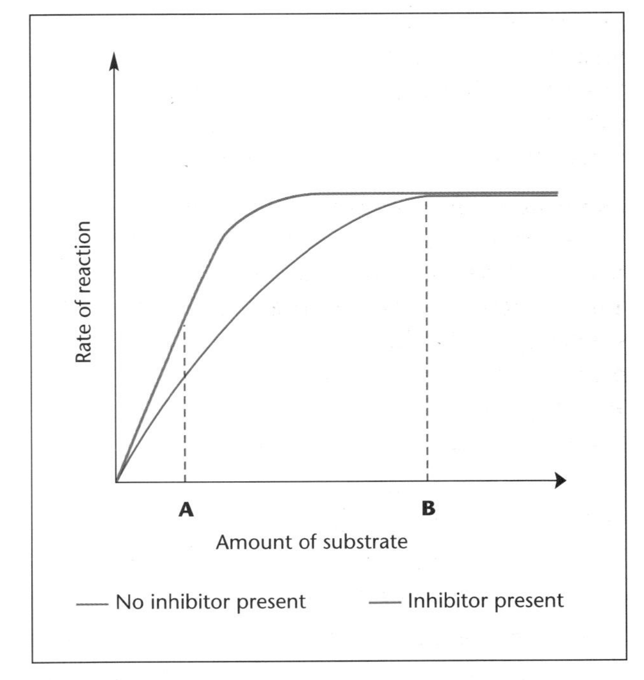

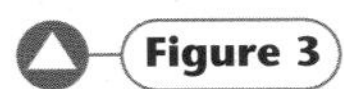

Figure 3 *The effect of a competitive inhibitor on an enzyme-controlled reaction over a range of different amounts of substrate. When inhibitor is present, the reaction is slow with small amounts of substrate. With large amounts of substrate, the rate is the same as when there is no inhibitor present.*

3 Explain why the trypsin inhibitor shown in figure 2 is able to bind to the enzyme.

4 Explain why the presence of a competitive inhibitor reduces the rate of reaction at point A on figure 3.

7 Being obstructive

Inhibitors do not all compete with the substrate. Some inhibitors slow down enzyme-controlled reactions by changing the shape of the enzyme in a way that prevents an enzyme–substrate complex being formed. The inhibitor acts by binding to the enzyme and causing the shape of the enzyme's active site to change.

The shape shifter – non-competitive inhibition

In figure 1, substance A has a different shape from the substrate, so substance A cannot bind to the enzyme's active site. However, substance A acts as an inhibitor by binding to an area on the enzyme away from the active site. Because the substrate and substance A are not competing for the active site, this is called **non-competitive inhibition**. Substance A is called a **non-competitive inhibitor**.

When substance A binds to the enzyme, the enzyme's shape changes. The active site changes shape. This means that the substrate cannot bind, an enzyme–substrate complex cannot be produced and no product will be formed.

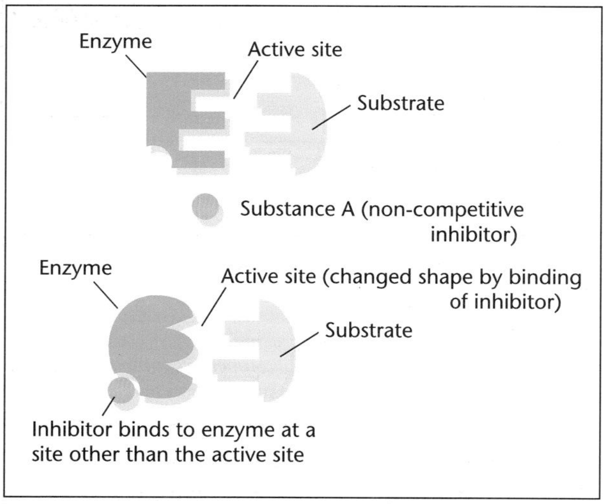

Enzyme
Active site
Substrate
Substance A (non-competitive inhibitor)
Enzyme
Active site (changed shape by binding of inhibitor)
Substrate
Inhibitor binds to enzyme at a site other than the active site

Figure 1 *Non-competitive inhibitors alter the shape of the enzyme's active site.*

Q

1 In figure 1, why can substance A not bind to the enzyme's active site?

Increasing the amount of substrate present does not overcome the effect of a non-competitive inhibitor. This is shown in figure 2.

At point **A**, the rate of reaction is much lower when the inhibitor is present. The inhibitor has bound to the enzyme, and has caused the active site shape to change.

Even when the amount of substrate is high at point **B**, the rate of reaction is still much lower when the inhibitor is present. The inhibitor is still bound to many enzyme molecules. The only way of reducing the effect of a non-competitive inhibitor is to remove the inhibitor.

Heavy metals such as cadmium, zinc, mercury and lead are non-competitive inhibitors. Before the introduction of unleaded petrol, lead from petrol exhaust fumes was readily absorbed into the body. Lead inhibits an enzyme that is involved in the synthesis of haemoglobin.

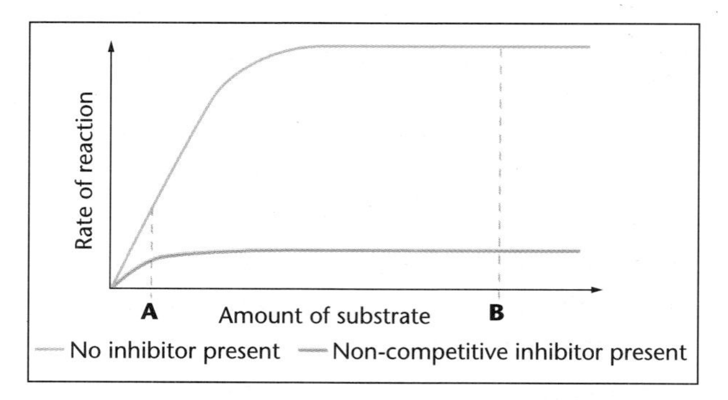

Figure 2 *The effect of a non-competitive inhibitor on the rate of an enzyme-controlled reaction. The rate of reaction is always lower with a non-competitive inhibitor, however much substrate is present.*

Keeping control

Many chemical processes that take place in the body involve a series of enzyme-controlled reactions. One example is blood clotting.

Figure 3 shows how the product from one reaction acts as the substrate for the next. Substance **A** is the initial substrate and substance **E** is the final or end-product. Substances **B**, **C** and **D** are intermediate products. There are four enzymes in the process – E_1, E_2, E_3 and E_4.

When enough **E** has been formed to meet the body's needs, no more is formed. To stop the process, **E** acts as a non-competitive inhibitor, preventing the formation of **B**. Without **B** there will be no further production of **C**, **D** or **E**. By acting as a non-competitive inhibitor, product **E** has prevented its own production. This is called **end-point inhibition**.

Specific enzymes

E_1 E_2 E_3 E_4

A → **B** → **C** → **D** → **E**

Initial substrate

Intermediate products

End-product

Level of end-product inhibits the activity of E_1 – **end-point inhibition**

Figure 3 *By acting as an inhibitor, the end-product of a series of reactions prevents its own production.*

A series of reactions in the body like that shown in figure 3 is called a **metabolic pathway**. An example of a metabolic pathway in both bacteria and plants is shown in figure 4. This series of reactions converts one amino acid, threonine, to another amino acid, isoleucine. The product, isoleucine, inhibits the first enzyme in the pathway, thereby regulating its own production.

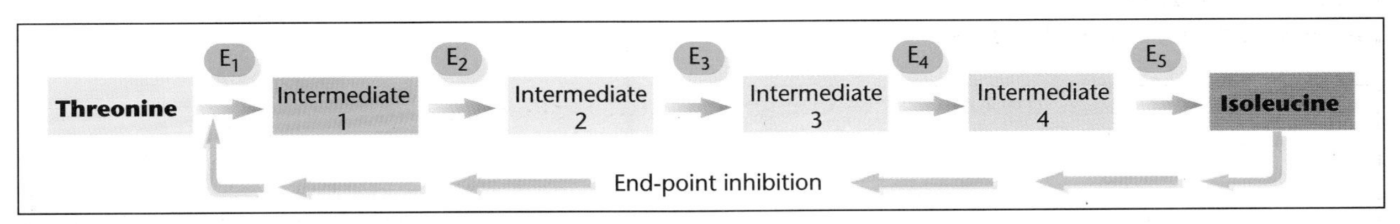

Isoleucine controls its own production by end-point inhibition. This is just one of thousands of metabolic pathways in living things.

2 **Why is it important to be able to control the amount of product made in a chemical process?**

Key ideas 14–17

The rate of an enzyme-controlled reaction depends on the amount of substrate and enzyme available.

A competitive inhibitor slows down the rate of an enzyme-controlled reaction because it has a shape similar to that of the 'true' substrate. It competes with the substrate for active sites.

A non-competitive inhibitor slows down the rate of an enzyme-controlled reaction because it binds to the enzyme, causing the enzyme's active site shape to change. This makes it impossible for the substrate to bind.

Unit 1 – Questions

8

1 a) Explain the following terms:
i) active site ii) enzyme specificity
iii) competitive inhibition iv) non-competitive inhibition.
(4 marks)

b) Figure 1 shows the effect of temperature on the rate of an enzyme-controlled reaction.

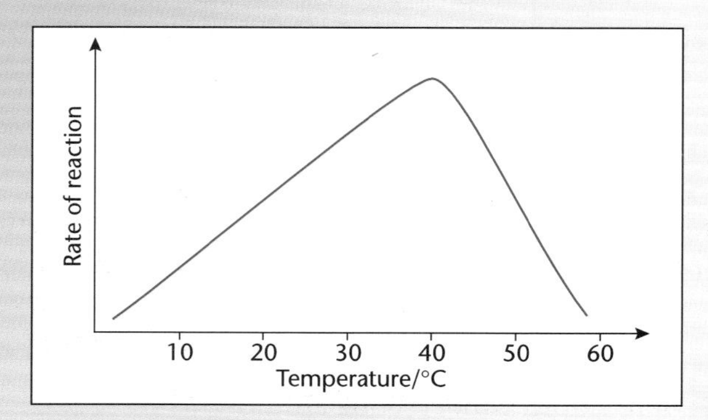

Figure 1

Describe and explain the shape of the curve:
i) between 15 °C and 40 °C
ii) from 50 °C to 60 °C.
(4 marks)
(Total 8 marks)

2 Figure 2 shows the changes in energy level that occur during an uncatalysed biological reaction.

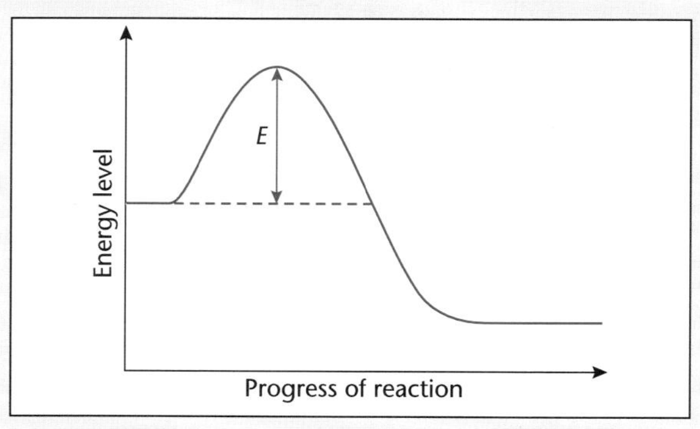

Figure 2

a) What does *E* represent? (1 mark)
b) Copy the graph and draw a second curve to show the changes in energy level that occur when the reaction is catalysed by an enzyme.
(2 marks)
(Total 3 marks)

3 a) List the properties of an enzyme. (4 marks)
b) Enzymes are affected by pH. Use the lock and key theory to explain the effect of pH on an enzyme-controlled reaction. (4 marks)
(Total 8 marks)

4 Amylase is an enzyme that breaks down starch. The effect of pH on amylase activity can be investigated using a starch–agar plate, as shown in figure 3.

Circular wells were cut into the plate using a cork borer. The wells were set up so that they each contained the same volume and concentration of amylase, and a solution of different pH. After 24 hours the starch–agar plate was flooded with iodine solution and then rinsed with water. Iodine is used to test for the presence of starch – if starch is present, a blue-black colour will appear.

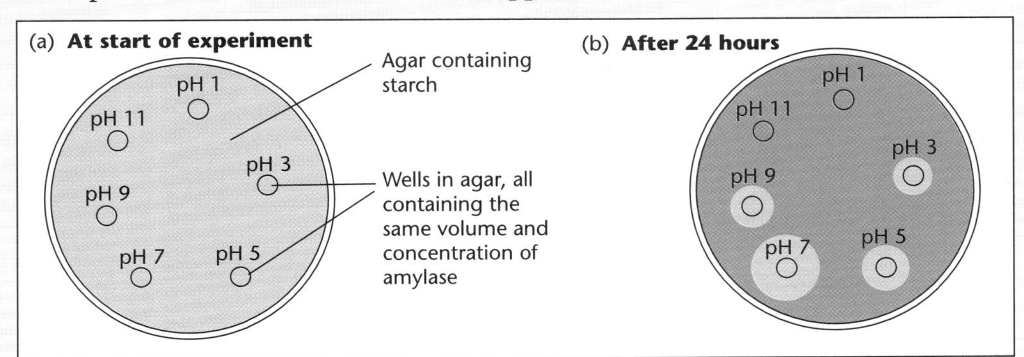

Figure 3

a) What was the optimum pH for the enzyme? (1 mark)
b) Why are there no clear zones at pH 1 and pH 11? (2 marks)
c) What controls would be needed for this investigation? (2 marks)

(Total 5 marks)

5 The conversion of succinate to fumarate is catalysed by the enzyme succinate dehydrogenase, and is inhibited by the competitive inhibitor malonate. Use your knowledge of enzyme specificity and the lock and key theory to explain:

a) why only succinate dehydrogenase catalyses this reaction (2 marks)
b) how malonate inhibits the enzyme. (2 marks)

(Total 4 marks)

6 Figure 4 shows the effect of increasing substrate concentration on the rate of an enzyme-controlled reaction at a temperature of 40 °C and pH 7.

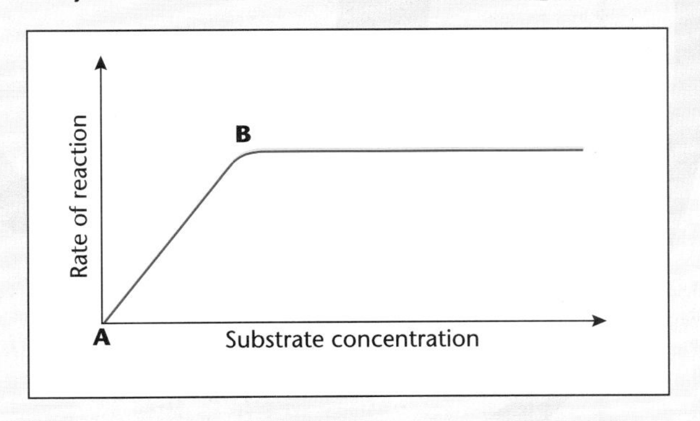

a) Explain the shape of the curve between points A and B. (2 marks)
b) Copy the graph and sketch a curve to show the effect of increasing substrate concentration on the rate of reaction at a temperature of 25 °C. (2 marks)

(Total 4 marks)

1 Food in humans

Most of the food we eat is made up of large, complex and often insoluble molecules. Before the nutrients in food can be used by the body's cells, these molecules must be broken down into smaller soluble molecules which can be carried in the blood. This breaking down of large molecules is called **digestion**. Enzymes are very important in digestion.

Organisation

Digestion takes place in the digestive system, which is shown in figure 1. The digestive system is a long tube (about 5–6 m long in an average adult) that begins with your mouth and ends at your anus. Sometimes it is simply called the **gut**.

The major parts of the gut are the oesophagus, stomach, small intestine and large intestine. Around the gut are a number of other organs that play an essential role in digestive processes, for example by producing chemicals needed for digestion, such as enzymes. We call these **digestive secretions**. These organs, such as the liver and pancreas, are also shown in figure 1.

Food enters the gut through the mouth, which does the initial processing. The teeth break the food up into smaller pieces, and **saliva** starts the process of breaking down large starch molecules. Saliva lubricates the food so that it is easier to swallow.

A ball of partially digested food called a **bolus** leaves the mouth when you swallow. It moves down the throat into the **oesophagus** and then the **stomach**. More physical breaking down and chemical digestion of the food takes place here. The partially digested food then passes into the **small intestine**, the longest part of the gut, where most of the digestion and absorption occurs. Some digestive secretions enter the small intestine from the liver and the pancreas. Other digestive secretions are produced by the cells lining the inside of the small intestine itself.

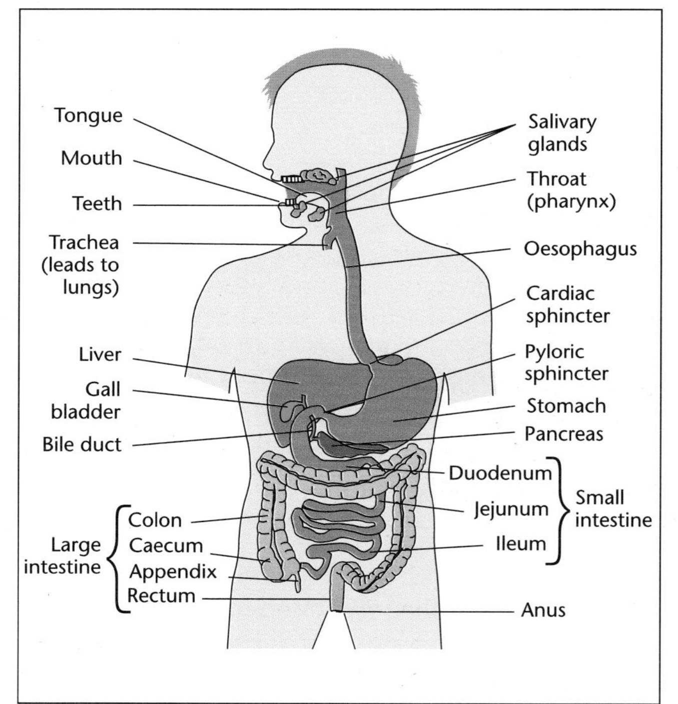

Figure 1 *The digestive system (gut) and associated organs.*

Q

1 By the time food enters the small intestine, where most of the chemical digestion takes place, it has been broken down into smaller pieces. How does this help the digestive enzymes do their job?

Tissues of the gut

The shape and dimensions of the parts of the gut vary, though the tissue layers that make up the gut wall are similar throughout. Look at figure 2. You can see that starting from the inside and moving outwards, there are three main layers in the gut wall – the **mucosa, submucosa** and **muscularis externa**. Each layer has different functions to perform and contains several different types of cell. The space in the middle through which food passes is called the **lumen**.

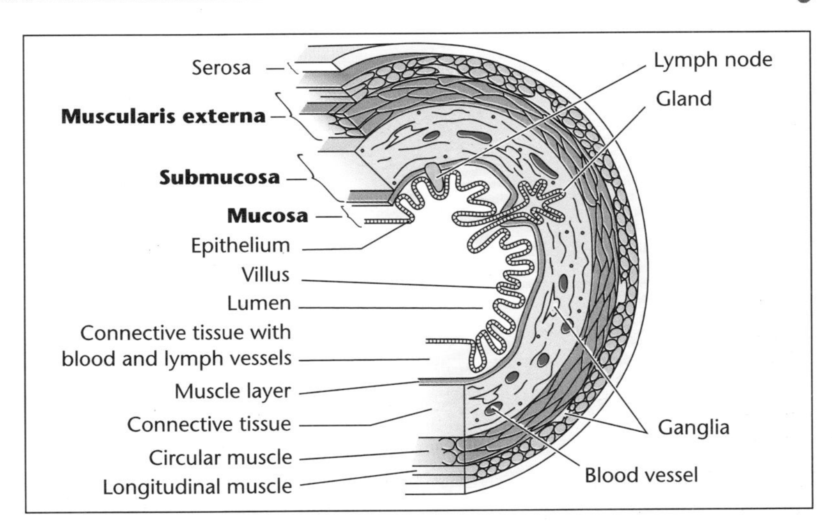

Figure 2 *The generalised structure of the gut wall.*

On the inside surface of the **mucosa** there is a layer of tissue called the **epithelium**. Epithelium is the type of tissue that lines the external and internal surfaces of the body. In some areas of the gut such as the oesophagus, where physical protection is needed, the epithelium is several layers thick. In most parts of the gut the epithelium is only a single cell thick, and the epithelial cells are specialised to carry out digestion and absorption.

Below the epithelium there is a layer of **connective tissue**. Connective tissue binds organs and tissues together. This layer is supplied with blood vessels and lymph vessels. The innermost part of the mucosa consists of a thin layer of **smooth muscle cells**. These are muscle cells that carry out automatic or involuntary actions in the body. The smooth muscle cell layer in the mucosa causes gentle movement of the mucosa.

2 The mucosa throughout the gut is folded. Suggest why this may be an advantage.

The **submucosa** is a loose matrix of connective tissue containing blood vessels, lymph vessels and **ganglia** which are made up of the cell bodies of nerve cells. Digested food is transported away from the gut in the submucosa.

The **muscularis externa** is a thick layer of smooth muscle. In most regions of the gut it consists of two separate muscle layers, one longitudinal and one circular, at right angles to each other. This muscle layer forces food along the gut by a process known as **peristalsis**. In peristalsis the smooth muscle cells of the muscularis externa contract behind the food bolus, but relax ahead of it, forcing the bolus to move along the gut.

Key ideas 20–21

The gut is divided into regions, each with its own functions.

The gut wall consists of three main layers – the mucosa, submucosa and muscularis externa.

2 Adapted for work

Each part of the gut carries out a specific role. To do this, the gut wall in each part is modified to carry out particular jobs. We shall look at the major parts of the gut to see how their structure helps their function.

A slippery slope – oesophagus

When food is swallowed, it enters a long tube called the **oesophagus** and is quickly transported to the stomach. To carry out this transport task the oesophagus has been adapted in a number of ways. Look at figure 1.

You can see that the epithelium is made of several layers of flattened cells. The outer cells are continually rubbed off by friction as solid food passes to the stomach. The oesophagus epithelium is therefore protected from damage by being several cells thick. The mucosa is folded, which allows expansion as the food passes along. The epithelial layer contains **mucus-secreting glands** to lubricate the passage of food.

The submucosa is elastic, allowing expansion. In this region of the gut, the muscularis externa is two layers thick to allow peristalsis, the muscular wave that forces the food into the stomach.

1 Explain how the structure of the oesophagus helps to get food into the stomach quickly.

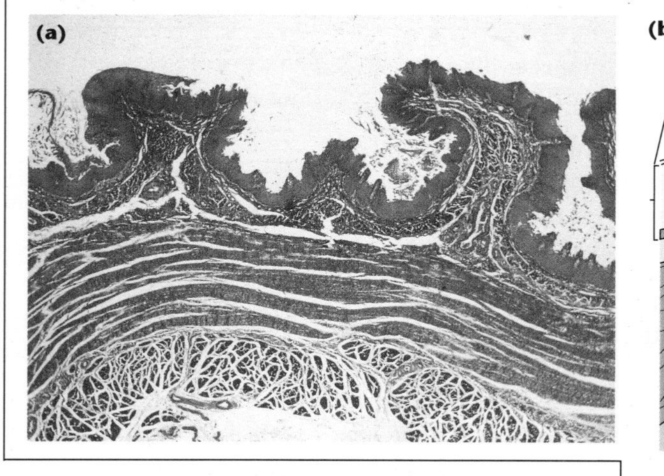

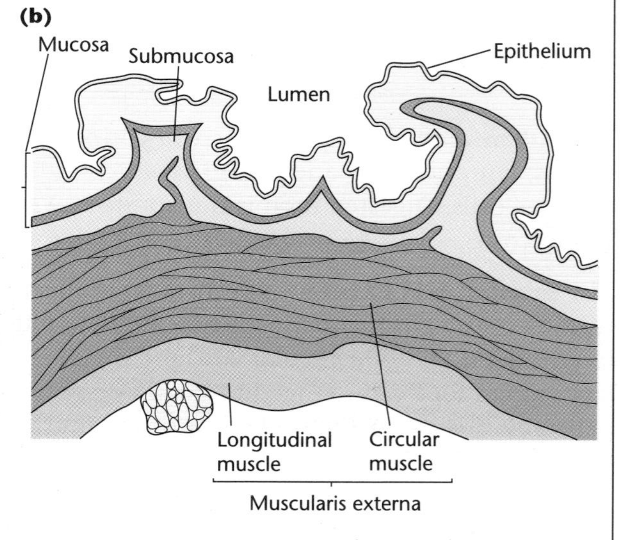

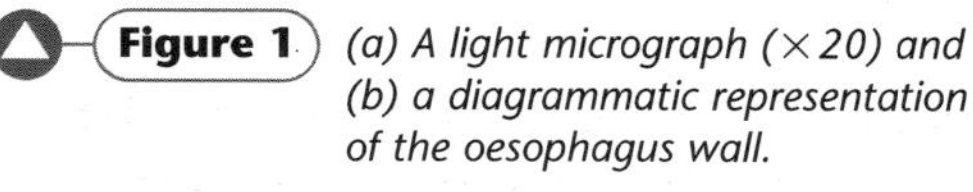

Figure 1 *(a) A light micrograph (×20) and (b) a diagrammatic representation of the oesophagus wall.*

A holding bay – stomach

The stomach is a muscular bag that can swell out when full of food. The main functions of the stomach are:

- temporary storage of food
- mixing of the stomach contents
- some digestion.

To understand how the stomach performs these functions, look at figure 2.

The mucosa is folded to allow for expansion, and it is lined with cells that secrete **mucus**. Mucus protects the stomach from enzyme action and acid. The mucosa also contains many **gastric glands**, which secrete acid, and a protease enzyme called **pepsin**, which helps break down proteins. The pH of the stomach contents is 1–2.5, which is the optimum pH range of pepsin.

The submucosa contains large numbers of nerve cell bodies. These are part of the nervous system that controls the production of gastric secretions.

The muscularis externa is three layers thick. The muscles mix (churn) the stomach contents to produce a mixture called **chyme**.

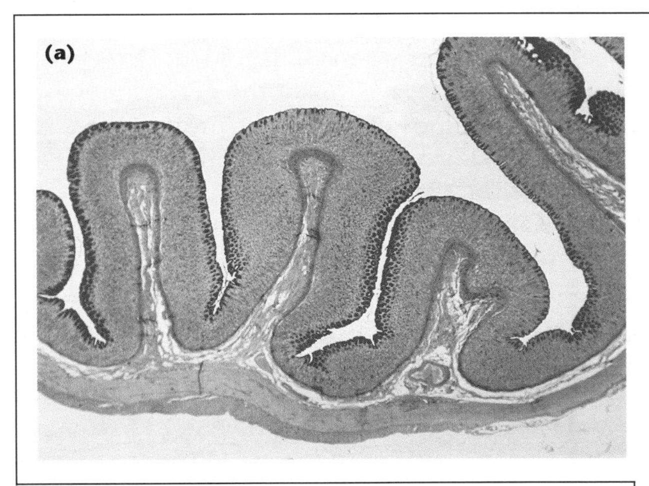

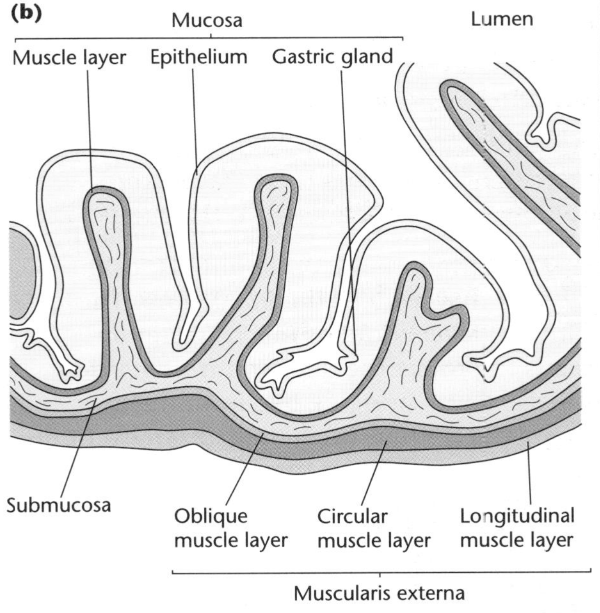

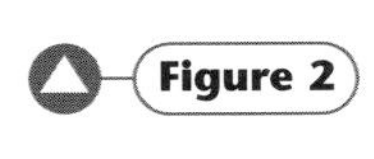
Figure 2 *(a) A light micrograph (×20) and (b) a diagrammatic representation of the stomach wall.*

2 The oesophagus and stomach have folds which increase their surface area. In each case, suggest why this is an advantage.

3 Why do you think the muscularis externa is three layers thick in the stomach?

4 Why do you think the production of gastric secretions needs to be controlled?

5 What is the role of acid in the stomach?

Key ideas 22–3

The mucosa, submucosa and muscularis externa of the oesophagus are adapted to allow quick passage of food to the stomach.

The mucosa and muscularis externa of the stomach are adapted to allow temporary storage, mixing of the stomach contents and some digestion.

3 Specially adapted

The food passes from the stomach into the small intestine. The small intestine performs two major functions:

1. It brings about most of the digestion of large food molecules into smaller and more soluble ones.
2. It brings about the absorption of digested food.

A large surface – small intestine

The small intestine is a long, coiled tube about 5–6 m long. It consists of an upper tube called the **duodenum**, into which open the **pancreatic duct** and **bile duct**. The duodenum leads via the jejunum to a lower tube called the **ileum**.

In the duodenum, some important digestive secretions are added to the food. Glands produce alkaline secretions which neutralise the acidity of the food leaving the stomach. They also produce the optimum pH for the enzymes that work in the duodenum. The epithelial layer contains mucus-secreting glands to protect the duodenum from acid damage. Ducts bringing bile from the liver and digestive secretions (including enzymes) from the pancreas also open into the duodenum.

As you can see from figures 1 and 2, the duodenum and ileum are very similar in structure. The small intestine, like the oesophagus and stomach, is folded. However, unlike the other regions of the gut, its mucosa also has millions of finger-like projections called **villi** (singular: **villus**). They greatly increase the surface area of the epithelium. There are about 20–40 villi per mm^2 of mucosa, and each villus extends about 0.5–1.5 mm into the lumen. The individual cells on the surface of the villi themselves have thin, closely packed finger-shaped projections, called **microvilli**, on their free surfaces. These microvilli form the **brush border** and further increase the surface area of the small intestine.

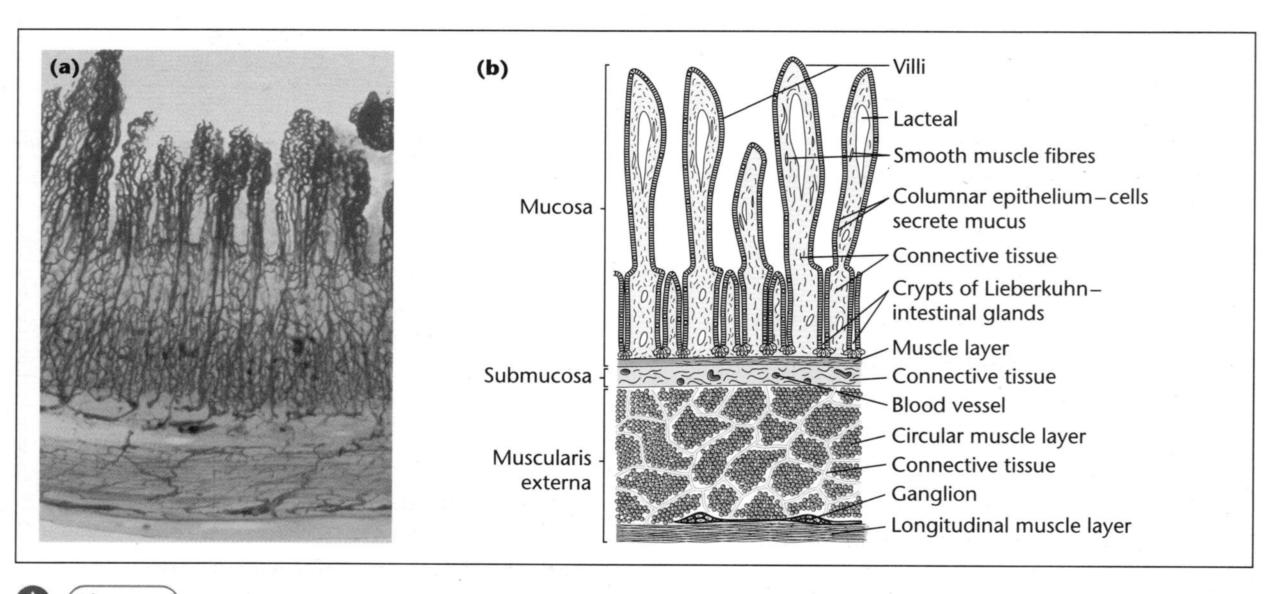

Figure 1 *(a) A light micrograph, stained to show the blood capillaries (× 10) and (b) a diagrammatic representation of the duodenum.*

The villi and the submucosa are well supplied with blood and lymph vessels, which absorb food products and transport them around the body. Between the villi you can see that there are deep folds. The cells at the base of these folds produce digestive enzymes, particularly the cells in the duodenum. In the duodenum, lying beneath these folds there are also glands that produce alkaline secretions and mucus.

Most of the epithelial cells of the small intestine have digestive enzymes embedded within their cell membranes and in their cytoplasm. The epithelium is a single layer of cells providing a short distance for the absorption of digested food.

The muscularis externa of the small intestine consists of two layers, enabling peristalsis to occur.

A vast surface – ileum

Only the first 30 cm of the small intestine is called the duodenum. The ileum forms most of the small intestine, and can be up to 6 m in length. Although some digestion does take place in the ileum, it is the main site for absorption of digested food. The digested food is moved from the lumen into the bloodstream or lymph for transport to the body tissues.

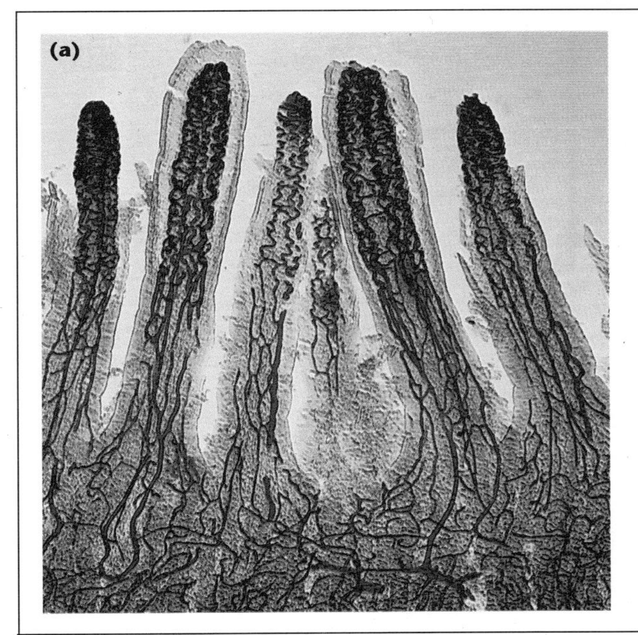

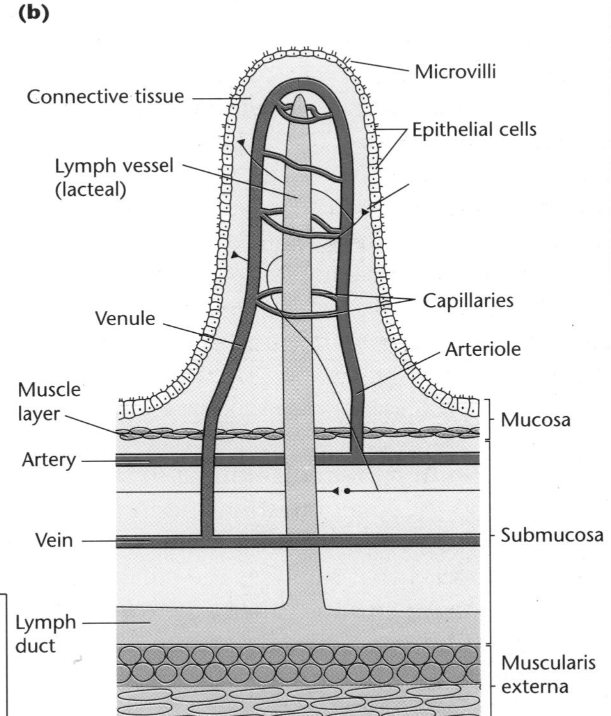

Figure 2 *(a) A light micrograph of the ileum (×10) (b) a diagrammatic representation of a villus.*

Q

1. **List the features of the ileum that increase its surface area, and suggest why this is an advantage.**
2. **Draw a table to summarise the functions and adaptations of the oesophagus, stomach, duodenum and ileum.**

Key ideas 24–5

The mucosa, submucosa and muscularis externa of the small intestine are adapted for digestion and absorption of food.

4 Making smaller

Enzymes help in the breakdown of food, in a process called **chemical digestion**. Food contains carbohydrates, proteins and lipids (fats), so a wide range of different enzymes is needed.

What happens to the food we eat?

Enzymes that break down carbohydrates are called **carbohydrases,** enzymes that break down proteins are called **proteases** and enzymes that break down lipids are called **lipases**. Most of the enzymes that catalyse these processes are present in the lumen of the gut, although a few occur inside the cells of the gut mucosa.

From figure 1, you can see that carbohydrate digestion involves two stages. First, the breakdown of starch to maltose is catalysed by the enzyme **amylase** in the mouth and the lumen of the small intestine. Secondly, the breakdown of maltose to glucose is catalysed by the enzyme **maltase** inside the mucosa cells of the small intestine.

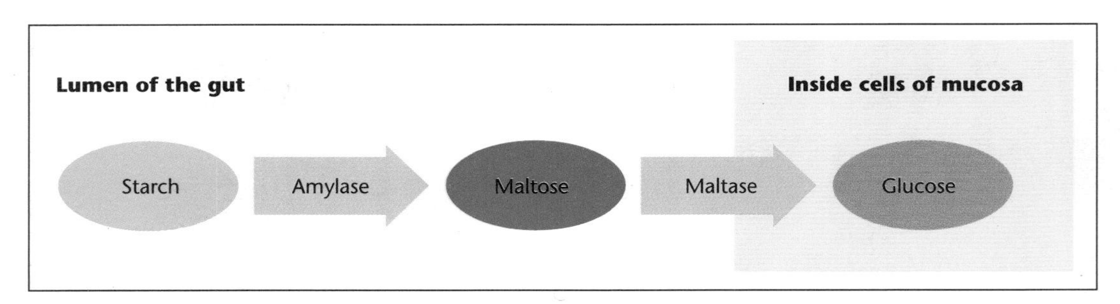

Figure 1 *A summary of carbohydrate digestion in humans.*

The processes of protein digestion also take place in the lumen of the stomach and the small intestine and in the mucosa of the small intestine. Protein digestion in the gut lumen starts with an enzyme called an **endopeptidase** that catalyses the breakdown of proteins to form polypeptides. An enzyme called an **exopeptidase** catalyses the breakdown of polypeptides to produce dipeptides. Inside the cells of the gut mucosa **dipeptidase** enzymes catalyse the breakdown of dipeptides to amino acids.

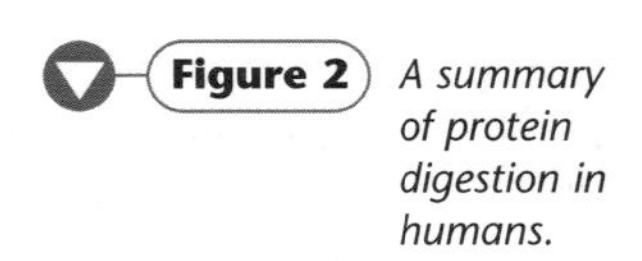

Figure 2 *A summary of protein digestion in humans.*

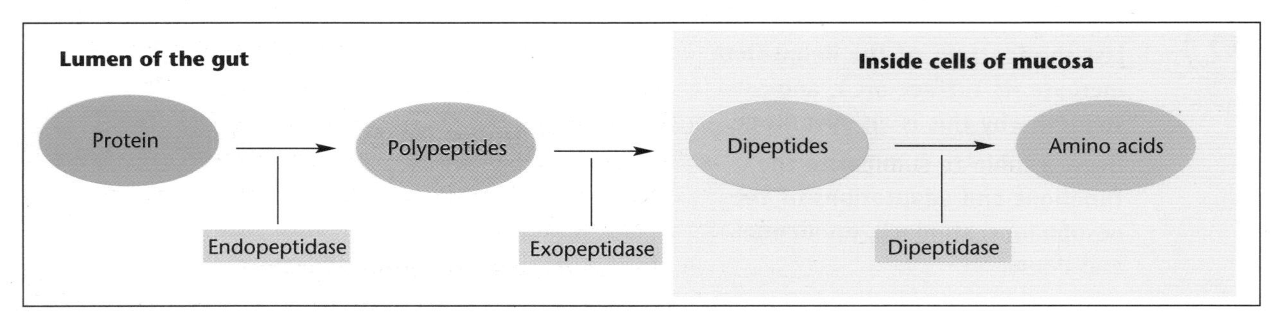

1 **List the similarities and differences between carbohydrate digestion and protein digestion.**

Fat busting

Fats and oils are **lipids**. Lipid digestion only occurs in the lumen of the small intestine. A fat-digesting enzyme called **lipase** and another substance called **bile** only occur in the lumen of the small intestine. Figure 3 outlines the digestion of lipids.

The stomach churns the solid lipids into a fatty liquid made of fat droplets. No chemical digestion takes place because the pH of the stomach is too acidic for lipase activity.

Once the fatty liquid passes into the duodenum, bile salts from the liver found in the bile bind onto the fat droplets. This breaks them down into smaller droplets. This process is called **emulsification**. It is a physical process which increases the surface area available for digestion in the presence of lipase. Lipase from the pancreas catalyses the breakdown of lipids into **fatty acids** and **glycerol**.

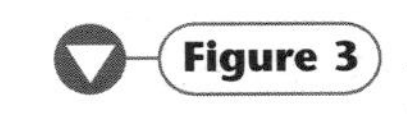

Figure 3 *A summary of lipid digestion in humans.*

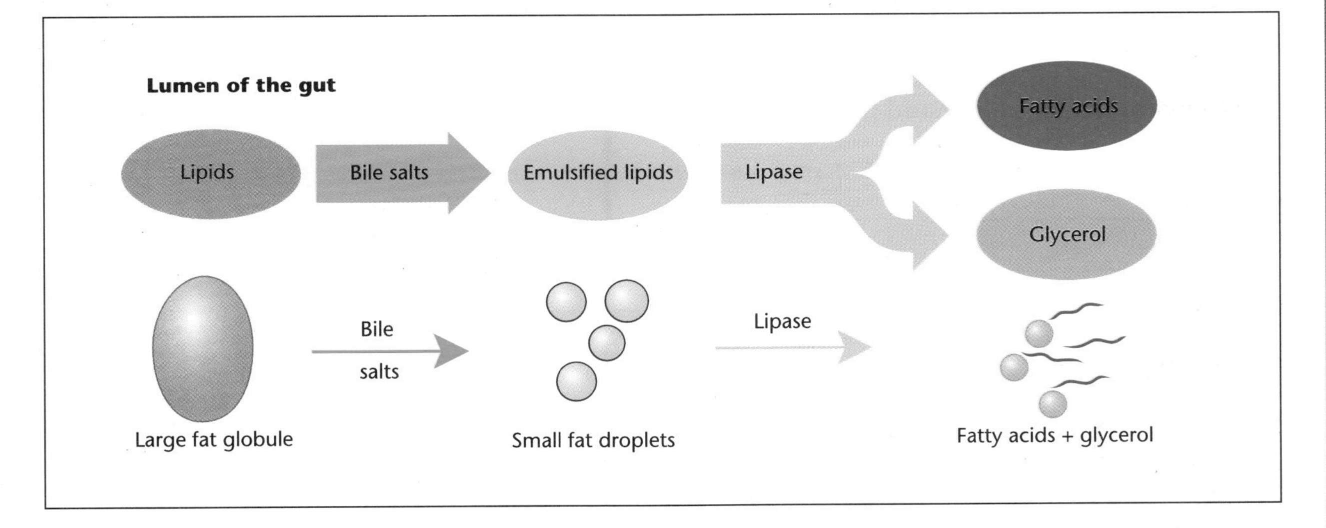

2 **How does lipid digestion differ from carbohydrate and protein digestion?**

Key ideas 26–7

Carbohydrate, protein and lipid digestion is catalysed by enzymes.

Amylases catalyse the breakdown of starch to maltose and maltase catalyses the breakdown of maltose to glucose.

Endopeptidases and exopeptidases are involved in protein digestion. Endopeptidases catalyse the breakdown of proteins to polypeptides. Exopeptidases catalyse the breakdown of dipeptides to amino acids.

Lipase and bile are required for lipid digestion.

5 More about digestion

Chemical digestion takes place at a number of areas throughout the digestive system. Some of the enzymes involved are produced and secreted in **digestive juices** by specialised epithelial cells. Other enzymes are not secreted but are part of the epithelial cell membrane.

Outside and inside the cells

The salivary glands, gastric glands and pancreas all secrete enzymes that pass into the lumen of the gut. This part of digestion takes place outside the cells that make up the gut wall – it is called **extracellular digestion**.

Maltase and the dipeptidases are found in the outer membranes and the cytoplasm of the epithelial cells lining the small intestine. This part of digestion takes place within the cells and is known as **intracellular digestion**.

Digestive juices

The glands involved in digestion are the salivary glands of the mouth, and the glands of the stomach, the small intestine, the liver and the pancreas. Table 1 summarises enzyme action and digestive juice secretion in the human gut.

Table 1 *A summary of enzyme action and digestive juice secretion throughout the human gut.*

Secretion	Site of production	Site of action	Enzyme	Substrate	Product/s
Saliva	Gastric glands	Mouth	Amylase	Starch	Maltose
Gastric juice	Gastric glands	Stomach	Endopeptidase	Protein	Polypeptides
Pancreatic juice	Pancreas	Lumen of the small intestine	Amylase Endopeptidases Exopeptidases Lipase	Starch Protein Polypeptides Lipids	Maltose Polypeptides Dipeptides Monoglycerides Fatty acids + glycerol
Bile	Liver	Lumen of the small intestine			Emulsified lipids
Enzymes	Small intestine	Cell surface membrane of epithelial cells of mucosa	Maltase Dipeptidases	Maltose Dipeptides	Glucose Amino acids
		Cytoplasm of epithelial cells of mucosa	Dipeptidases	Dipeptides	Amino acids

Q

1 **Draw a diagram of the digestive system. On your diagram identify the areas involved in carbohydrate, protein and lipid digestion.**

Intracellular digestion

The digestion of maltose and dipeptides is completed by enzymes in the microvilli on epithelial cells in the small intestine. Look at figure 1. The enzymes are found either in the cell surface membrane or the cytoplasm of the epithelial cells.

Look at figure 2. You can see that maltase and the dipeptidase enzyme are part of the cell surface membrane. Maltose molecules diffuse towards the outer membrane of the microvilli, where they bind to the enzyme maltase.

Maltase catalyses the breakdown of maltose into two glucose molecules. These glucose molecules pass through the membrane into the cytoplasm.

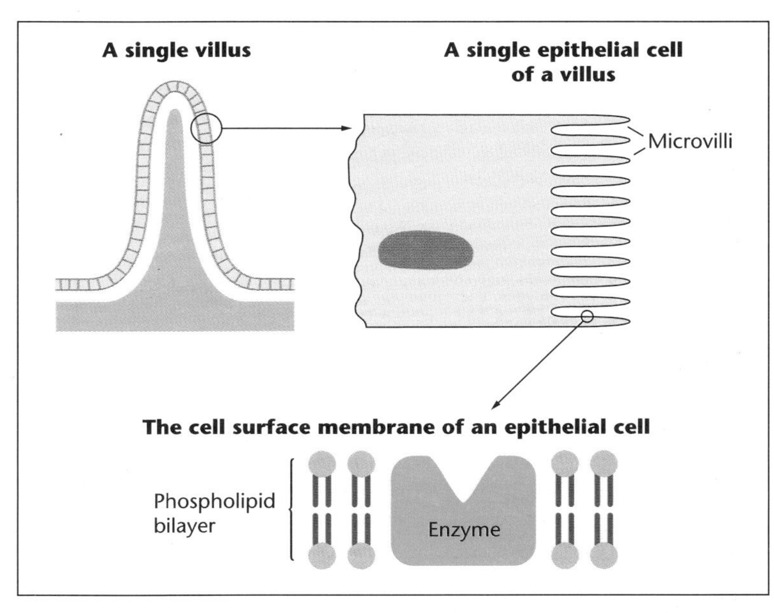

Figure 1 *The position of enzymes on the cell surface membrane of the microvilli.*

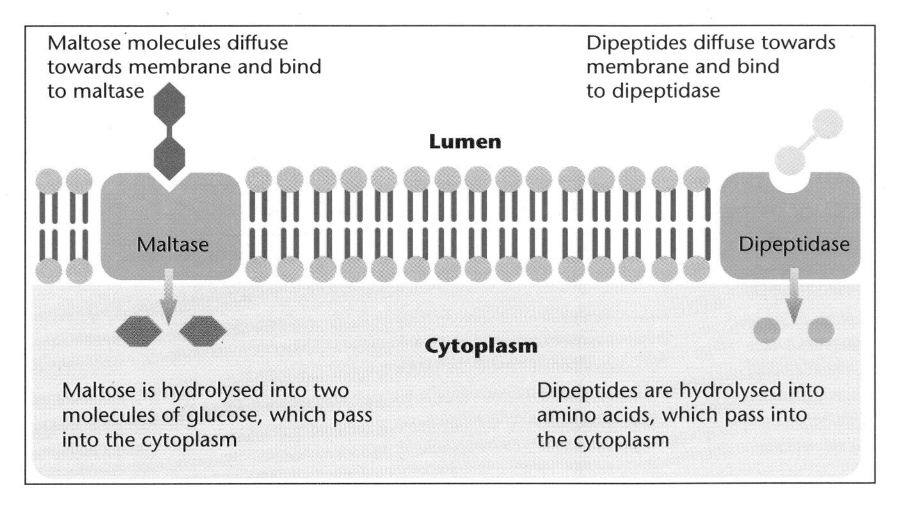

Figure 2 *Intracellular digestion of carbohydrate and protein in the outer membrane of the ileum.*

Dipeptides also diffuse towards the outer membrane of the microvilli, where they bind to dipeptidase enzymes. Dipeptidases catalyse the breakdown of dipeptides into amino acids, which pass into the cytoplasm. Dipeptidases are found in the cytoplasm as well as the cell surface membrane, suggesting that some dipeptides are transported directly into these cells.

2 Draw flow diagrams to summarise the digestion of:
a starch
b protein
c lipid.

Key ideas 28–9

The digestive juices secreted by the salivary glands, gastric glands and pancreas carry out extracellular digestion.

Maltase and dipeptidases in the small intestine carry out intracellular digestion.

6 Absorbing food

Digestion breaks down large molecules of insoluble food into small soluble molecules, which can be used by the body's cells. These molecules reach the rest of the body by passing through the walls of the small intestine and into the blood or lymph. This process is called **absorption** and it takes place mainly in the ileum.

The fate of digested food

The ileum provides a large surface area – the mucosa has large numbers of villi and the epithelial cells have microvilli. Each villus also has an extensive capillary network so that absorbed food is transported away quickly. Lipids are absorbed into a vessel in the villus called a **lacteal**.

Most of the molecules that are the final products of digestion are absorbed by the epithelial cells of the villi into the blood vessels. They are then transported directly to the liver where they are processed.

Glucose and amino acids are absorbed partly by a process called **facilitated diffusion**, and partly by a process called **active transport**. In facilitated diffusion, a molecule is moved across a cell membrane with the help of a protein called a channel protein. In active transport, a molecule is moved across a membrane with the help of a protein called a carrier protein, and the process uses energy. The products of lipid digestion are absorbed by a process called **simple diffusion**. Simple diffusion is the movement of a molecule from an area of high concentration to an area of low concentration. There is more about how substances cross membranes on pages 82–7.

1 Look at the epithelial cells in figure 1. Notice the many closely packed microvilli at the top (the brush border region). Suggest how the structure of these cells is ideally suited for the function of absorption.

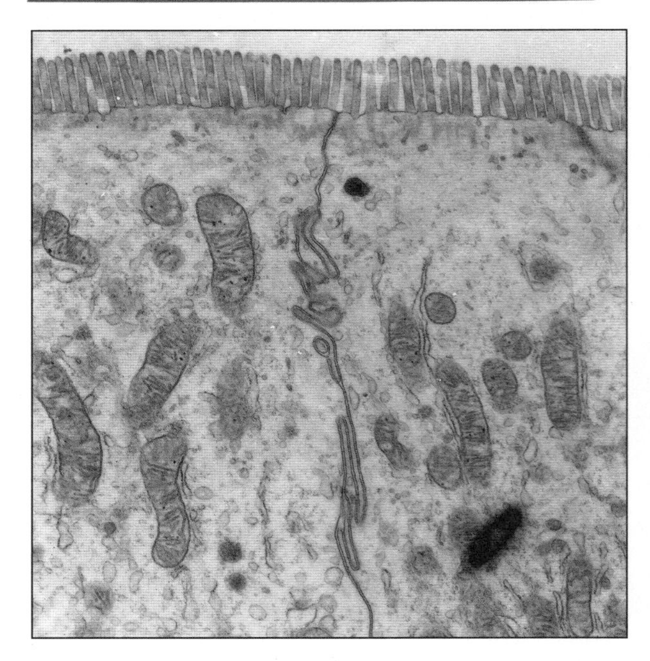

Figure 1 *An electron micrograph of epithelial cells from a villus (× 10 000).*

Transporting glucose

In the membrane of the epithelial cells, there are glucose carrier proteins which are dependent on sodium ions. The process involves a number of steps, shown in figure 2.

A sodium/potassium pump (**A**) transports sodium ions out of the cell by active transport. Glucose molecules and sodium ions bind to the carrier protein (**B**) and the sodium ions diffuse into the cells, carrying the glucose molecules with them. Inside the cells, the glucose molecules and sodium ions leave the carrier protein. The glucose concentration of the cell rises and glucose diffuses to the other end of the cell. It then moves into the blood by facilitated diffusion.

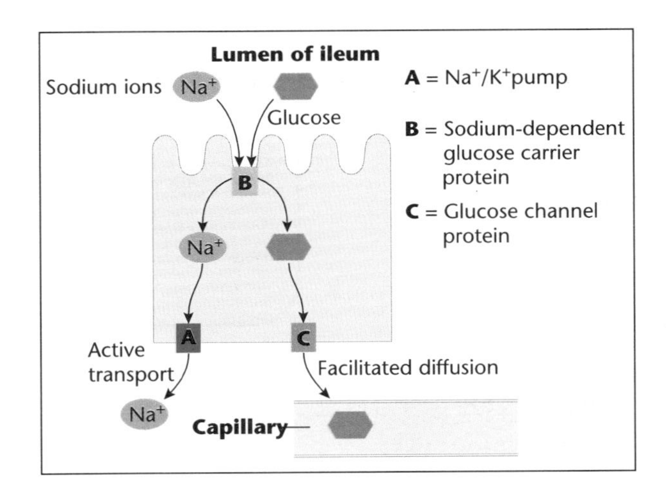

Figure 2 *Absorption of glucose from the lumen of the ileum to the blood capillaries.*

Transporting amino acids

In the membrane of the epithelial cells, there are also amino acid carrier proteins. These too rely on the help of sodium ions. Look at figure 3. The sodium/potassium pump transports sodium ions out of the cell by active transport. Amino acids and sodium ions bind to the carrier protein (**D**). As the sodium ions diffuse into the cell, amino acids are carried too.

The amino acids diffuse to the other end of the cell. They are then transferred to the capillaries by facilitated diffusion (**E**).

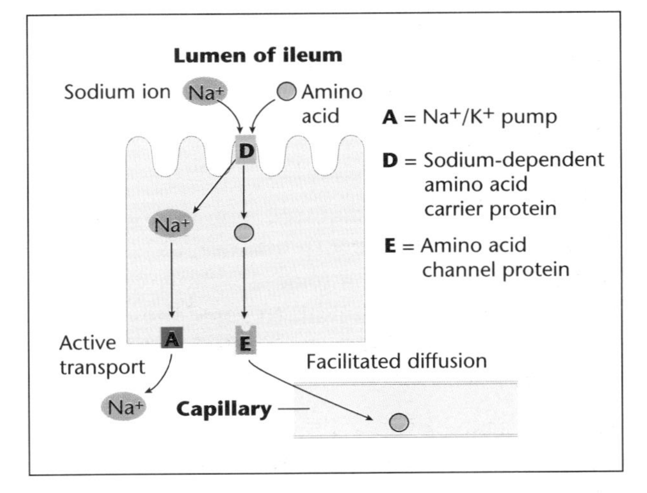

Figure 3 *Absorption of amino acids from the lumen of the ileum to the blood capillaries.*

Transporting lipids

Lipid absorption is different. Look at figure 4. Lipids are broken down to **fatty acids**, **glycerol** and **monoglycerides** (partially digested lipids). Fatty acids vary in the length of their chain.

Short fatty acid chains diffuse directly into the blood from the lumen of the ileum via the epithelium. Longer chain fatty acids, monoglycerides and glycerol diffuse into the epithelial cells where they recombine to form **triglycerides**. A triglyceride is a molecule produced by joining three fatty acid molecules and one molecule of glycerol. These triglycerides are packaged with cholesterol and phospholipid to form water-soluble fat droplets, called **chylomicrons**. These are transferred to the lacteal by **exocytosis** – membrane-bound sacs are emptied at the surface of the cell.

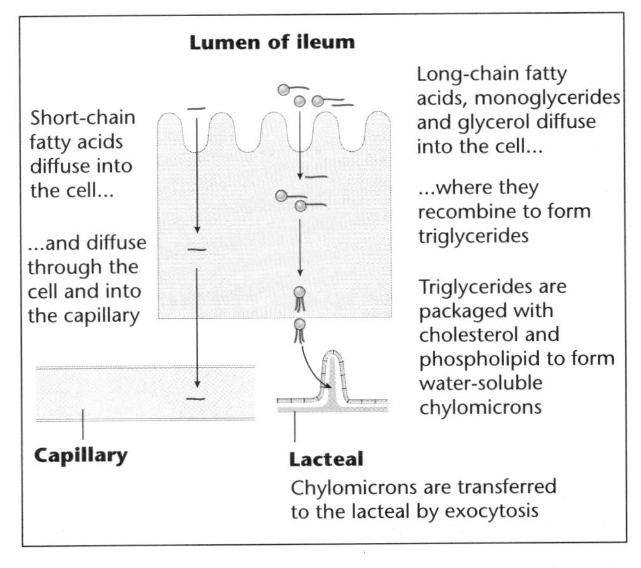

Figure 4 *Absorption of lipids from the lumen of the ileum to the blood capillaries and the lymph.*

7 When something goes wrong

The cells in the lining of the small intestine normally produce an enzyme called lactase, which catalyses the breakdown of lactose (a sugar found in milk). In the small intestine, lactose is digested into simple sugars by the action of lactase. The simple sugars produced are **glucose** and **galactose**.

Milk sugar

Lactose is a sugar found in milk and milk products such as ice cream, cheese and butter. Lactose is also added to some processed foods such as bread and some breakfast cereals. Figure 1 shows a range of food products that contain lactose.

1 Lactose is digested and absorbed in a similar way to maltose, as described on page 29. Draw a fully labelled diagram to show the intracellular digestion of lactose.

Figure 1 *These products contain lactose.*

Bothered by milk

Some people do not have enough lactase enzyme to digest the lactose they eat. If the lactose is not digested, it can cause nausea, bloating, diarrhoea, gas and stomach cramps. People who have this problem are considered to be **lactose intolerant**.

A few of the causes of lactose intolerance are known. Some diseases and injuries to the small intestine can reduce the amount of lactase produced. Occasionally children are born without the ability to produce lactase, but more often lactase deficiency develops gradually from about the age of two.

Treating lactase deficiency

Fortunately, lactose intolerance is not life threatening and is fairly easy to treat. The symptoms can be relieved by a change in diet. Sufferers start to feel better as soon as they stop eating foods containing lactose, or reduce the amount of lactose-containing food they eat. Different sufferers can tolerate different amounts of lactose. Medication is available for those who cannot tolerate even small amounts of lactose.

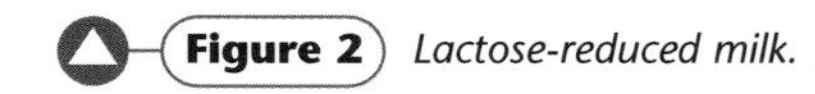

Figure 2 *Lactose-reduced milk.*

One medical product is lactase enzyme, available from local pharmacies. A liquid form can be added to milk, and a chewable tablet can be used to help the digestion of solid foods containing lactose. Lactose-reduced milk is also available.

Poor absorption

Gluten is a protein found in wheat, rye and some other cereals. Sufferers of **coeliac disease** cannot tolerate gluten.

The effect of gluten on the small intestine of sufferers is severe – the villi are lost and the small intestine becomes smooth. Figure 3 shows some of the effects of the disease. Loss of villi and elongation of the crypts of Lieberkuhn are typical in people who have coeliac disease.

The symptoms of coeliac disease usually start within a few weeks of cereals being introduced into a baby's diet. The baby does not put on weight easily, and may even lose weight through loss of appetite. Other symptoms include diarrhoea, stomach cramps and vomiting.

Fortunately the condition is treatable, although it can lead to long-term problems such as brittle bone disease, infertility and cancer. The main treatment is to remove cereals from the baby's diet. Sufferers can eat rice and maize, and there are a number of gluten-free products available. A short time after changing the diet, the baby's symptoms clear up.

2 Describe the effect the loss of villi will have on absorption.

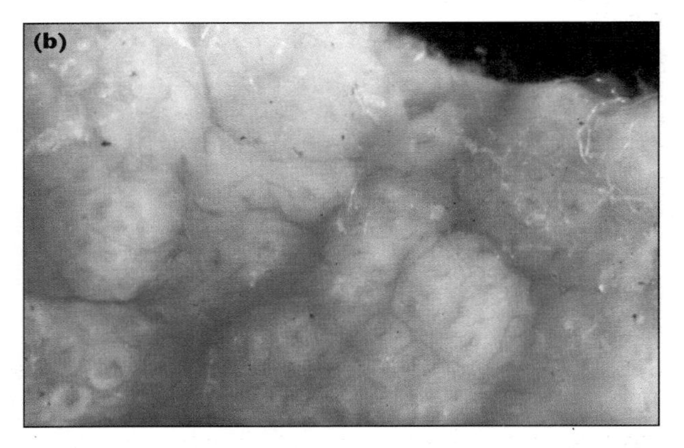

Figure 3 *(a) Surface view of normal villi in the small intestine. (×20)*
(b) The small intestine of a coeliac disease sufferer shows a loss of villi and a reduced surface area. (×20)

Key ideas 30–33

The ileum of the small intestine is the main site for the absorption of digested food.

Glucose and amino acids are absorbed partly by active transport and partly by facilitated diffusion into the blood capillaries.

The products of lipid digestion are absorbed into the blood capillaries and the lymph by simple diffusion.

8 Feeding from dead organisms

Some organisms digest their food outside the cells of their bodies. Fungi are good examples of this. They obtain nutrients from dead and decaying organisms by secreting enzymes directly onto them. Organisms that obtain nutrients in this way are called **saprophytes**.

Mouldy bread

Bread mould (*Mucor hiemalis*) is a common fungus that grows on damp, stale bread and rotting fruit. Look at figure 1(a). *Mucor* starts as cotton-like white threads on the surface of the bread. The network of threads is called the **mycelium**. After a few days, masses of tiny black **sporangia** appear, resembling pinheads.

Some saprophytes live in soil. Figure 1(b) shows mushrooms, which are a type of fungus. They live in soil and produce nutrients or humus, on which they feed.

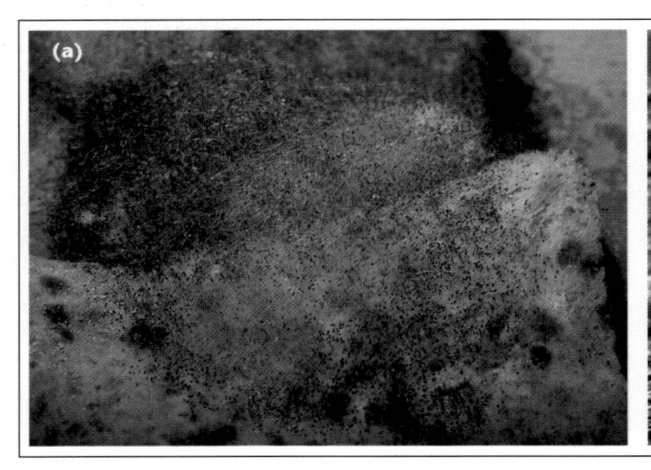

Figure 1 *(a) The saprophyte* Mucor hiemalis *growing on bread. (b) Mushrooms growing on a tree stump.*

A microscope reveals that the bread mould mycelium is made up of a network of hollow tubes called **hyphae**. A single tube is called a **hypha**. Aerial hyphae spread over the food and produce tufts of branched hyphae where they touch.

Figure 2 shows a portion of a mycelium with three fruiting bodies. Look at the network of hyphae spreading outwards. The hyphae branch repeatedly to produce the mycelium. It is the growing mycelium that can be seen as a white mass on the surface of rotting food.

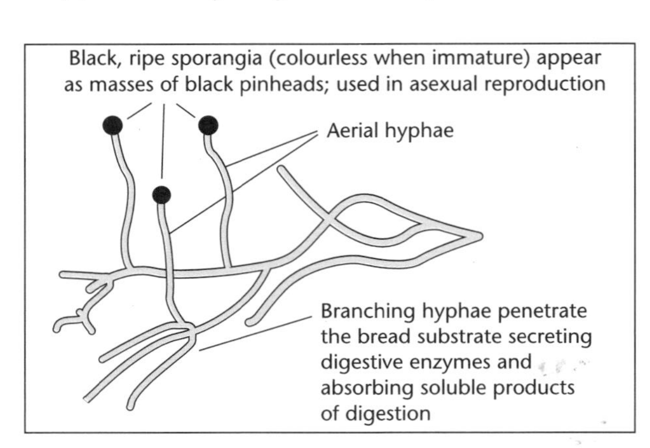

Figure 2 *The structure of* Mucor.

A mycelium starts with the germination of a single spore, which grows a hypha. The hypha branches, eventually forming a mat extending over the surface of the bread. There is no limit to the size of the mycelium – it will grow wherever there are enough nutrients.

Fungal feeding

Fungi secrete enzymes from the growing tip of the hyphae. Digestion takes place outside the fungi.

Figure 3 shows a single hypha. You can see many nuclei and mitochondria in the cytoplasm. There are no chloroplasts. Cytoplasm fills the tips of growing hyphae, and surrounding each hypha is a cell wall and a cell membrane.

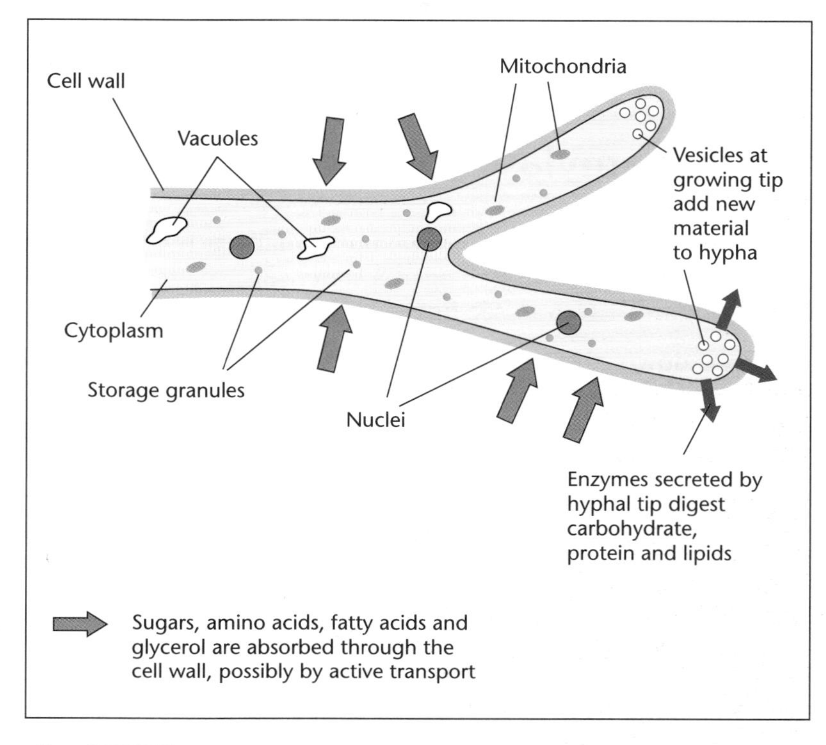

Figure 3 *A single hypha showing structures visible with a light microscope.*

The growing tips of the branching hyphae penetrate the food, secreting enzymes. The enzymes diffuse out through the cell wall onto the surface of the food (substrate). These enzymes digest the material in the food into small soluble products. The soluble products of this digestion are absorbed into the hyphae through the cell wall and the cell membrane by facilitated diffusion or active transport. The soluble products are then transported to all parts of the fungus. If excess nutrients are available, they are stored within the mycelium as glycogen. Since digestion has taken place outside the body of the fungus, this is known as **extracellular digestion**.

1 **Three main types of enzyme are secreted by the fungus: carbohydrases, proteases and lipases. Name the substrate that each type of enzyme acts on.**

Key ideas 34–5

Fungi obtain food by extracellular digestion.

Fungi secrete enzymes onto the food substrate. These enzymes break down the food, which is then absorbed through the cell wall into the hyphae.

9 Looking for enzyme activity

The fungus *Rhizopus* can be grown in the laboratory on starch–agar plates. *Rhizopus* digests the starch on which it is growing. The amount of starch digestion can be measured using an iodine solution. Iodine changes colour in the presence of starch. It changes from yellow-brown to blue-black.

Testing amylase for carbohydrase activity

Agar is a gel at room temperature, but it melts at high temperatures. If starch is mixed with molten agar, a starch–agar plate can be prepared. Look at figures 1 to 5 to see how a starch–agar plate is produced.

The breakdown of starch is catalysed by a **carbohydrase** enzyme called **amylase**. Amylase catalyses the breakdown of starch to glucose. *Rhizopus* secretes amylase from the growing tips of its hyphae onto the surface of its substrate. When iodine is poured onto a starch–agar plate, areas of undigested starch are visible as a deep blue colour and areas of digested starch are colourless. The larger the colourless area, the more active the enzyme has been.

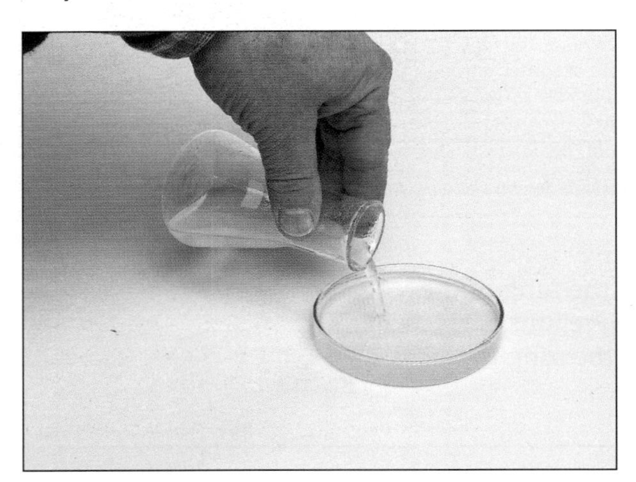

Figure 1 *To make a starch–agar plate, the starch–agar mixture is poured into a plate known as a Petri dish.*

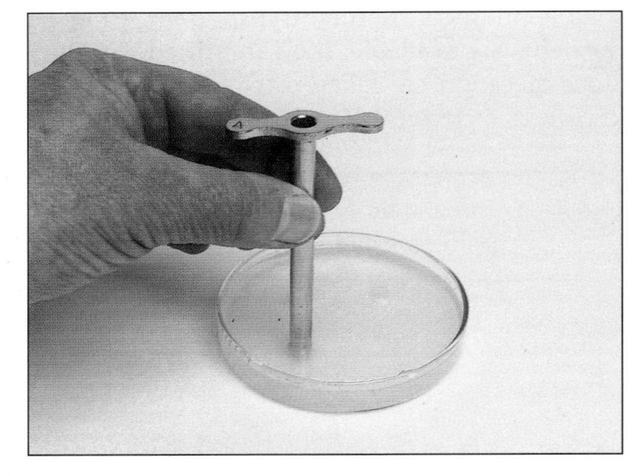

Figure 2 *Once the starch and agar has cooled and set, holes known as wells are cut into the starch–agar using a cork borer.*

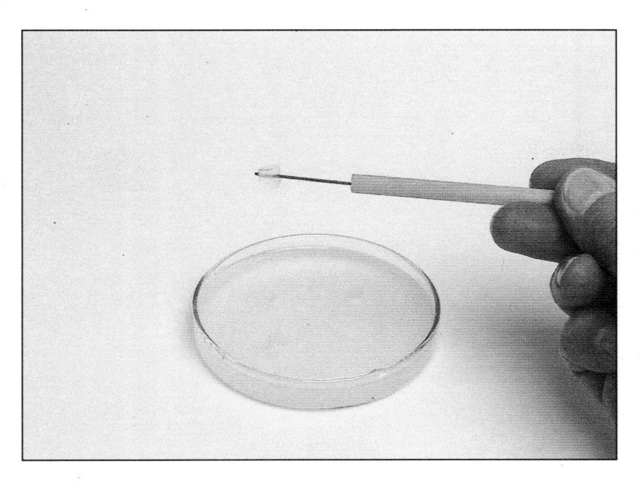

Figure 3 *The cylinders of starch–agar are removed. The wells are now ready for use. A different concentration of amylase is put in each well. The dish is then placed in an incubator for 48 hours at 25 °C.*

Figure 4 *After 48 hours, the plates are removed from the incubator and iodine solution is poured over the starch – agar surface.*

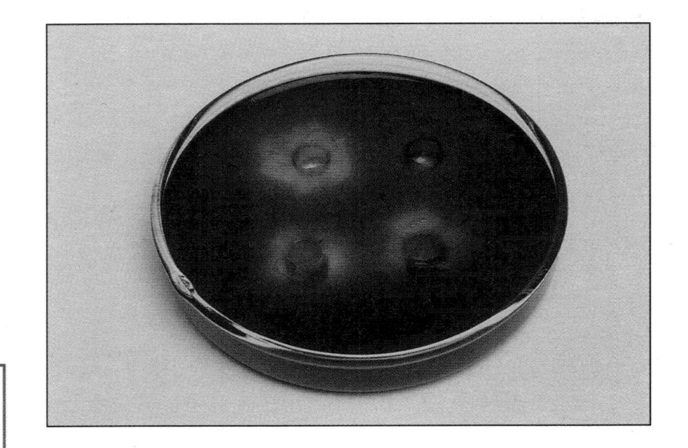

Figure 5 *After 1 minute, the iodine is poured away. Areas of undigested starch are visible as a deep blue colour. Areas where the starch has been broken down are colourless. The size of the colourless area gives an indication as to the activity of the enzyme. The larger the colourless area, the more active the enzyme.*

Q

1. **Look at figure 5. Which well contained the highest concentration of amylase?**
2. **Explain the results using the lock and key theory of enzyme action.**
3. **Describe an experiment using starch–agar plates to investigate amylase activity in *Rhizopus*.**

Key ideas 36–7

Starch–agar plates can be used to look for carbohydrase activity.

The size of the colourless area gives an indication as to the activity of the enzyme. The larger the colourless area, the more active the enzyme.

Unit 2 – Questions

10

1. Figure 1 shows a fungus.

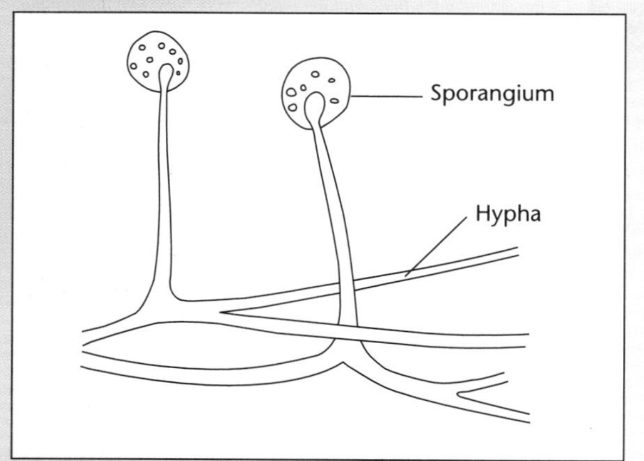

a) Define the term saprophyte. (1 mark)
b) Describe how the fungus in the diagram obtains food. (3 marks)
c) Describe an experiment that can be performed to determine whether the fungus secretes a carbohydrase enzyme. (3 marks)

(Total 7 marks)

2. Figure 2 shows a drawing made from an electron micrograph of epithelial cells from the small intestine of a human.

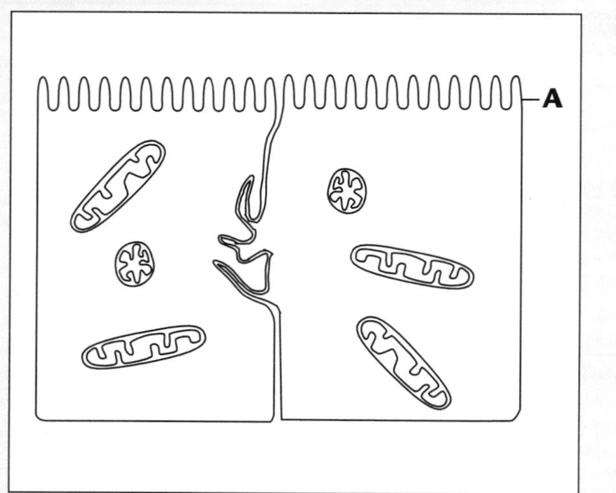

a) Name the structure labelled **A**. (1 mark)
b) Suggest how **A** increases the rate of uptake of substances from the small intestine. (2 marks)

(Total 3 marks)

3) In humans, protein digestion involves a number of steps and uses more than one type of enzyme.

a) Copy and complete table 1. (4 marks)

Enzyme	Site of action	Substrate	Product
Endopeptidase			Polypeptides
Exopeptidase		Polypeptides	

b) Give a reason why the combined action of these two enzymes is more efficient than an exopeptidase on its own. (2 marks)

(Total 6 marks)

4) **a)** Name the products of lipid digestion. (1 mark)

b) Describe lipid digestion and absorption. (6 marks)

(Total 7 marks)

5) Figure 3 represents a magnified section through a region of the human gut wall as seen through a light microscope.

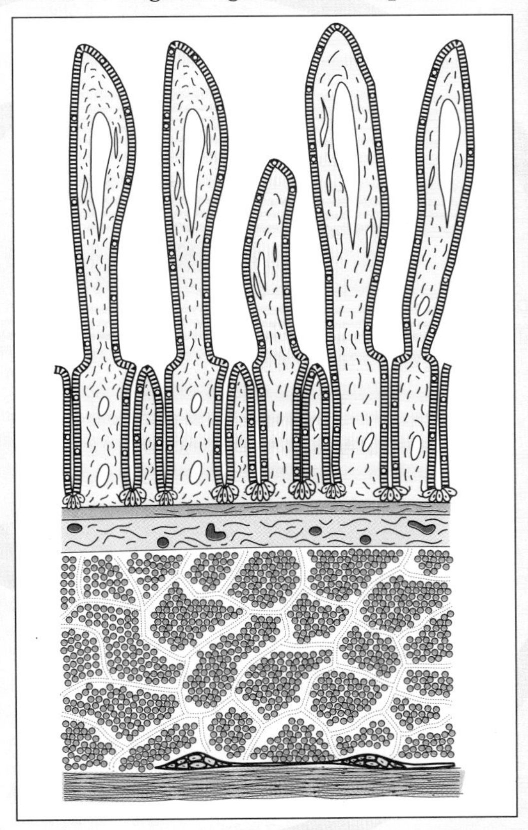

a) Identify the region of the gut from which the section is taken. (1 mark)

b) Give a reason for your answer. (1 mark)

c) Explain how this region of the gut is suited to its function. (2 marks)

(Total 4 marks)

1 Keeping order

The basic unit of any organism, such as a plant or an animal, is the **cell**. However, in the organism there is division of labour – there are many different kinds of cell, each with a particular job to do. You have already seen how similar cells group together to form **tissues**. Tissues group to form **organs** and organs group to form **systems**.

On a smaller scale

The cell is the basic unit of an organism, but the cell itself is made up of lots of atoms grouped in different ways. Look at figure 1. You can see that atoms join together to form simple **molecules**, for example, amino acids, carbon dioxide and water. Simple molecules join together to form larger molecules called **macromolecules**, such as proteins. Macromolecules combine together to carry out metabolic reactions, or to form structures in the cell such as membranes. The different structures inside a cell are called **organelles**. Each organelle carries out a special activity.

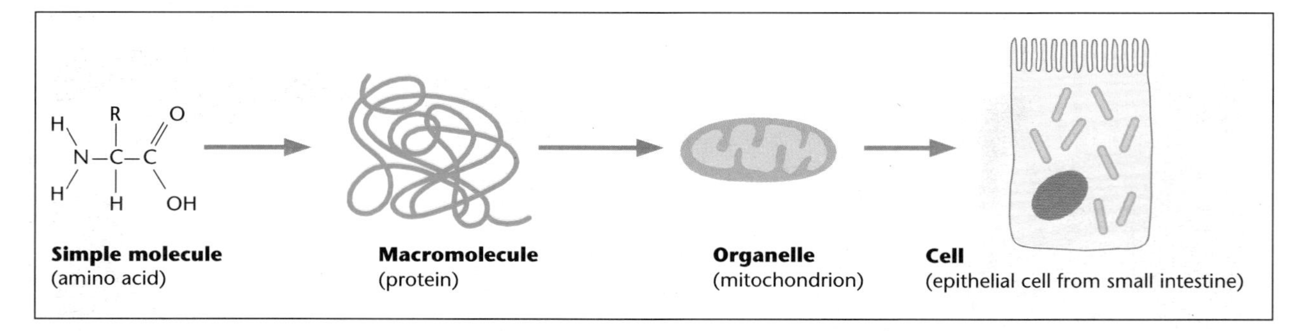

Figure 1 *Levels of organisation inside a cell.*

On the inside

If you look at figures 2 and 3, you can see that cells contain several different kinds of organelle. An **organelle** is a subunit of the cell, designed to carry out its own specific function separate from all the other activities going on in the cell. Figure 2 shows a cell from the epithelium of the small intestine, and figure 3 shows a spongy mesophyll cell from the leaf of a plant. Notice how some kinds of organelle are found in both types of cell, but other types of organelle are only found in particular kinds of cell.

1 The magnification of the electron micrograph in figure 3(b) is ×7000. Calculate the actual length in μm of the organelle marked X. (A μm, micrometre, is one-thousandth of a millimetre, or 10^{-6} m.)

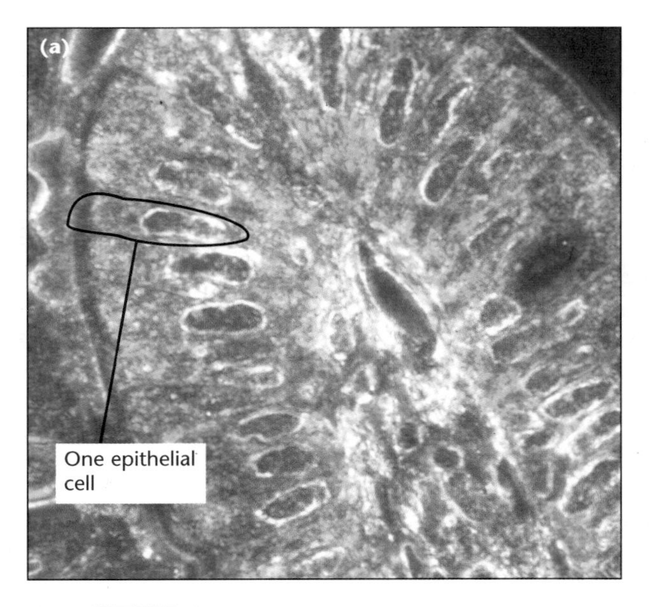

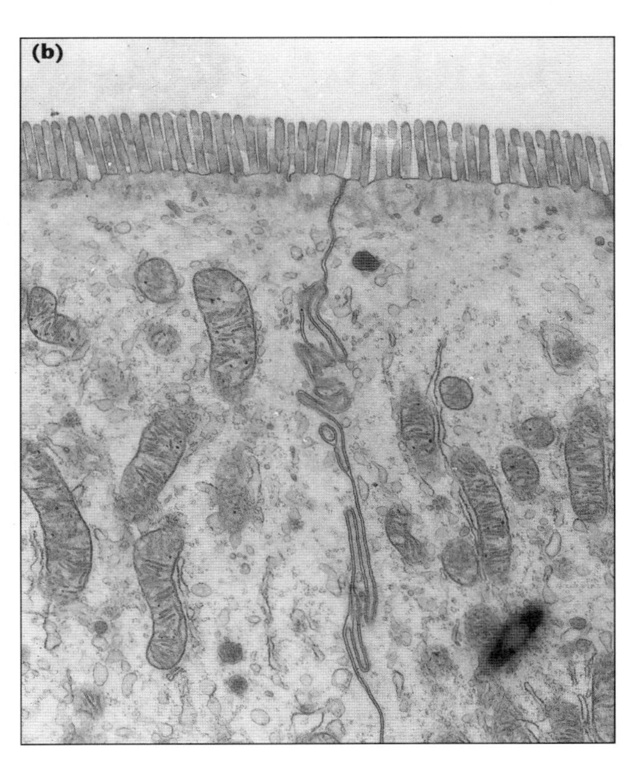

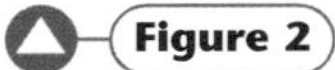
Figure 2 *(a) Light micrograph of the tip of a villus in the small intestine, showing epithelial cells (×4000). (b) Electron micrograph of epithelial cells from the small intestine (×10 000).*

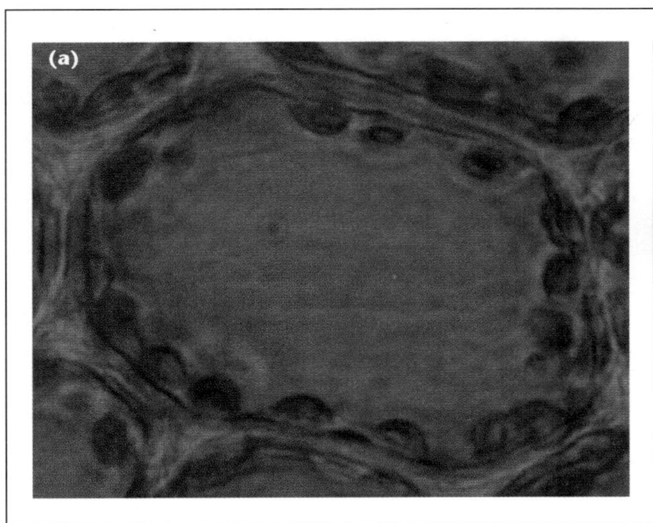

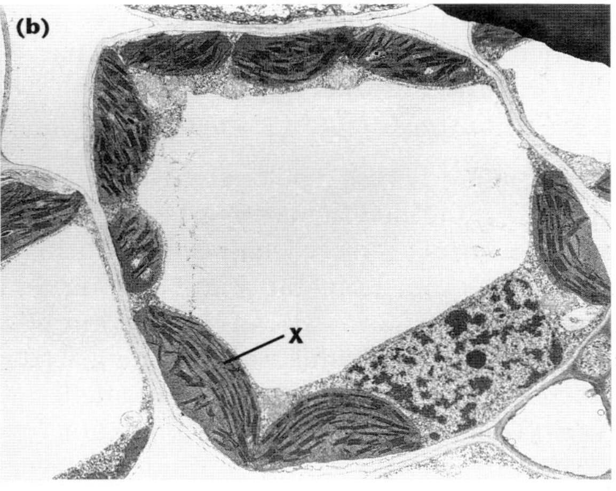

Figure 3 *(a) Light micrograph (×7000) and (b) electron micrograph (×7000) of a plant spongy mesophyll cell.*

Key ideas 40–41

Cells are the basic units of living things. They combine to form tissues, tissues combine to form organs and organs can combine to form systems.

Within cells there are smaller structures called organelles, which are subunits of the cell each designed to carry out a specific function.

2 Finding out about cells

Cells are the basic units of which living things are made. They are so small that we need to use a microscope to see them. Microscopes can magnify things many times. You are probably already familiar with a **light microscope**, which shines light through a thin sample of biological material, and magnifies it using lenses. A good light microscope can give a magnification of ×1500. However, if two structures inside a cell are closer than 0.2 mm, they cannot be seen as separate objects under a light microscope. Many structures inside cells are very small and close together, so we need a different kind of microscope to look at them.

The electron microscope

The **electron microscope** is very useful for helping us to find out about the detailed structure of cells. It uses a beam of electrons instead of light. Electron beams have a much smaller wavelength than light, which means the electron microscope can show two objects that are very close together as separate objects. In other words, the electron microscope has better **resolution** than a light microscope. This allows us to see structures in much more detail.

Look at figure 1. This type of electron microscope is called the **transmission electron microscope**. The specimens being observed are called **sections**, and they need to be very thin to allow electrons to pass through. Once prepared, individual sections are placed in a vacuum, as any air molecules would deflect the electron beam. Since your eyes are not sensitive to electron beams, you cannot view the specimen directly. Instead, the image has to be viewed in black and white on a screen or a photograph. Sometimes computer software is used to add colour to these pictures, but they are not the real colours of the specimen.

Another kind of electron microscope is the **scanning electron microscope**. The scanning electron microscope allows you to see the three-dimensional shape of a specimen. This is particularly useful for looking at structures such as viruses.

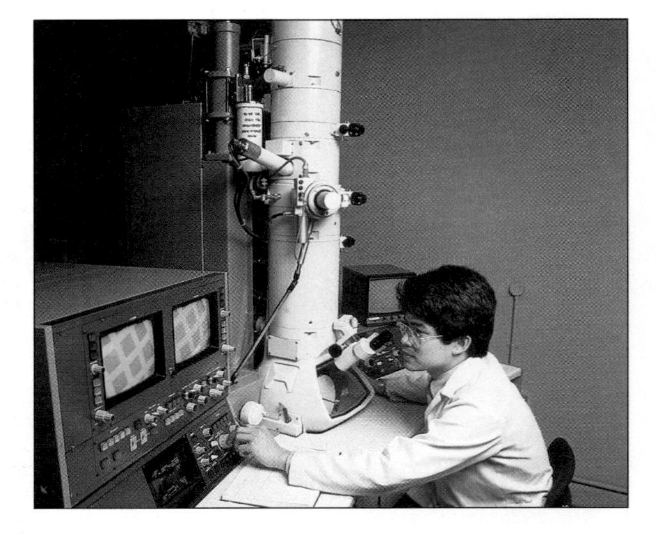

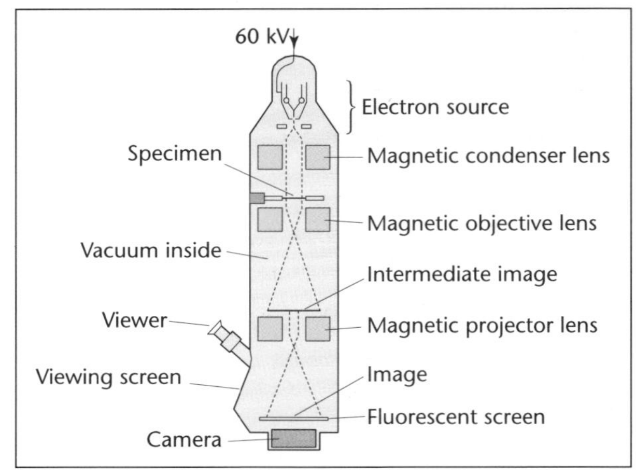

Figure 1 *How the electron microscope works.*

Looking inside

Look at figure 2. These two photographs show the same structure (pancreas cells) at the same magnification (×1200). The top photograph was taken using a light microscope and the bottom one was taken using an electron microscope. You will notice that the bottom photograph shows much more detail, because the electron microscope has better resolution than the light microscope.

When you use an ordinary light microscope, some areas seem darker than others. This is because light can pass through certain parts of the specimen more easily than others. Electron microscopes work in a similar way. The beam of electrons passes through certain parts more easily than others, so when you view the image on a screen, some parts are darker and some are lighter.

Figure 3 shows how the specimens are prepared for a scanning electron microscope.

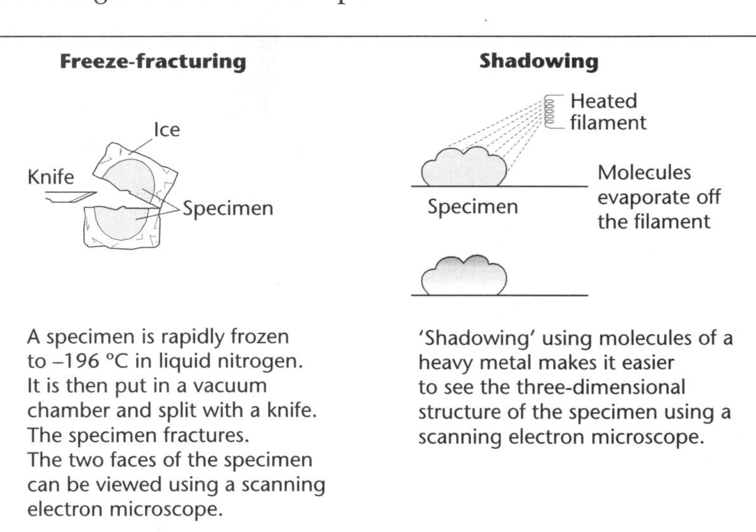

Figure 3 *Freeze-fracturing and shadowing.*

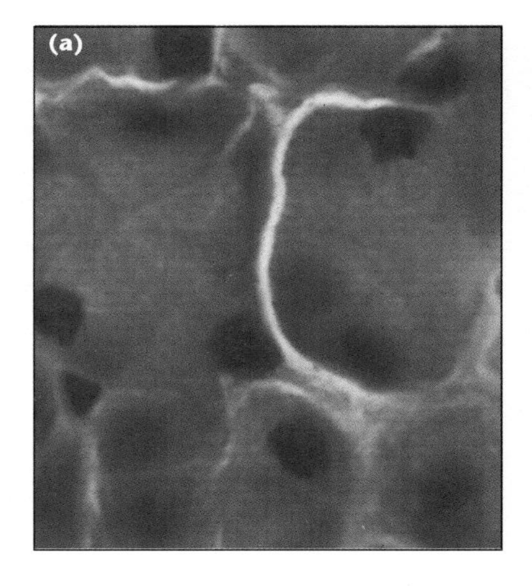

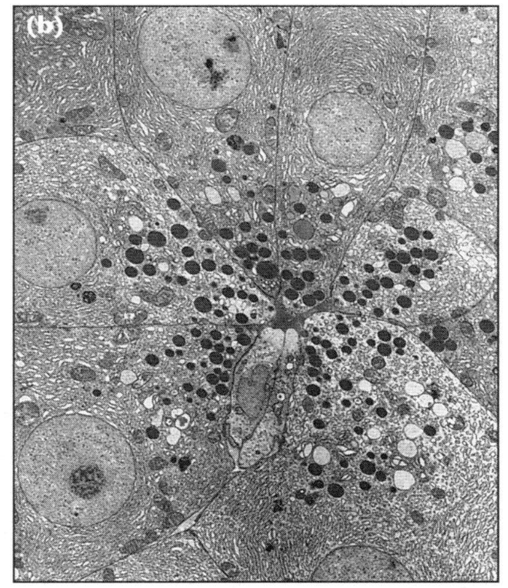

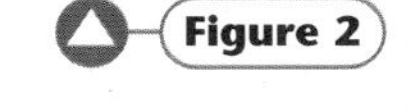
Figure 2 *A photograph of pancreas cells taken using (a) a light microscope and (b) an electron microscope.*

Q

1. **Give two reasons why we cannot view living specimens using an electron microscope.**
2. **Give one advantage and two disadvantages of using the electron microscope rather than a conventional light microscope to study the structure of a cell.**

Key ideas 42–3

The electron microscope is useful for studying cells because it has better resolution than a light microscope.

Transmission electron microscopes show thin sections of specimens, and scanning electron microscopes can show the three-dimensional structure of a specimen.

3 Cells with a nucleus

Cells with a nucleus are called **eukaryotic cells**, which means 'cells with a true nucleus'. Animal cells and plant cells are eukaryotic. Look at the photographs on page 43. You can see that some of the organelles within eukaryotic cells can be seen using a light microscope, but to see all the organelles in detail you need to use an electron microscope.

Animal cell

Figure 1 shows the **ultrastructure** of one type of animal cell – it shows the organelles you can see with an electron microscope.

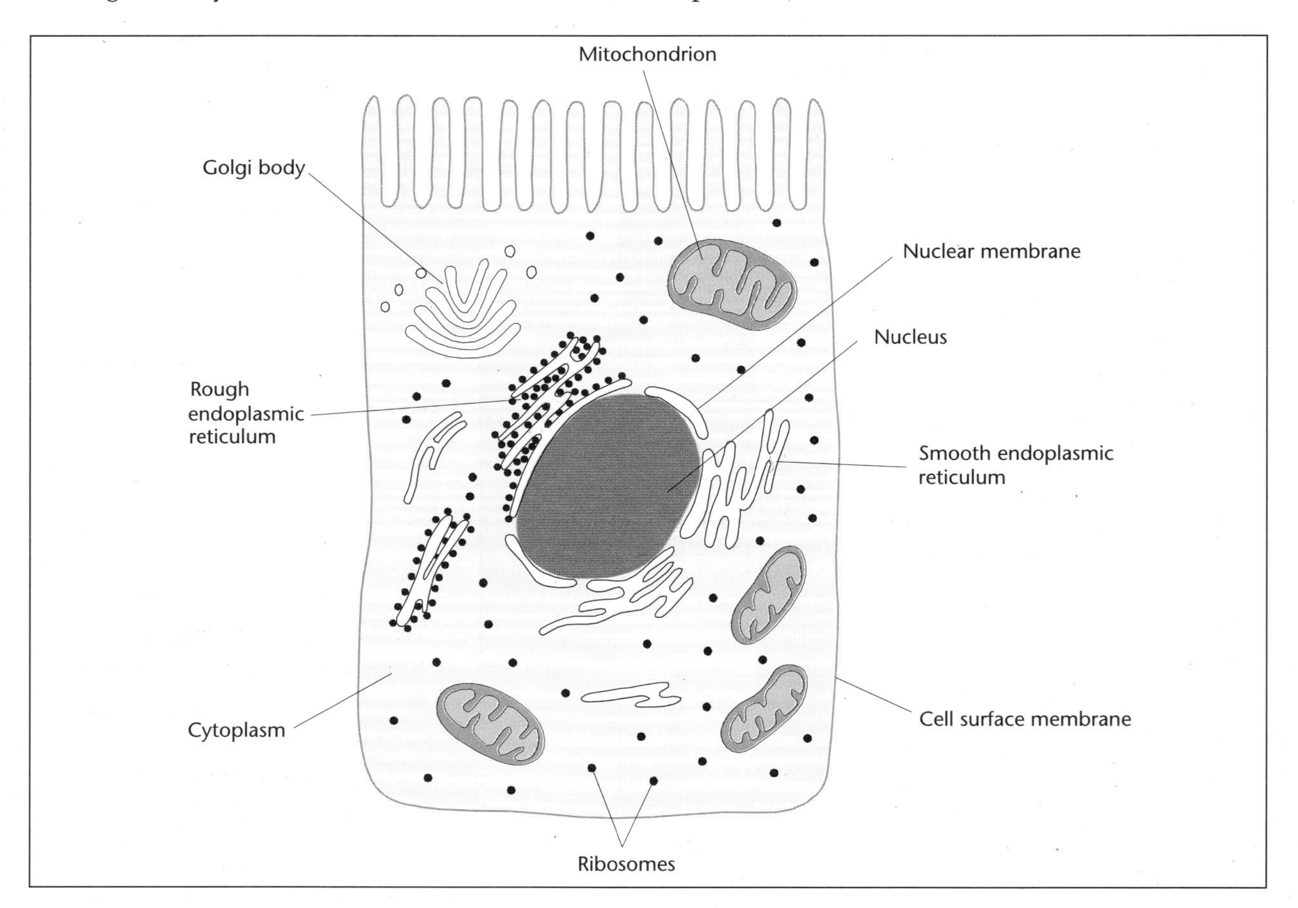

Figure 1 *The ultrastructure of an epithelial cell from the small intestine.*

Plant cell

Figure 2 shows the ultrastructure of one type of plant cell. You can see that some of the organelles shown are also present in the animal cell. However, some organelles are only found in plant cells.

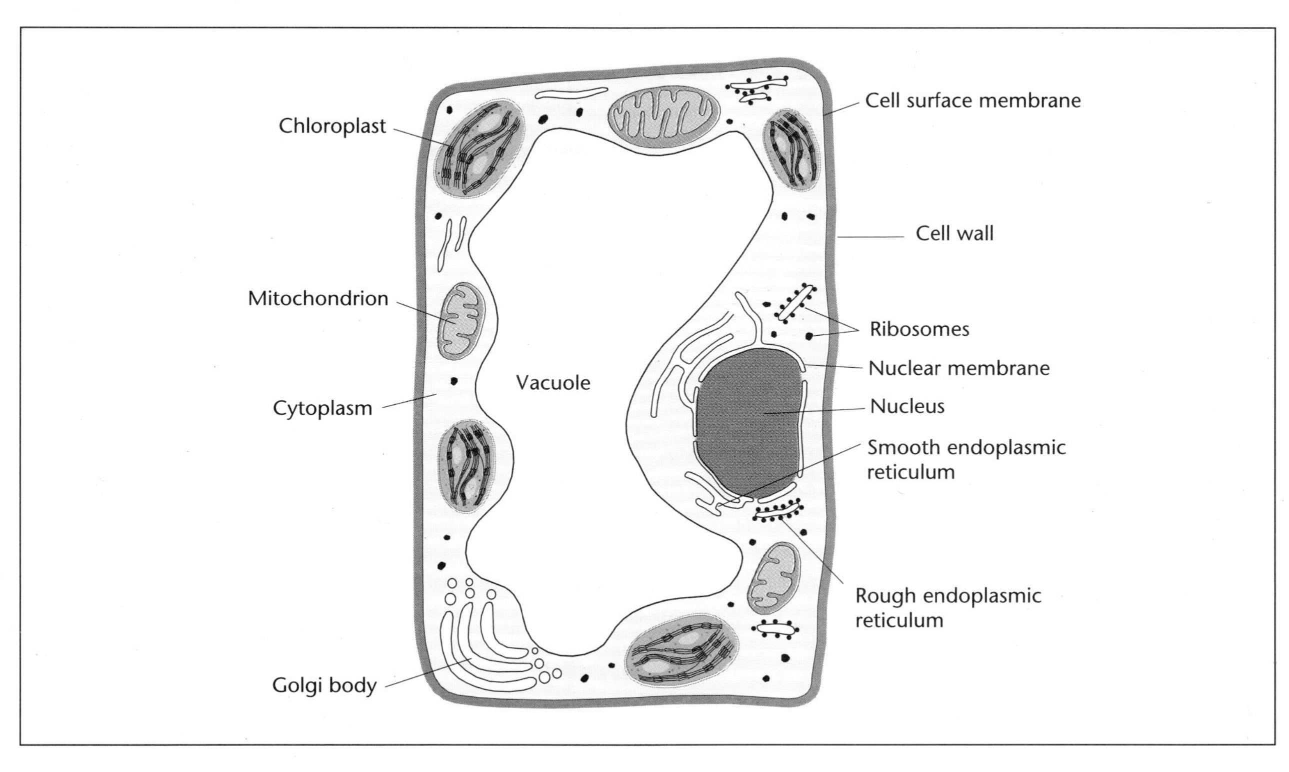

Figure 2 *The ultrastructure of a palisade mesophyll cell from a plant leaf.*

Comparing animal cells and plant cells

Table 1 summarises the similarities and differences between animal cells and plant cells.

Table 1 *Animal cells and plant cells both have many organelles. Unlike animal cells, plant cells have a cell wall and may have chloroplasts.*

Organelles	Animal cell	Plant cell
Nucleus	✓	✓
Ribosomes	✓	✓
Cell wall	✗	✓
Cell surface membrane	✓	✓
Golgi body	✓	✓
Mitochondria	✓	✓
Chloroplasts	✗	✓
Rough endoplasmic reticulum	✓	✓
Smooth endoplasmic reticulum	✓	✓
Permanent vacuole	✗	✓

Q

1 What three organelles may plant cells have that animal cells do not?

2 Compare the shapes of the animal cell and plant cell.
a Which is more regular?
b What feature causes this?

Key ideas 44–5

Animal cells and plant cells are eukaryotic cells.

Plant cells have a cellulose cell wall and may contain chloroplasts and a permanent vacuole.

4 Hives of activity

Organelles are found inside cells, in the **cytoplasm**. The cytoplasm is a watery solution containing glucose, proteins and ions. Each organelle in a cell has a different function to perform, amongst all the other activities going on in the cell.

Controlling the cell

Look at figure 1. You can see that the **nucleus** has a double membrane around it containing pores. The nucleus contains chromosomes, which are made of **DNA**. Sections of the DNA are **genes**. These hold the blueprint for every feature of the body. They carry the information needed to make proteins, including the enzymes needed for most of the processes going on in the cell. Making proteins is called **protein synthesis**.

The **cell surface membrane** controls the entry of substances into and out of the cell. For more details of how the membrane does this, see page 78.

1 What kind of electron microscope was used to obtain the electron micrograph in figure 1?

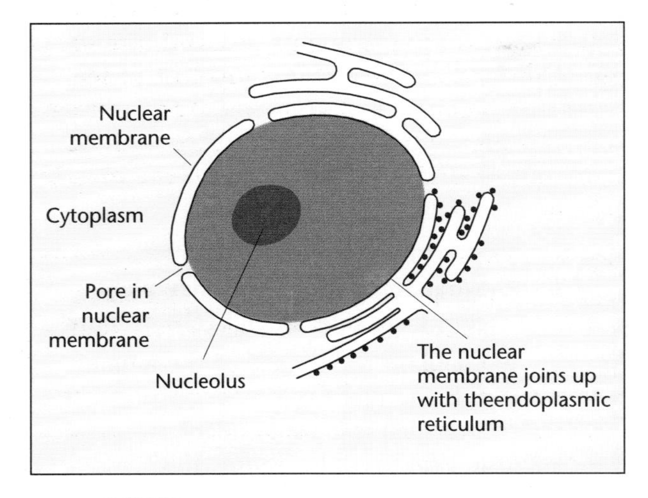

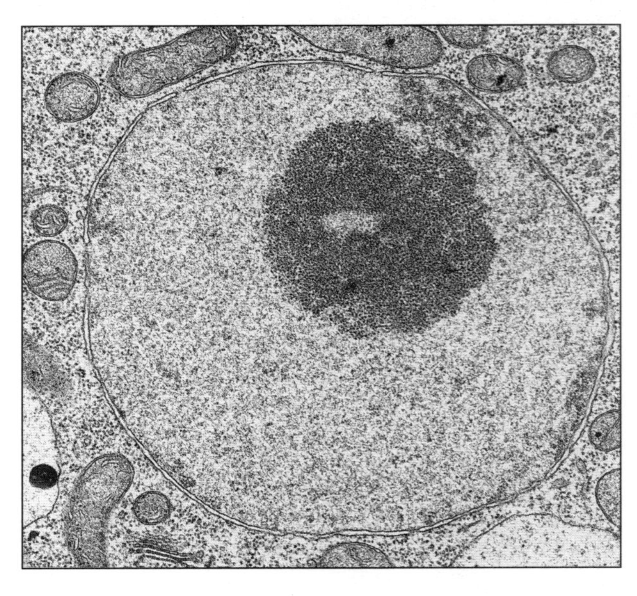

Figure 1 *The nucleus. The electron micrograph shows the nuclear membrane containing nuclear pores (× 20 000).*

Mature red blood cells do not have a nucleus. Instead, the cell is packed with the protein **haemoglobin** which it uses to carry oxygen. However, developing red blood cells do have a nucleus.

2 Explain why developing red blood cells need a nucleus.

The powerhouse of the cell

The **mitochondrion** is the site of most of the stages of **aerobic respiration**. Look at figure 2. You can see that the mitochondrion has a double membrane around it, and the inner membrane is highly folded to form **cristae**.

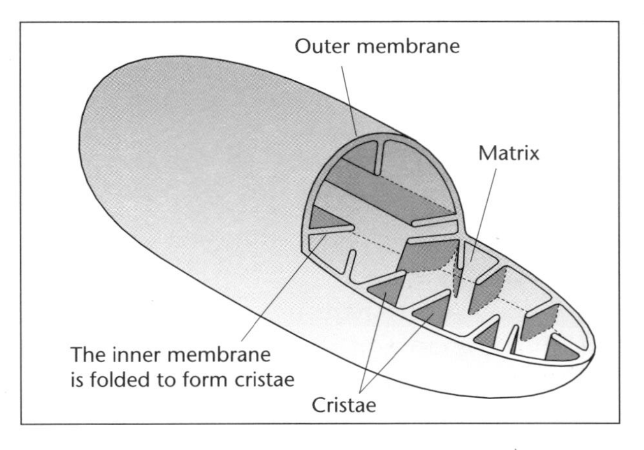

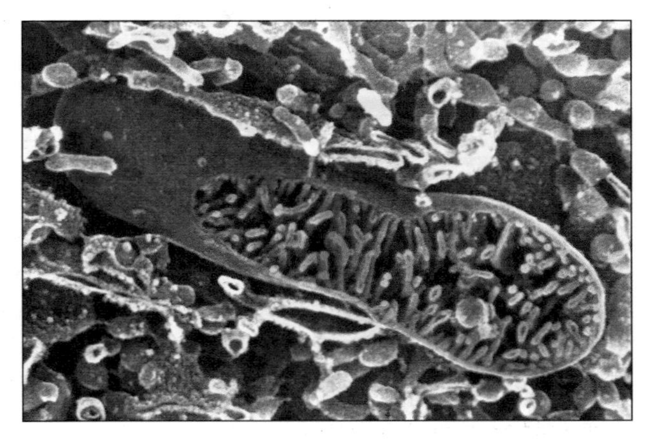

Figure 2 *A mitochondrion as seen under an electron microscope. The mitochondrion is shown pink in this false-colour scanning electron micrograph (× 60 000).*

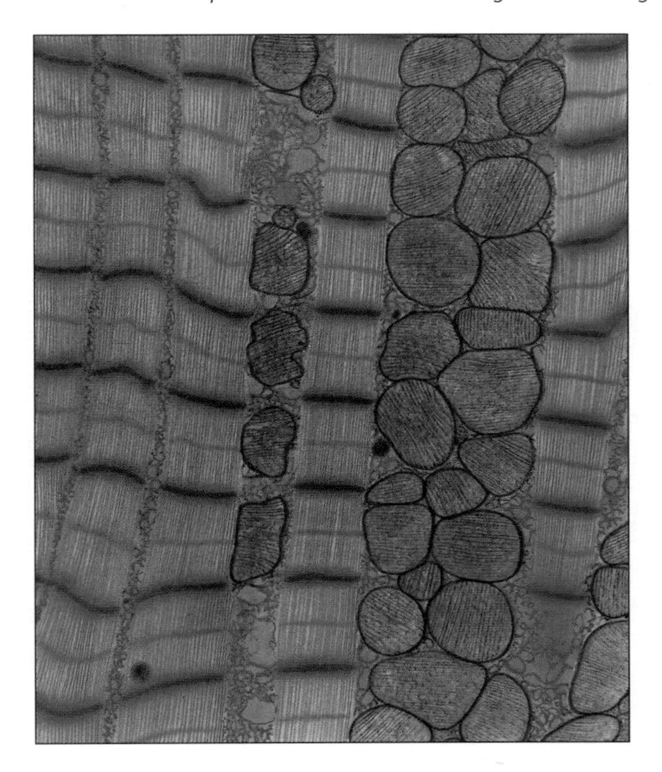

Figure 3 *This electron micrograph shows a section through heart muscle. The mitochondria (shown blue) lie between the muscle fibres (pink).*

Mitochondria provide the cell with energy in the form of energy-storage molecules called **ATP**. All cells have many mitochondria, but if the cell is very active, the cell will be packed with mitochondria. Some muscle cells are so full of mitochondria that it is difficult to see any other organelles. If you look at the muscle cells of a highly trained athlete, there will be more mitochondria present than in the muscle cells of a non-athlete.

3 Explain why muscle cells need more mitochondria than many other kinds of cell.

Key ideas 46–7

The cytoplasm is the fluid part of the cell.

The nucleus contains the genetic material of the cell.

The cell surface membrane controls the entry of substances into and out of the cell.

The mitochondrion is the organelle where most of the processes concerned with aerobic respiration take place.

5 Making and transporting substances

Cells need to make many substances, such as enzymes, structural proteins, mucus and hormones. Some organelles are specialised for this function. Once made, the substances have to be transported to where they are needed. This transport job is carried out by other specialised organelles.

Making proteins

Protein synthesis takes place on **ribosomes**. Look at figure 1. Some ribosomes are attached to the **endoplasmic reticulum**, making it look like a 'string of beads'. An endoplasmic reticulum with ribosomes attached is called **rough endoplasmic reticulum** (**RER**). The RER is a series of flattened sacs and sheets, which transport proteins around the cell. Ribosomes on the rough endoplasmic reticulum make proteins that will be secreted by the cell to be used elsewhere in the body. Ribosomes that are free in the cytoplasm make proteins to be used inside the cell itself.

The **smooth endoplasmic reticulum** (**SER**) is another membrane system, but the sacs and sheets are more tube-shaped than in the rough endoplasmic reticulum. The enzymes found in the smooth endoplasmic reticulum are important for synthesising fats, phospholipids, steroids and other lipids.

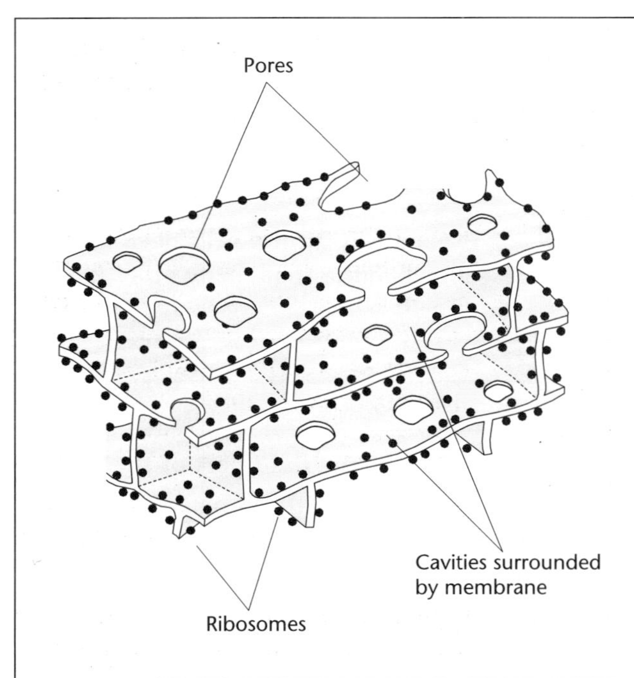

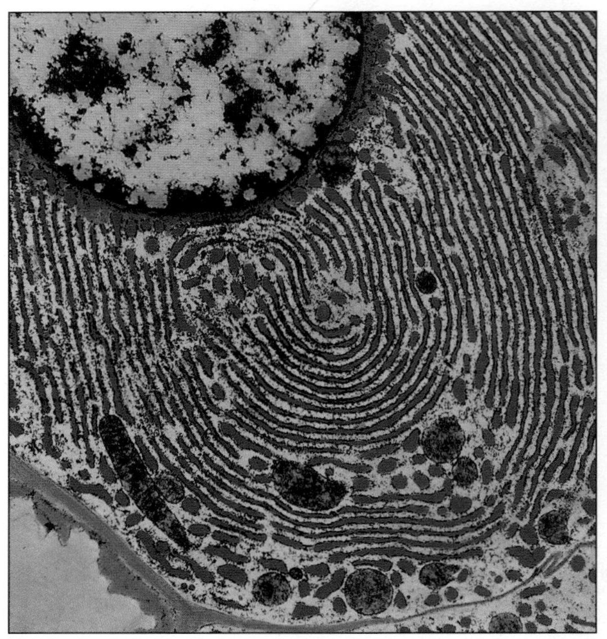

Figure 1 *The rough endoplasmic reticulum with ribosomes. The electron micrograph shows the nucleus (green) and rough endoplasmic reticulum (× 5500).*

Secreting substances

The **Golgi body** receives substances from the endoplasmic reticulum. The Golgi body modifies the substances made in the cell before they are secreted. Look at figure 2. You can see that the Golgi body is made of a stack of membrane-bound sacs. It produces **vesicles**, small sacs which carry secretions to the surface of the cell, such as mucus in animal cells and cell wall materials in plant cells.

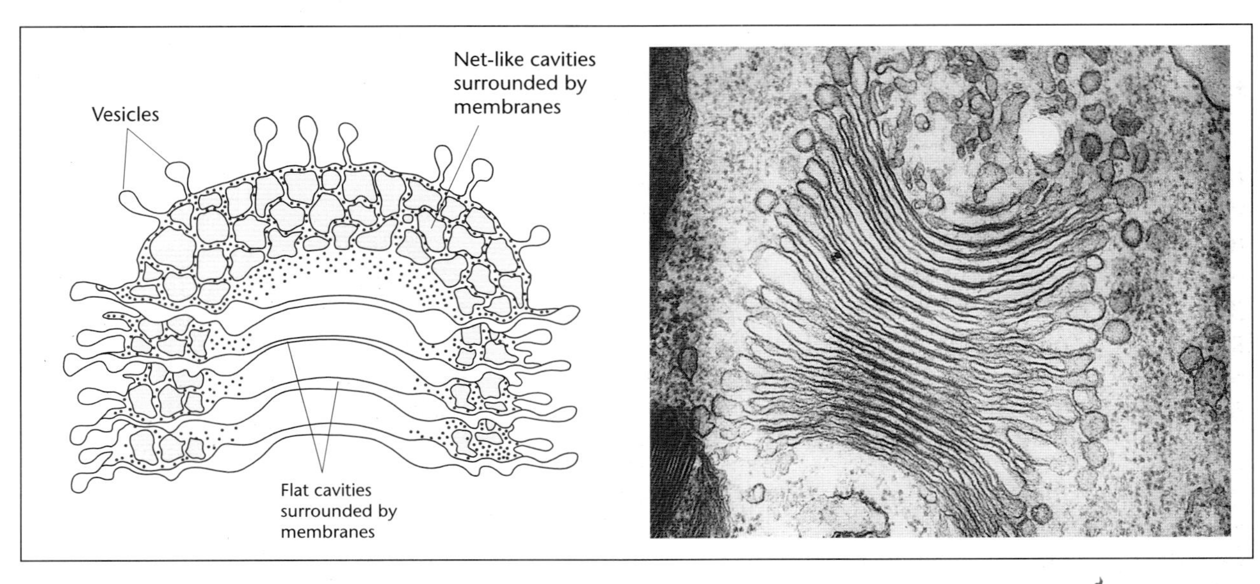

Figure 2 *A Golgi body as seen under an electron microscope (× 56 000).*

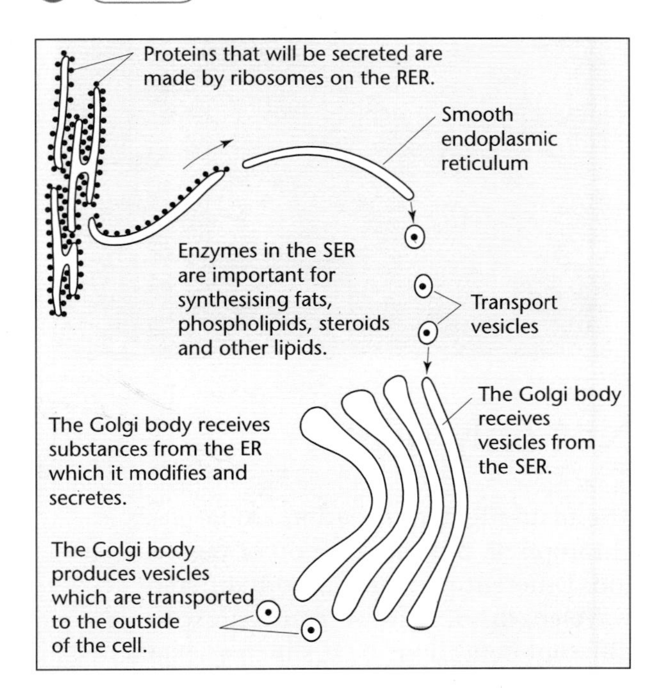

Figure 3 *The rough endoplasmic reticulum, smooth endoplasmic reticulum and Golgi body are all involved in transport and secretion in a cell.*

The endoplasmic reticulum and Golgi body work together to transport substances through the cell and secrete them at the cell surface. This is shown in figure 3.

Q

1 **Look at the electron micrograph of the epithelial cell from the lining of the small intestine on page 41. What features of this cell help it in its function of absorbing dissolved nutrients from the gut?**

Key ideas 48–9

Ribosomes carry out protein synthesis in the cell.

Rough endoplasmic reticulum, smooth endoplasmic reticulum and the Golgi body are involved in transporting substances around the cell and secreting them at the cell surface.

6 Only found in plants

Plant cells differ from animal cells in that they have a cellulose cell wall around them. This is important for support, and also stops the cells taking in too much water by osmosis. Some plant cells are able to carry out **photosynthesis**. This means they can take in carbon dioxide from the air, and use energy from sunlight to convert this to carbohydrates and other useful organic substances.

Solar power

Look at figure 1, which shows a **chloroplast**. You can see that it has a double membrane around it. Different plant species have chloroplasts with different shapes and sizes. Chloroplasts are used for photosynthesis, so they are only found in parts of the plant that are exposed to the light. This means that chloroplasts are found mainly in the leaf. The space inside the chloroplast is called the **stroma**, in which you can see long structures called **thylakoids**. The thylakoids stack to form a **granum**. These grana contain the pigment **chlorophyll**, which is used in photosynthesis. Chlorophyll is a pigment that can trap the energy from sunlight and use it to convert carbon dioxide to carbohydrates.

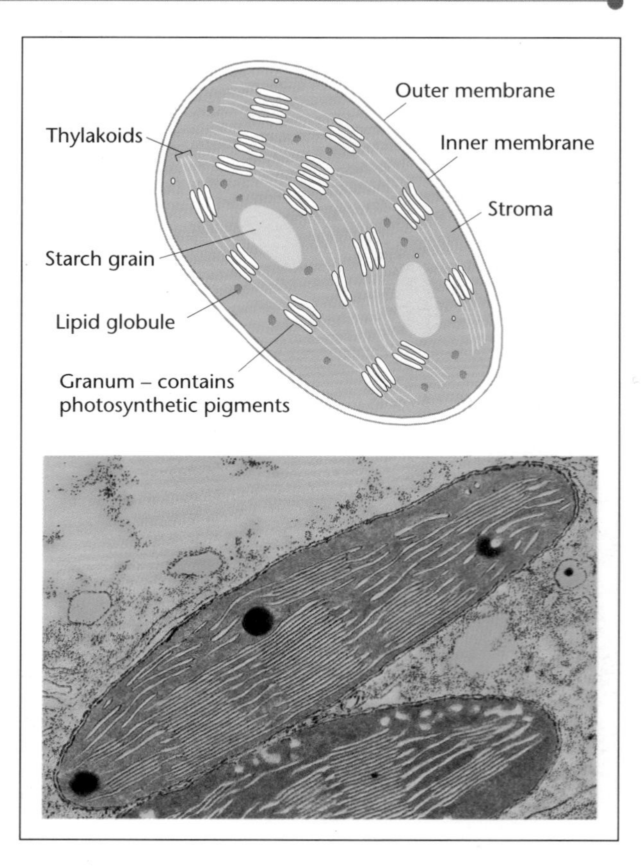

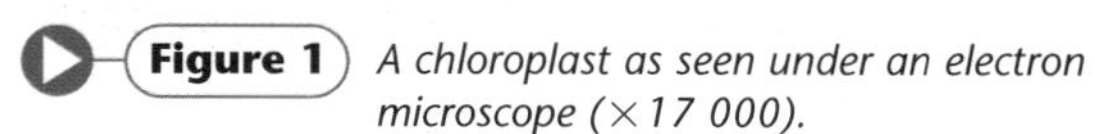

Figure 1 *A chloroplast as seen under an electron microscope (× 17 000).*

Figure 2 *Red and brown seaweeds have different pigments to absorb the light that reaches them in the sea.*

Not only green

The main pigment found in chloroplasts is chlorophyll, but there are other pigments too. Different pigments absorb different wavelengths of light, so plants growing in different conditions have different pigments. Some seaweeds (algae) contain red or brown pigments, which enable them to photosynthesise under the sea.

Holding a plant cell together

The plant cell wall is visible with a light microscope. It can be seen as a clear boundary. It is made of long cellulose fibres which make it rigid and strong. The cell wall prevents the cell bursting when it takes in water by osmosis, and helps to support the plant. The **primary cell wall** is laid down in younger growing cells. The **secondary cell wall** is found in mature cells and is waterproof. You can see the structure of the cell wall in figures 3 and 4.

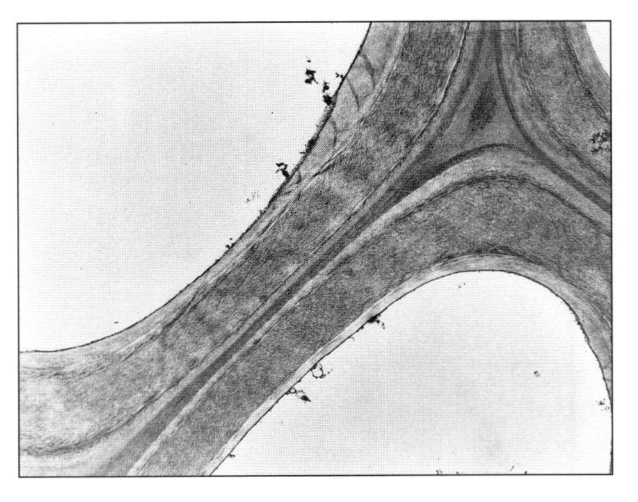

Figure 3 *Electron micrograph of a section through a cell wall (×8000).*

Figure 4 *Electron micrograph of the surface of a cell wall showing the cellulose fibres (×30 000).*

1. **Use figure 4 to help you explain why the cell wall is very rigid and strong.**
2. **Name a type of plant cell in which you would be unlikely to find chloroplasts.**

Supporting the plant

Mature plant cells contain a large cell vacuole. This has a membrane around it. The vacuole is filled with a solution of pigments, nitrogenous waste and other solutes. It is important in keeping the plant cells turgid. You can read more about this on page 107.

Key ideas 50–51

Plant cells have a cellulose cell wall.

Many plant cells contain chloroplasts, which are the site of photosynthesis.

7 Different densities

One way of finding out how different organelles in the cell work is to study them in isolation, away from all the other parts of the cell. Before you can do this you have to open up the cell and remove the organelles. You then have to isolate the organelle you want to study.

Density

The **density** of a substance is its mass divided by its volume. In other words, if you had two balls of the same size (and therefore the same volume), one made of polystyrene and the other made of metal, you could say that the metal ball was denser, because it would have a greater mass for the same volume. The organelles in the cell have different densities, and this fact can be used to separate them.

Spinning fast

Scientists have developed a technique called **differential centrifugation** that allows you to isolate individual organelles from cells. Figure 1 shows the different steps.

The cells are broken down using a blender called a **homogeniser**. The liquid that is produced is called the **homogenate**. This liquid is placed in a **centrifuge**, which spins the homogenate. When spun at high speeds, solid material forms a **pellet** at the bottom of the tube. The liquid above the pellet is called the **supernatant**. It is possible to separate the different organelles in a cell by spinning the homogenate at different speeds. At first slow speeds and short spin times are used, causing the denser organelles such as nuclei and chloroplasts to form a pellet. The supernatant is then spun a second time at a faster speed and for longer. This time, the slightly less dense organelles such as mitochondria form a pellet. To isolate the least dense organelles, RER and ribosomes, the second supernatant is spun again at even faster speeds and for even longer.

1 a If the second supernatant is spun again at a faster speed, what would you expect to find in the sediment?
b How would you use this technique to obtain a sample of chloroplasts?

In stage **1** of figure 1, the buffer solution keeps the pH of the cell contents constant. Any change in pH could denature the enzymes in the mixture, and this would affect any investigation carried out on the isolated organelles. Everything is kept ice-cold so that the enzymes do not become denatured. However, keeping them ice-cold stops them from working. If the mixture was warmer, enzymes such as proteases could digest and destroy the organelles being investigated.

1
Chop up fresh liver tissue in ice-cold buffer solution.

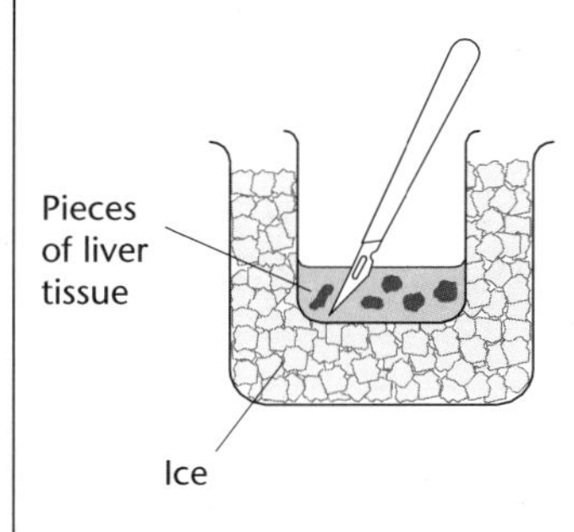

2
Put the chopped tissue into a blender or **homogeniser** which breaks open the cells.

3
Filter the mixture to remove the debris.

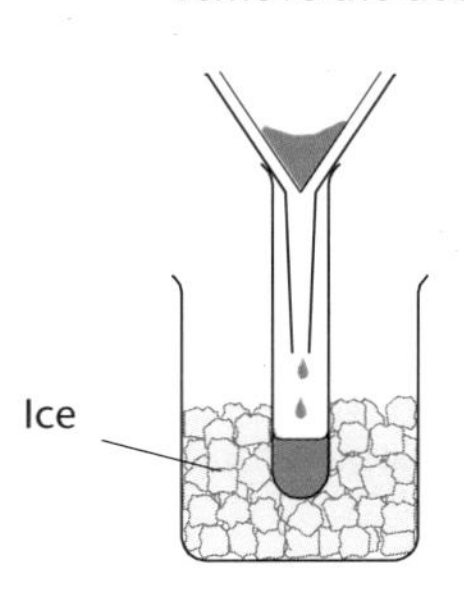

4
Pour the mixture into tubes and spin very quickly in a centrifuge. This works rather like a spin-dryer. The denser parts of the mixture get spun to the bottom of the tube where they form a 'pellet' called the **sediment**.

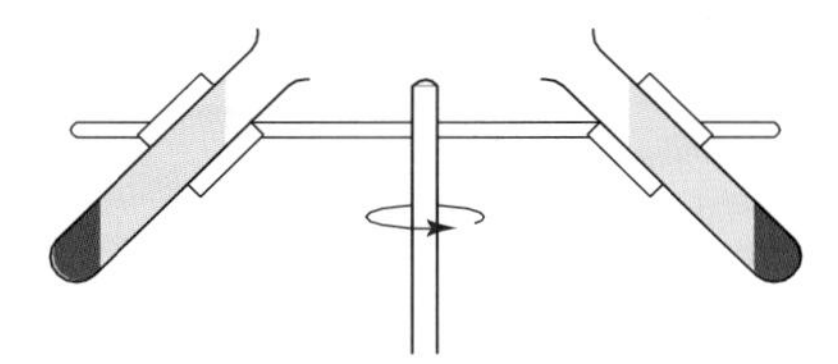

5
The liquid layer on top (the **supernatant**) is poured into a fresh tube, leaving the sediment behind. This contains the nuclei.

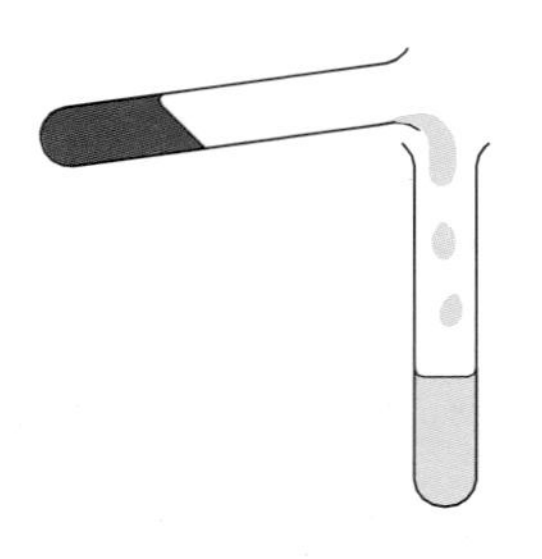

6
This supernatant may then be spun again at a faster speed, to produce a sediment containing mitochondria.

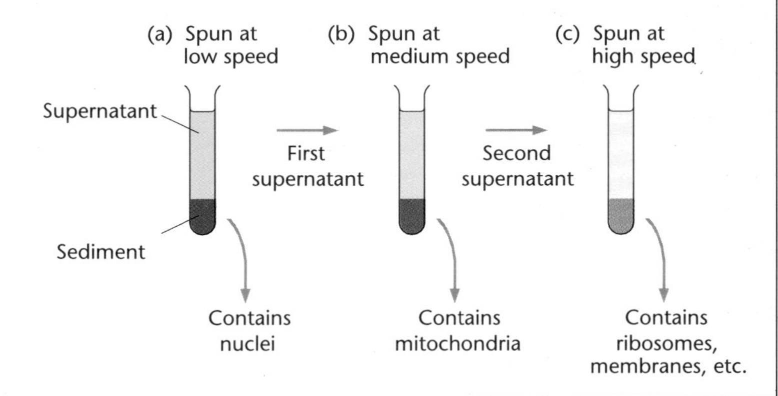

Figure 1 *Outline of the steps in differential centrifugation.*

Key ideas 52–3

Differential centrifugation is a technique used to break open cells and obtain large numbers of one kind of organelle, so that we can study its function.

8 Cells without a nucleus

Bacteria have a different kind of cell structure from animals and plants. Bacterial cells are said to be **prokaryotic**, which literally means 'before the nucleus'. Prokaryotic cells are smaller than eukaryotic cells, and are simpler in structure. Biologists believe that prokaryotes evolved much earlier than eukaryotic cells.

The structure of prokaryotic cells

As you will see in figure 1, prokaryotic cells do not have a nucleus to contain their genetic material. Their DNA is circular. They do not have membrane-bound organelles, such as mitochondria. They have a cell wall, although this is made of a polymer called **murein** instead of cellulose. Bacteria often have hair-like **flagella** so that they can move around. Bacterial flagella are made of a protein called flagellin, and there is a 'motor' at the base of the flagellum, which causes it to rotate. Some eukaryotic cells, such as sperms, have flagella too, but their structure is different from prokaryotic flagella.

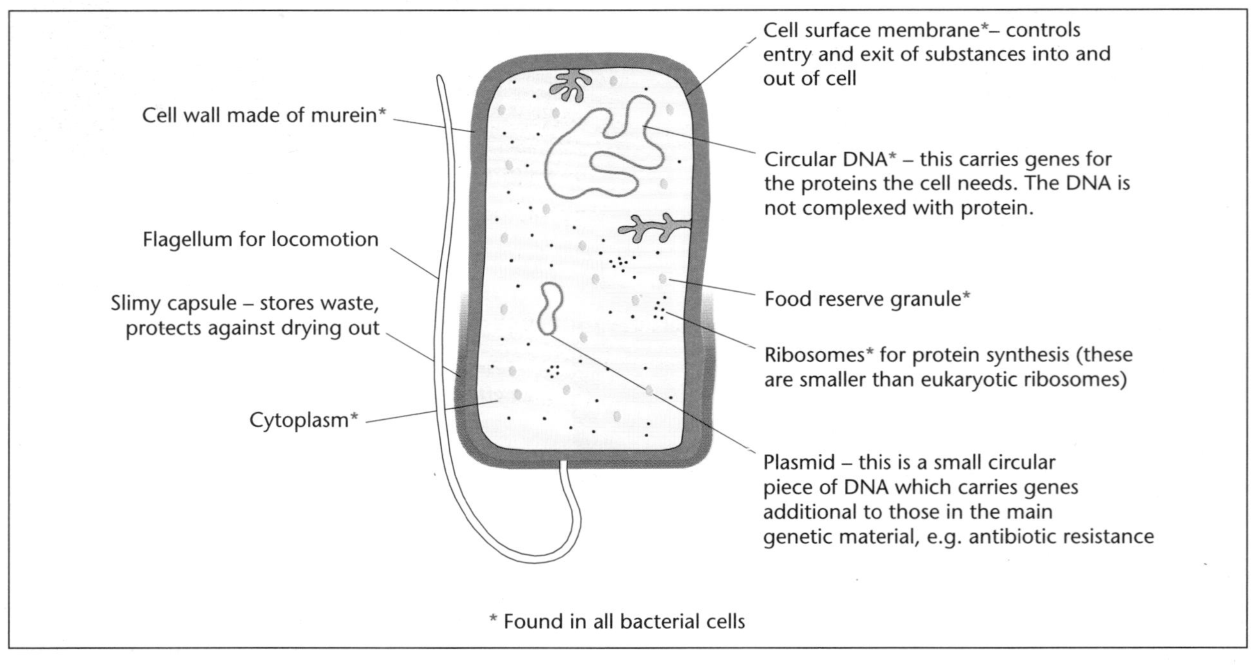

Figure 1 *The structure of a typical bacterial cell.*

In addition to the main bacterial DNA, some bacteria contain **plasmids**. These are small, circular pieces of DNA, which carry additional genes, for example, for antibiotic resistance. Bacteria can pass plasmid DNA from one cell to another. Antibiotic resistance genes are often passed between bacteria in this way.

Bacteria have ribosomes, which carry out protein synthesis just like eukaryotic ribosomes, but they are smaller than the ribosomes found in eukaryotic cells.

A slimy capsule surrounds some bacterial cells. This can help to protect the bacterium from drying out. Some disease-causing bacteria have a capsule which makes them slippery, so it is harder for white blood cells to engulf them by phagocytosis.

Figure 1 shows a typical bacterial cell, but bacteria may have many different shapes and sizes, as shown in figure 3.

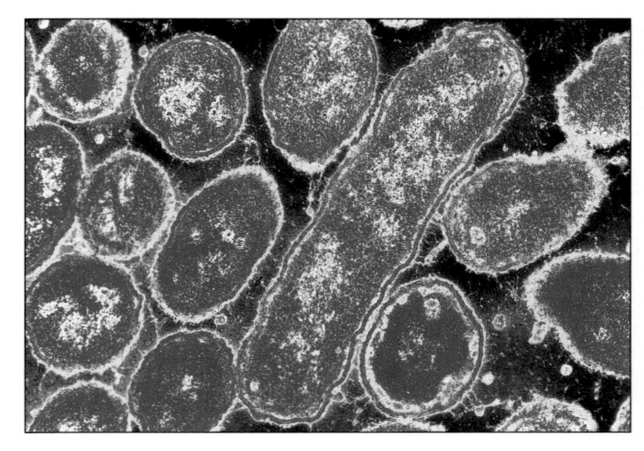

Figure 2 *A transmission electron micrograph of bacterial cells (× 32 000).*

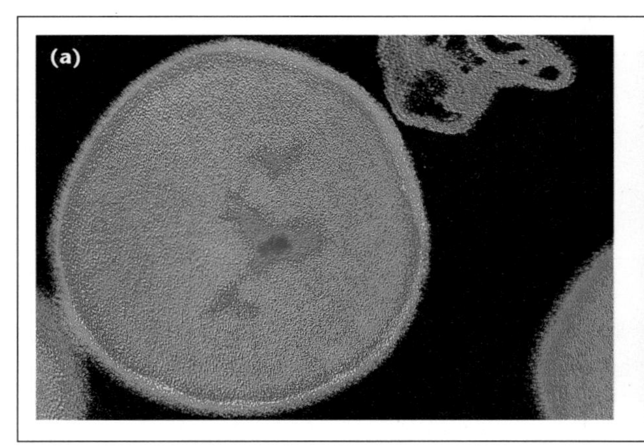

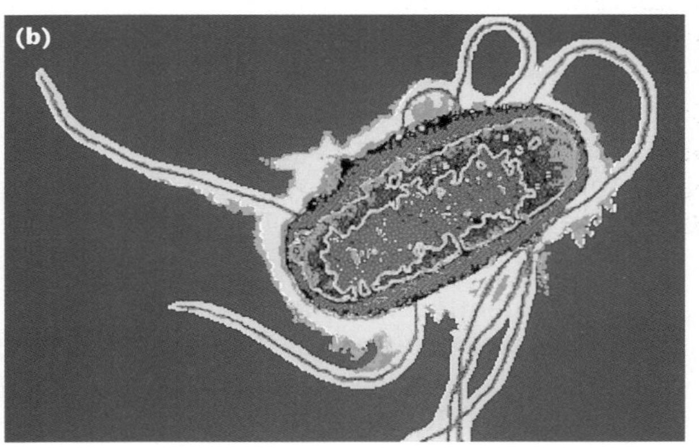

Figure 3 *False-colour transmission electron micrograph of (a)* Staphylococcus aureus *(× 20 000). (b)* Escherichia coli *(× 9000).*

1 The magnification of the electron micrograph in figure 2 is × 32 000. Calculate the actual length of the longest bacterium.

2 Make a list of differences between prokaryotic and eukaryotic cells. (You should be able to find at least four.)

3 Copy and complete table 1 for prokaryotic cells.

Structure	Function
Cell wall	
Cell membrane	
Genetic material	
Ribosomes	
Flagellum	
Plasmid	
Capsule	

Table 1

Key ideas 54–5

Bacterial cells are prokaryotic, which means they do not have a nucleus.

They are much smaller than eukaryotic cells, and do not contain membrane-bound organelles.

Unit 3 – Questions

9

1) Figure 1 shows the electron microscope appearance of part of a cell at a junction of two other cells.

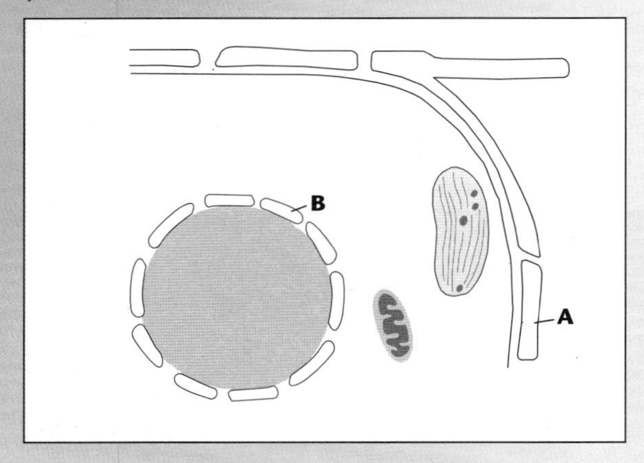

a) Identify structures **A** and **B**. (2 marks)
b) Give two features that show the cell is a eukaryotic cell. (2 marks)
c) Does the diagram show a plant cell or an animal cell? Give the reason for your answer. (2 marks)

(Total 6 marks)

2) Figure 2 shows a drawing of an electron micrograph of a typical liver cell. Identify parts **A** to **C**. **(Total 3 marks)**

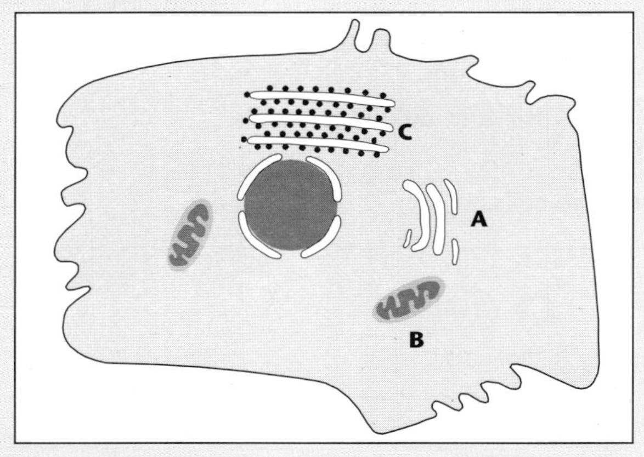

3) Give three differences between a prokaryotic cell and a eukaryotic cell. **(Total 3 marks)**

4) Give two ways in which an electron microscope and a light microscope differ. **(Total 2 marks)**

5) Give three similarities and three differences between a plant cell and an animal cell. **(Total 6 marks)**

6) Describe the function of each organelle:
a) chloroplast
b) Golgi body
c) nucleus
d) cell wall. **(Total 4 marks)**

7) Figure 3 shows the structure of a bacterial cell.

Figure 3

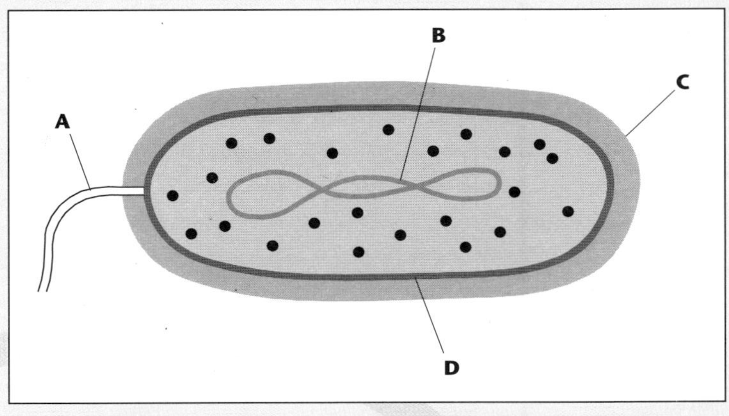

a) Identify structures **A** to **D** and describe their functions. (4 marks)
b) Give one difference between the DNA of a prokaryotic cell and that of a eukaryotic cell. (1 mark)
(Total 5 marks)

8) Figure 4 shows some of the features of a cell visible with an electron microscope.

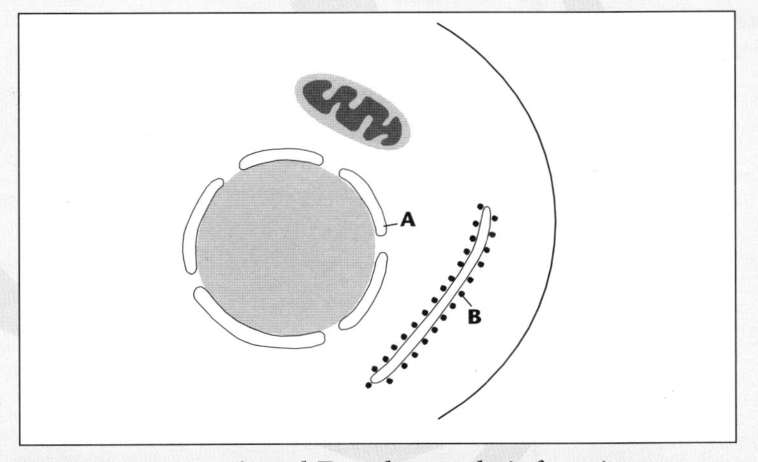

Name structures **A** and **B** and state their functions. **(Total 4 marks)**

9) Describe how differential centrifugation can be used to separate different organelles.

(Total 4 marks)

1 Biomolecules

All living things are made up of chemicals. As well as water, these chemicals are mainly carbohydrates, proteins and fats. Organisms are constantly taking in a range of chemicals and using them to make other substances that they need. Large molecules are broken down to smaller ones inside the organism. These may be broken down further, to release energy for the organism to use, or they may be used to build up more complex molecules that the organism needs.

Making chains

Many important biological molecules are **polymers**. Figure 1 shows how polymers are made from a series of smaller molecules called **monomers**, joined together to form a chain. Biological polymers include **proteins**, such as haemoglobin, which carries oxygen in the blood, keratin, which is found in hair, and enzymes, which control all the chemical reactions in the body. Many **carbohydrates** are also polymers, such as starch which acts as a food store in plants, or cellulose which makes up plant cell walls.

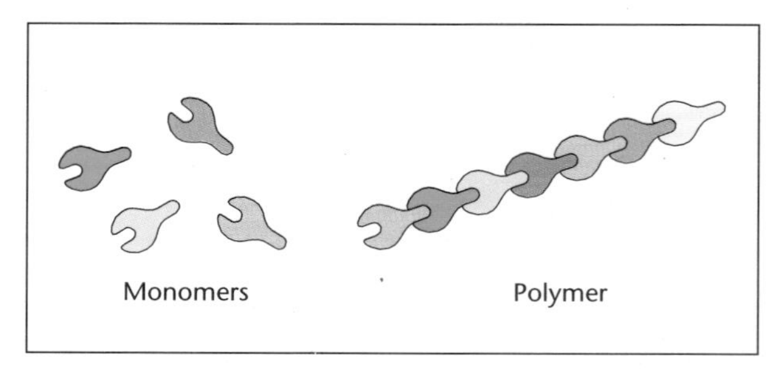

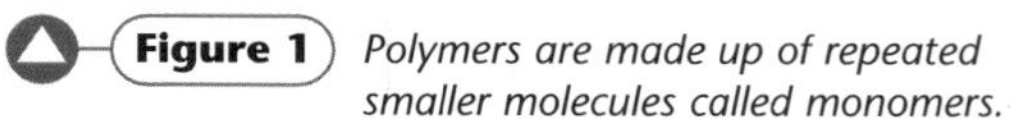
Figure 1 *Polymers are made up of repeated smaller molecules called monomers.*

Joining by a condensation reaction

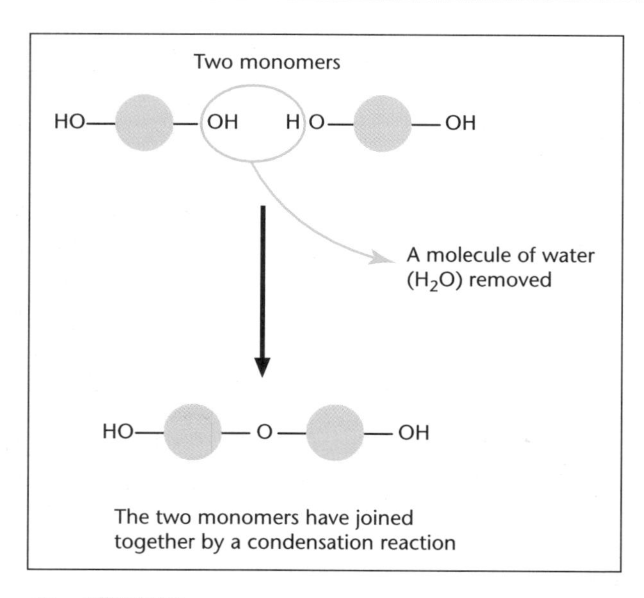

Figure 2 *A condensation reaction.*

The bonds that hold monomers together are often formed by **condensation** reactions. Figure 2 shows how a condensation reaction occurs. When a bond forms, water is removed. This type of reaction is involved in the formation of proteins, starch and many other biological polymers.

Making a polymer inside cells

Figure 3 shows an investigation carried out to find out how the carbohydrate polymer starch is made by cells in potato plants. The results are given in table 1.

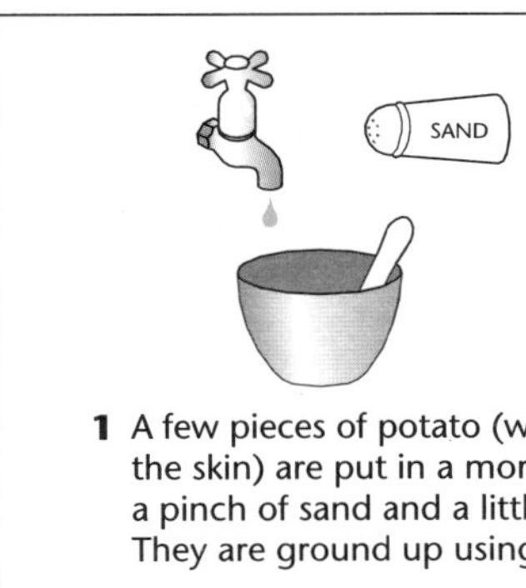

1 A few pieces of potato (without the skin) are put in a mortar with a pinch of sand and a little water. They are ground up using a pestle.

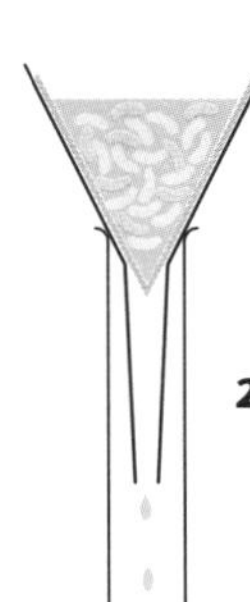

2 The potato pulp is filtered into a test tube.

Potato juice

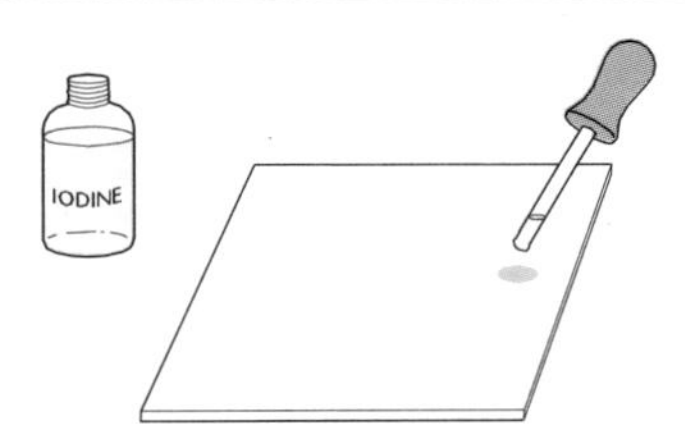

3 A drop of potato juice is placed on a white tile and a drop of iodine solution is added. The iodine stays browny-yellow in colour.

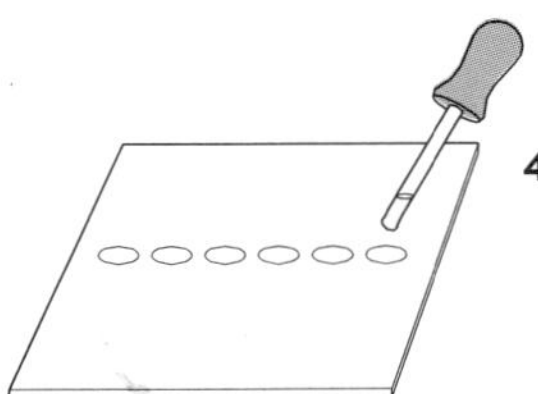

4 Six drops of glucose-1-phosphate are placed side by side on another white tile. (Glucose-1-phosphate is an active form of glucose.) A drop of potato juice is added to each drop of glucose and mixed in.

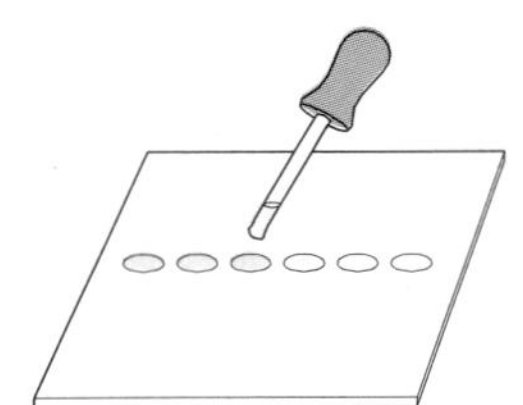

5 Every 2 minutes, a drop of iodine solution is added to one of the drops.

Figure 3 *An experiment to see if potato juice will turn glucose into starch.*

1 a Why does the potato need to be ground up?

b Why does the potato pulp need to be filtered?

c Why was the potato pulp tested for starch after being filtered?

d What did the test show?

e Suggest what is present in potato juice which turns glucose into starch.

f Describe a suitable control for this investigation.

Table 1 *Results of iodine test on mixture of potato juice and glucose-1-phosphate.*

Time/ minutes	Results of iodine test
0	Negative
2	Negative
4	A few black specks
6	More black specks
8	Turns black
10	Very black

Key ideas 58–9

Polymers are large molecules made by joining together many small molecules called monomers.

When biological polymers are formed, the monomers usually join by a condensation reaction, which involves the removal of a molecule of water.

2 Carbohydrate polymers

All carbohydrates contain carbon, hydrogen and oxygen. Carbohydrates include simple sugars like **glucose** and large polymers such as **starch** and **cellulose**. Some carbohydrates also form parts of other molecules, such as the sugar deoxyribose which is part of DNA.

Simple sugars

Carbohydrate polymers are made from monomers called **monosaccharides**. The best known monosaccharide is glucose, which contains 6 carbon atoms, 12 hydrogen atoms and 6 oxygen atoms. Therefore, the **general formula** for glucose is $C_6H_{12}O_6$. Figure 1 shows how the atoms are arranged in glucose. A diagram such as this, showing the arrangement of atoms in a molecule, is called the **structural formula**.

Monosaccharides are very soluble, so they can be transported easily in living organisms, and they can easily be broken down by respiration to make energy in the form of ATP.

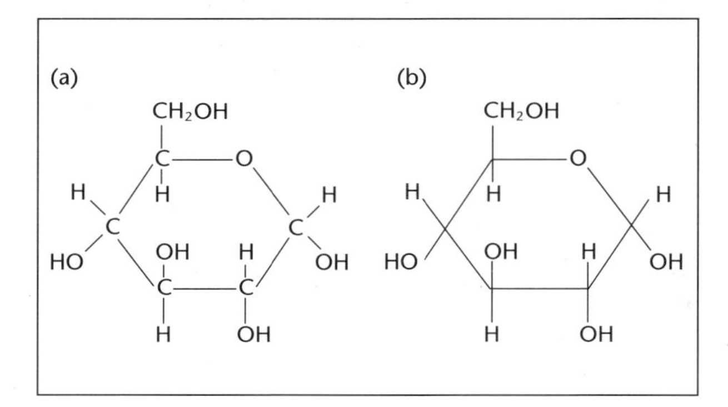

Figure 1 *The structural formula of glucose. Sometimes structural formulae are drawn without showing the carbon atoms in the ring, as shown in figure (b).*

Making small chains

Two monosaccharide monomers are joined together by a condensation reaction to form a **disaccharide**. If two glucose molecules join together, they form a disaccharide called **maltose**. You can see in figure 2 that when maltose is made from glucose, one molecule of water is produced.

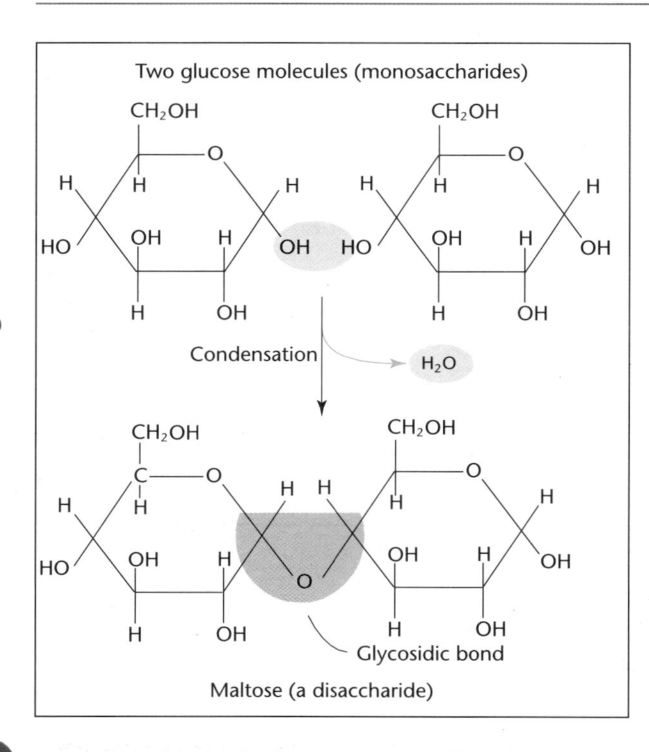

Figure 2 *The formation of maltose from glucose.*

Making long chains – and breaking them

Polymers made from monosaccharides are known as **polysaccharides**. One of the most important polysaccharides is **starch**, which is made up of long chains of glucose molecules. You can see in figure 3 that the starch molecule has many branches. This makes it a good **storage molecule**, because it is compact and can form an approximately spherical shape. Starch is insoluble in water, which makes it a very good storage molecule in plants.

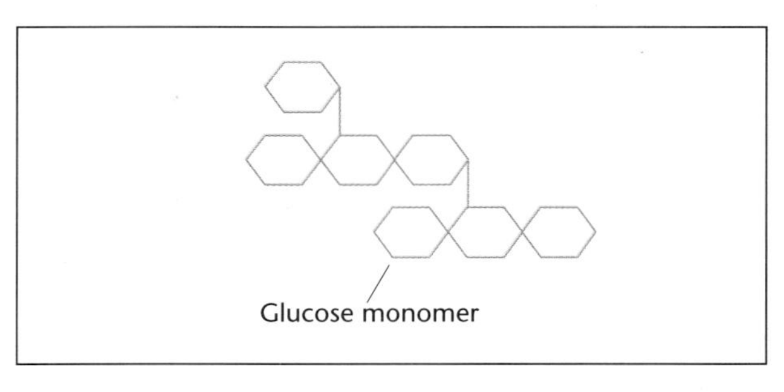

Figure 3 *The structure of starch.*

The bonds between the monomers in disaccharides and polysaccharides can be broken by a **hydrolysis** reaction. Hydrolysis is the opposite of condensation. Look at figure 4. You can see that bonds are broken by the addition of water.

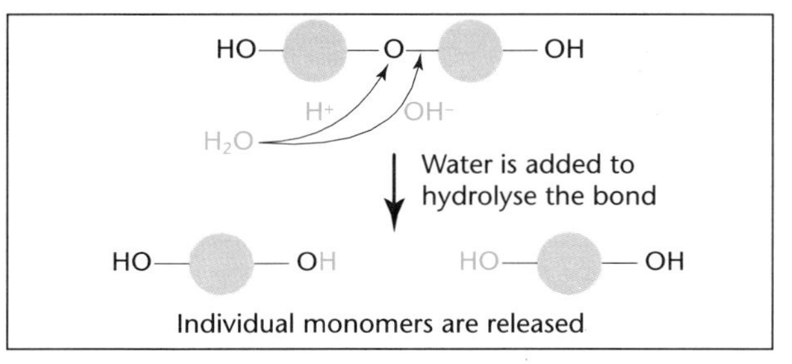

Figure 4 *A hydrolysis reaction. An enzyme is needed for the reaction – it does not happen if you just dissolve the carbohydrate in water.*

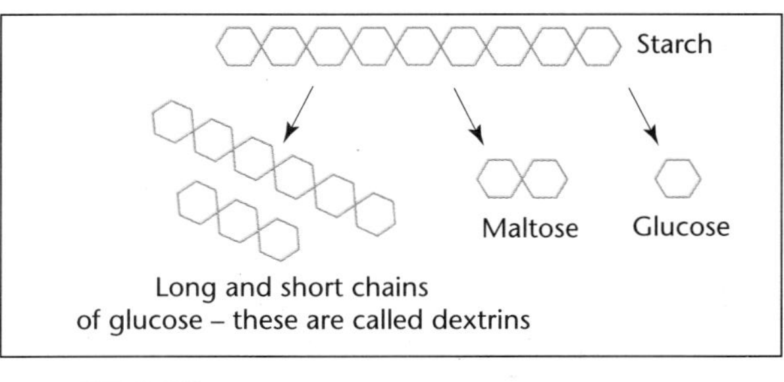

Figure 5 *The products of hydrolysing starch using amylase.*

1. **Carbohydrates can be hydrolysed by boiling them with acid. Give another method of hydrolysing carbohydrates.**
2. a **Name the products of the hydrolysis of maltose.**
   b **Draw a diagram to show the hydrolysis of maltose.**
3. **List the properties of starch that enable it to carry out its function as a storage molecule.**

Key ideas 60–61

Carbohydrates contain carbon, hydrogen and oxygen.

Monosaccharides are the basic units (monomers) of which other carbohydrates are made.

Two glucose molecules join together by a condensation reaction to form the disaccharide maltose.

Polysaccharides are polymers of monosaccharides.

Starch is a polymer of glucose. It is insoluble and useful as a storage molecule in plant cells.

The bonds between the monomers in disaccharides and polysaccharides can be broken by hydrolysis.

3 New arrangements

Monosaccharide units join together in many different ways to form simple carbohydrates called sugars. In animals, the storage carbohydrate is not starch but a polysaccharide called **glycogen**.

Fruit sugar

You will see from food labels that foods such as fruit and honey contain a sugar called **fructose**. Fructose is very similar to glucose. It even has the same molecular formula as glucose, $C_6H_{12}O_6$, but a different structural formula. Like glucose, fructose has a ring structure, but the atoms are arranged differently.

Figure 1 shows how a molecule of glucose bonds with a molecule of fructose to form a disaccharide called **sucrose**. Notice that water is removed to form the bond between fructose and glucose. In other words, a **condensation** reaction takes place.

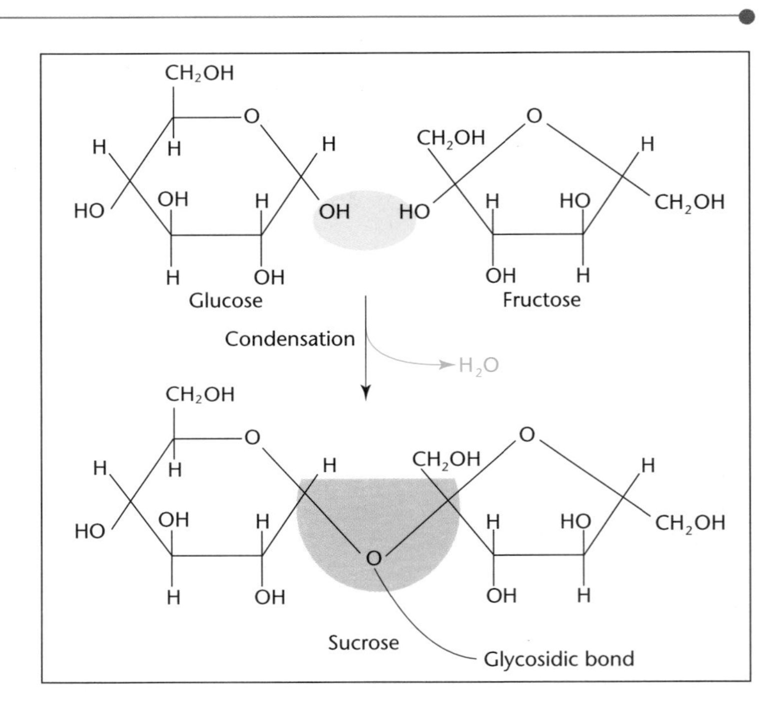

Figure 1 *The formation of sucrose from glucose and fructose.*

Polysaccharides – animal starch and cellulose

Glycogen is sometimes called 'animal starch' because it is used as a storage polysaccharide in animal cells. Glycogen is a polymer made of glucose units. Look at the diagram of glycogen in figure 2. You can see that it is very similar to starch, but with many more branches. Glycogen is insoluble in water, which makes it a good storage molecule.

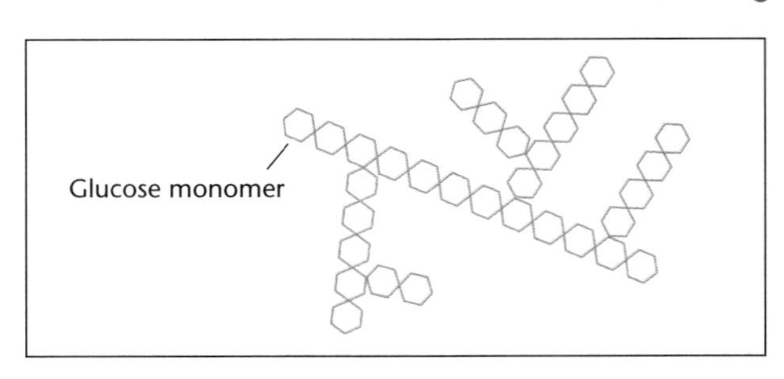

Figure 2 *The structure of glycogen.*

Figure 3 shows the structure of **cellulose**. Notice that cellulose is another polymer made from glucose units. Many long parallel polysaccharide chains are held together in a bundle by hydrogen bonds, forming fibres which are very strong. The structure of cellulose makes it a useful **structural** molecule. It is found in plant cell walls where its function is to prevent the cell from bursting when it takes in water.

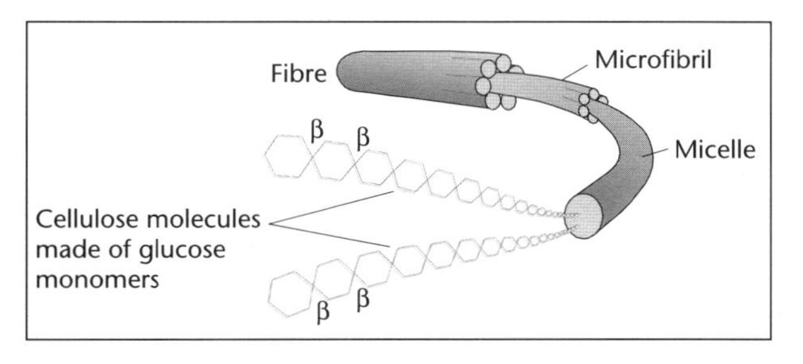

Figure 3 *The structure of cellulose.*

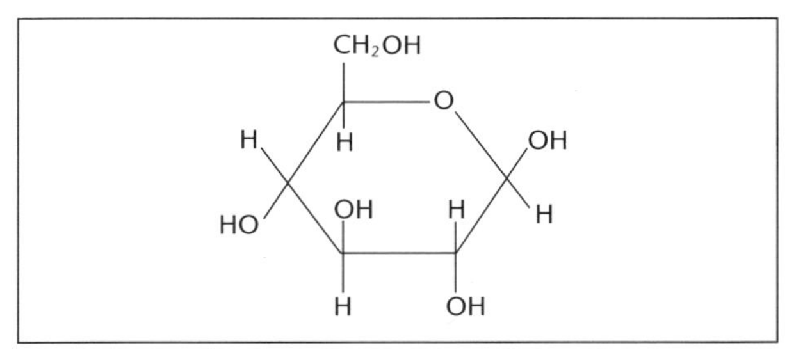

Figure 4 *The structure of β-glucose.*

1 Cellulose is made from β-glucose. Figure 4 shows a molecule of β-glucose. Draw a sketch to show how two β-glucose molecules join together.

Testing for sugars and starch

Carbohydrates can be detected using simple biochemical tests. **Benedict's solution** is used to detect monosaccharides and disaccharides. **Iodine** is used to detect starch.

Put a sample of the food to be tested in a test tube

Add Benedict's reagent (alkaline copper sulphate) and place in a boiling water bath

If a reducing sugar is present a yellow or orange precipitate is formed

Figure 5 *Benedict's test for reducing sugars.*

Some sugars carry out reduction reactions. These sugars are called **reducing sugars**. All monosaccharides and some disaccharides are reducing sugars. When a reducing sugar such as glucose is heated with Benedict's solution, the colour changes from blue to orange, as shown in figure 5.

Sucrose is a disaccharide that does not react with Benedict's reagent – it is an example of a **non-reducing sugar**. However, if sucrose is hydrolysed with acid first and then heated with Benedict's solution, the solution does turn orange. The hydrolysis splits the sucrose into monosaccharides, which are reducing sugars.

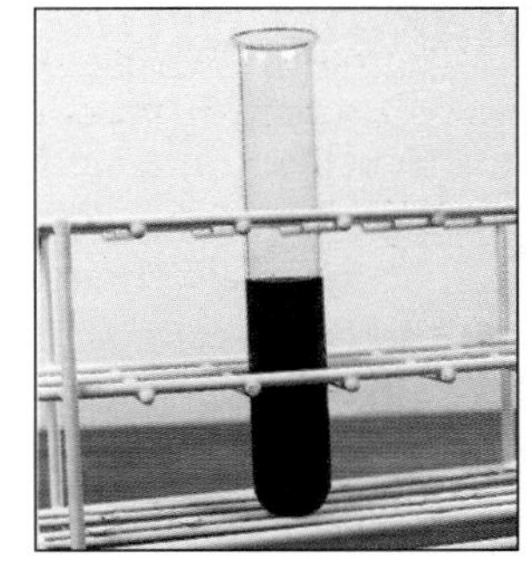

Figure 6 *Iodine test for starch.*

The presence of starch can be tested using the **iodine test**. Look at figure 6. If you add iodine solution to starch, a blue-black colour is formed. The iodine solution stays yellow-brown with other polysaccharides.

Key ideas 62–3

Glucose and fructose can join together in a condensation reaction to form the disaccharide sucrose.

Glycogen is an insoluble polymer of glucose, used as a storage polysaccharide in animals.

Cellulose forms fibres, which are very strong, so it is ideal for its function of making plant cell walls.

Benedict's solution changes from blue to orange in the presence of a reducing sugar.

Sucrose is a non-reducing sugar, which gives a negative result with Benedict's solution unless hydrolysed with acid first.

Iodine solution changes from yellow-brown to blue-black in the presence of starch.

4 Proteins

Proteins are very important biological molecules. Proteins carry out essential functions in organisms, such as **haemoglobin** used to transport oxygen. All enzymes are proteins. Some proteins give cells and tissues strength – these are structural proteins, for example, **keratin** found in hair and nails.

Amino acids

Proteins contain carbon, hydrogen, oxygen, nitrogen and sometimes sulphur. The basic building blocks, or monomers, of which proteins are made are **amino acids**. Amino acids have three groups: an **amino group** ($-NH_2$), a **carboxylic acid group** ($-COOH$), and a side-chain or **R group**. These are shown in figure 1. The R group varies between amino acids. There are 20 different types of amino acid that make up the proteins in the body, each with a different side-chain.

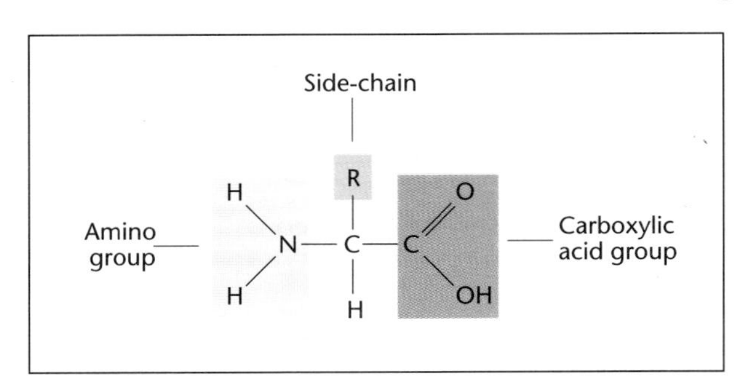

Figure 1 *The structure of an amino acid.*

Making proteins

Amino acids join together in long chains to form proteins, by a condensation reaction. Look at figure 2. The amino acids line up so that the carboxylic acid group of one is next to the amino group of the other. The bond is formed with the removal of water. The bond formed between the two amino acids is called a **peptide bond**. Two or more amino acids joined together by peptide bonds form a **peptide**.

Figure 2 shows how two amino acids join to form a **dipeptide**. It is possible for many more amino acids to join on to the chain, forming a **polypeptide**. Some proteins are made up of one polypeptide, but others have two or more polypeptides in them.

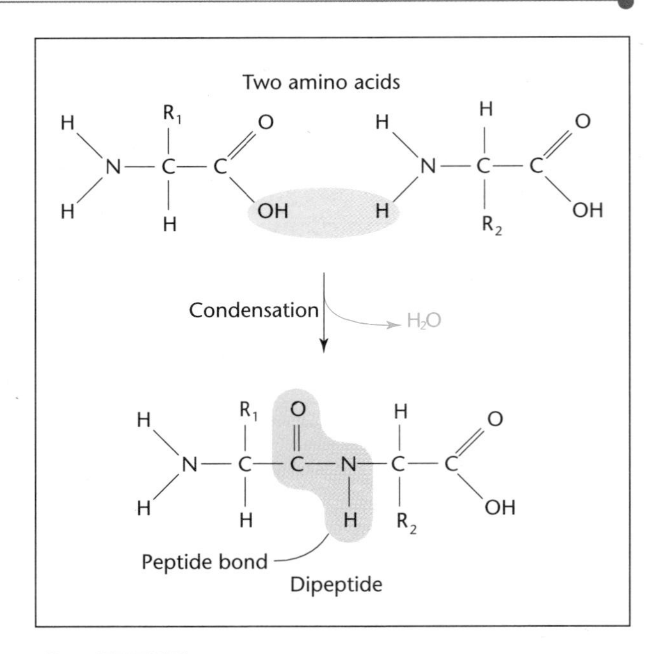

Figure 2 *The formation of a peptide bond by the condensation of two amino acids.*

Breaking down proteins

Peptide bond

Dipeptide

H_2O

Two amino acids

Figure 3 *The hydrolysis of a dipeptide.*

The peptide bonds in proteins can be broken by hydrolysis. Proteins are hydrolysed into peptides and then to amino acids by boiling with dilute acid or by using a protease enzyme. Figure 3 shows the hydrolysis of a dipeptide. To break the bond, water has to be added.

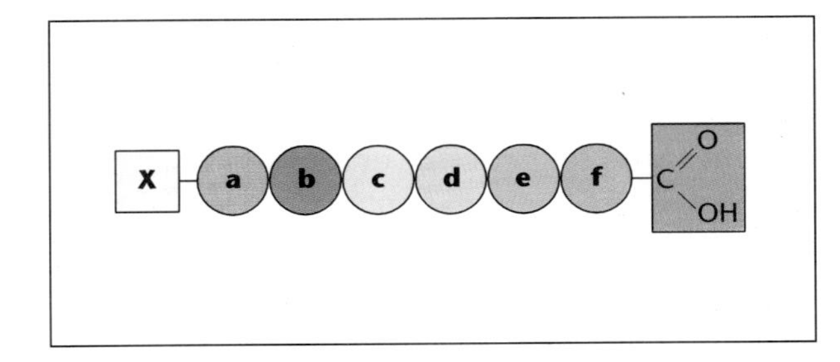

Figure 4

1 **Name the enzyme that can be used to catalyse the hydrolysis of a dipeptide.**

2 **Figure 4 shows a short peptide made up of the amino acids a, b, c, d, e and f.**

a **What group should be present at point X?**

b **How many peptide bonds are there?**

c **Draw a diagram to show the effect of breaking the bond between amino acid a and amino acid b.**

Looking for proteins

A simple biochemical test can be used to see if proteins are present. The test for protein is called the **Biuret test**. Biuret reagent is added. This contains sodium hydroxide and copper sulphate. Biuret reagent is blue, because of the copper sulphate, but in the presence of protein the blue colour changes to lilac, as shown in figure 5.

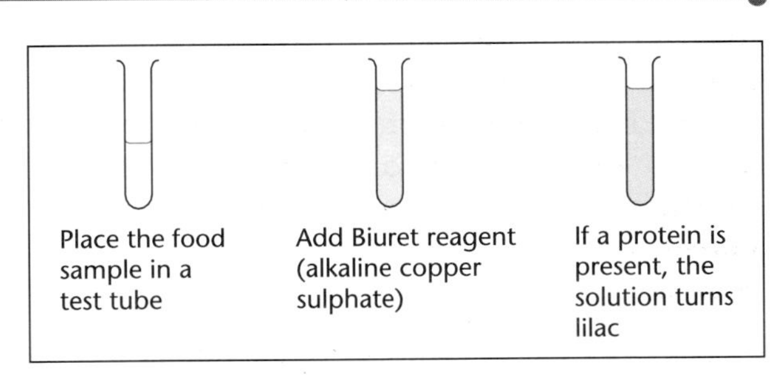

Figure 5 *The Biuret test for proteins.*

Key ideas 64–5

All proteins contain carbon, hydrogen, oxygen and nitrogen, and some contain sulphur.

Amino acids are the monomers that make up proteins.

Amino acids join together by condensation reactions to form dipeptides and polypeptides.

The bond between two amino acids is called a peptide bond, and it can be broken by hydrolysis.

5 Getting into shape

Proteins are very large, complex molecules. Since they are so complex, biochemists describe their structure at three different levels – primary, secondary and tertiary.

Primary structure

The **primary structure** of the protein is the sequence or order of amino acids in the polypeptide chain. The primary structure of a very small protein is shown in figure 1. A real protein has many more amino acids than this, often hundreds or even thousands.

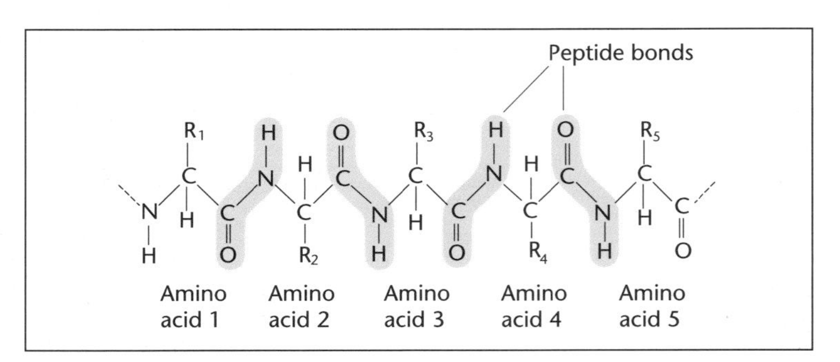

Figure 1 *The primary structure of a short protein.*

Secondary structure

Once several amino acids have joined together in a chain, the chain tends to make certain shapes or patterns. Peptide bonds contain polar hydrogen atoms (with a small positive charge) and polar oxygen atoms (with a small negative charge). This allows **hydrogen bonds** to form between peptide bonds in different parts of the chain. Because of this, the polypeptide chain can take on different shapes or patterns in different parts of the chain, and these patterns are called the **secondary structure** of the protein.

The two main types of secondary structure in proteins are the **alpha helix** (α helix) and the **beta-pleated sheet** (β-pleated sheet). These are shown in figure 2.

The secondary structure of a protein depends on the amino acids it contains, and the order in which they join together. In other words, it depends on the primary structure.

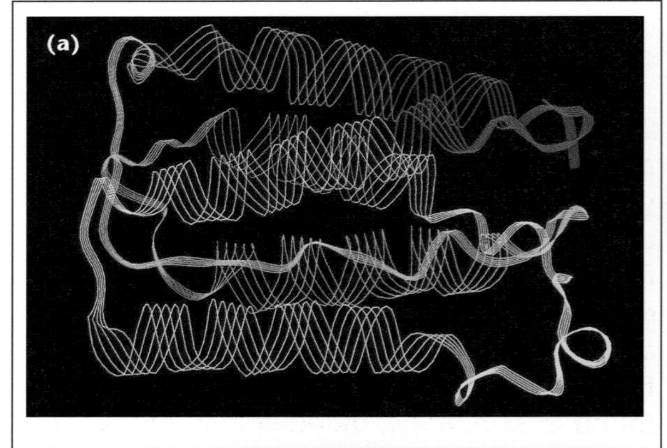

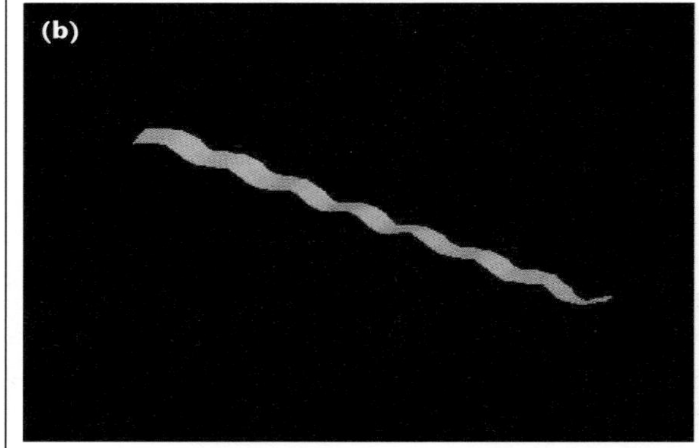

Figure 2 *Computer-generated models of (a) α helices and (b) β-pleated sheet.*

Tertiary structure

The **tertiary structure** of a protein is its overall three-dimensional shape. Figure 3 shows a protein. You can see that it has a specific shape. This shape is held together by weak bonds between the side-chains (R groups) of the different amino acids in the chain.

The tertiary structure of a protein creates the specific shape the protein needs to carry out its function. For example, enzymes are protein molecules which need to be exactly the right shape to catalyse specific reactions.

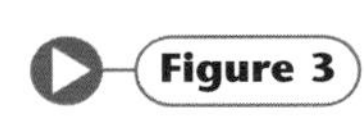
Figure 3 *The tertiary structure of a protein.*

Shape – fibrous and globular

There are two main kinds of protein, **fibrous** proteins and **globular** proteins. In figure 4, you can see that fibrous proteins have polypeptides that join together to form long fibres or sheets. These are strong proteins that do not dissolve in water, and they usually have a structural function. For example, keratin is found in fingernails and hair, and collagen is found in skin, bone, blood vessels and teeth.

1 **Why is it important that keratin and collagen are insoluble?**

Look at the globular protein in figure 4. You will notice that globular proteins have an approximately spherical shape. They are usually soluble in water, and they tend to have a biochemical function rather than a structural one. For example, enzymes are globular proteins.

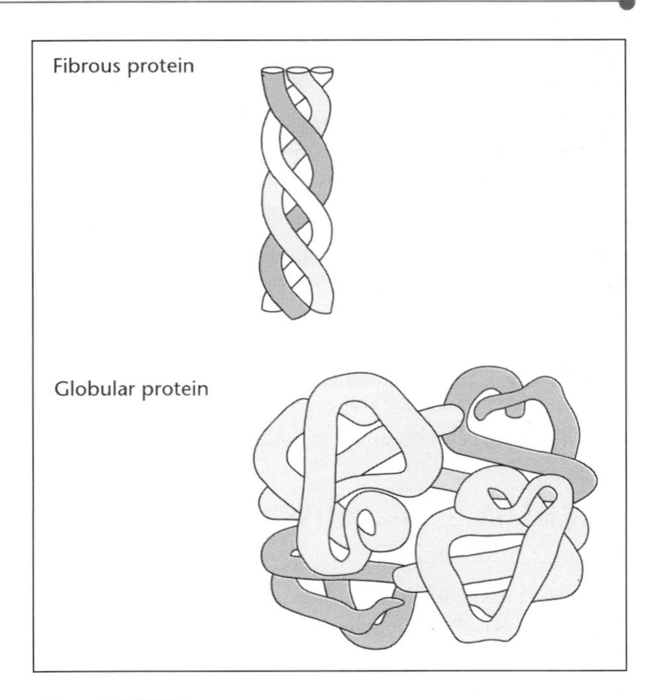

Figure 4 *Fibrous and globular proteins.*

6 Body building

Proteins are very important molecules in the body. You have already seen that enzymes are soluble globular proteins, controlling important reactions in the body. However, there are many other useful proteins in the body.

Collagen – holding you together

Collagen is a fibrous protein found in skin, bone, cartilage, tendons, blood vessels and teeth. It makes up a quarter of all the protein in the body and is the longest protein molecule known. Look at figure 1.

You will notice that collagen is made up of three helices, which are held together by hydrogen bonds. These hydrogen bonds make the molecule stable. Lack of vitamin C in the diet affects these hydrogen bonds, causing the collagen to break down. This is what happens in the disease **scurvy**. As the collagen breaks down, breaks in the skin called lesions form, and the gums become weakened causing the teeth to fall out.

There is an inherited condition called **osteogenesis imperfecta**. In this condition, collagen is not formed properly, and the bones are brittle. People with this condition are likely to suffer from multiple fractures, particularly in childhood.

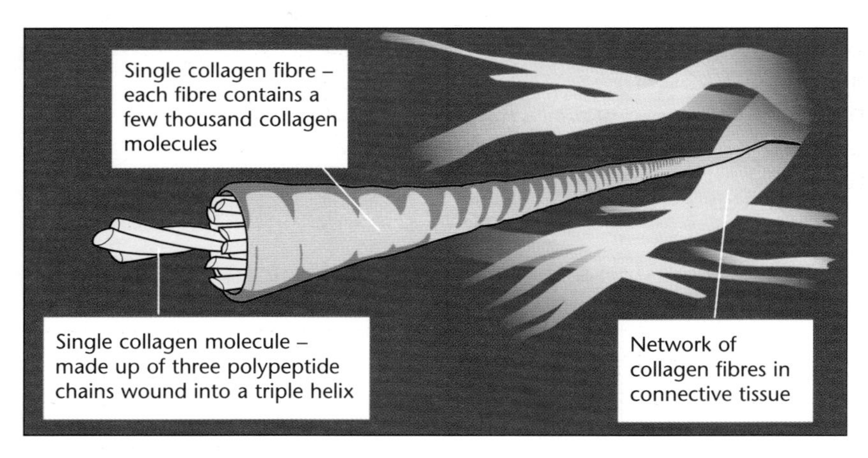

Figure 1 *The structure of collagen.*

Keratin – making you look good

Hair is made of the fibrous protein **keratin**. If you look at figure 2, you will see that the keratin molecule is made of three helices. They are held together by strong covalent bonds called sulphur bonds. Eleven of these molecules group together to form a microfibril, and then hundreds of microfibrils join together to form a single hair.

Shampoos and conditioners change the ionic charge on the protein molecules, making the coils tighter, so that they reflect more light and look shiny. Hair products can also cause the hairs to repel each other, giving the hair more 'body'.

If you have your hair permed, a lotion is added which breaks the sulphur bonds. The helices are unwound as the hair is styled, then a neutralising solution is added to make the sulphur bonds re-form. This results in a 'permanent wave'.

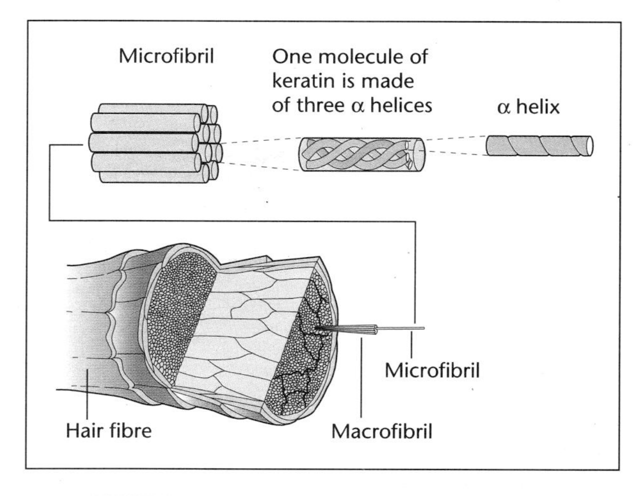

Figure 2 *The structure of a hair.*

1 Is each of the following a fibrous or globular protein?
a collagen
b keratin

Haemoglobin – a carrying molecule

Figure 3 shows haemoglobin. Notice that haemoglobin is a large globular protein made of four subunits joined together.

Haemoglobin is vitally important in the body, as it carries oxygen from the lungs to all parts of the body. In a fetus, there is a special kind of haemoglobin called fetal haemoglobin, which can combine with oxygen even more readily than adult haemoglobin. Without the additional oxygen-carrying ability of fetal haemoglobin, a fetus would not be able to take oxygen from its mother's blood.

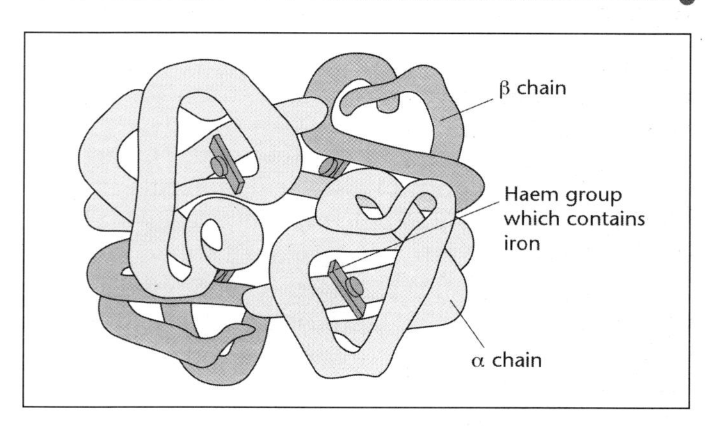

Figure 3 *The structure of haemoglobin.*

2 Explain why it is important for haemoglobin to be soluble.

Key ideas 66–9

The primary structure of a protein is the order or sequence of amino acids it contains.

The secondary structure of a protein is the way the polypeptide chain folds and forms hydrogen bonds.

Two important kinds of secondary structure are the α helix and the β-pleated sheet.

The tertiary structure of a protein is the overall shape of the molecule.

Fibrous proteins tend to be insoluble and have structural roles.

Globular proteins tend to be soluble and have biochemical roles.

7 Greasy substances

Lipids are fats and oils, which are important sources of energy in the diet. They have other uses as well. Energy is stored in the body as fat. As well as being an important energy store, the fat stored under the skin of mammals is an important insulation layer which helps to keep the body warm. Lipids are also important in the structure of cell membranes.

The structure of fats and oils

Fats and oils are not polymers like carbohydrates and proteins, but are made up of **fatty acids** and **glycerol**. Like carbohydrates, they are made up of carbon, hydrogen and oxygen, but in different amounts.

Look at figure 1. You can see that fatty acids have an acid group and a side-chain or R group. The R group is made up of a **hydrocarbon** chain, which means it contains carbon and hydrogen only.

Carbon atoms can bond with other carbon atoms to form a **carbon–carbon** bond. There are lots of these bonds in fatty acid molecules. Sometimes there is a double bond between two carbon atoms in a fatty acid. Figure 2 shows two fatty acids. If all the carbon–carbon bonds in the R group are single bonds, the fatty acid is said to be **saturated**. However, if some of the carbon–carbon bonds are double bonds, the fatty acid is said to be **unsaturated**.

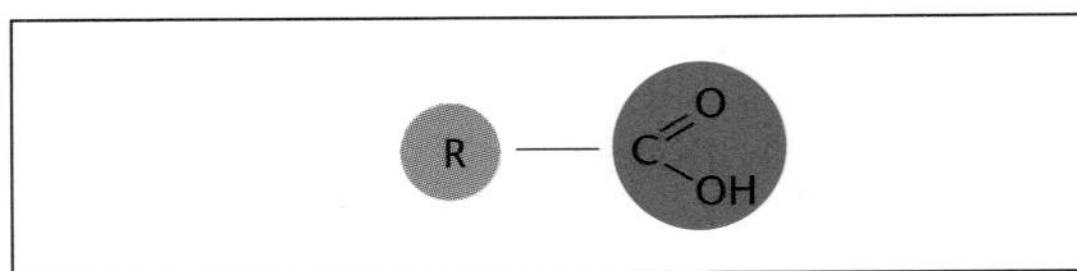

Figure 1 *The structure of a fatty acid.*

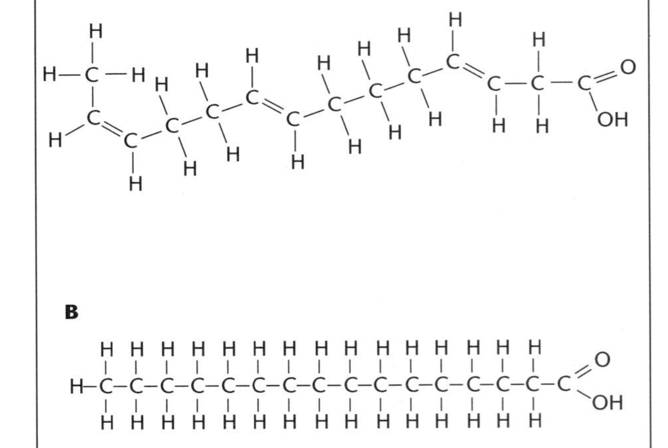

Figure 2 *Saturated fatty acids contain just single carbon–carbon bonds, while unsaturated fatty acids have one or more double bonds.*

1 Which fatty acid in figure 2 is saturated, A or B?

Triglycerides

Most fats and oils are made by joining one glycerol molecule to three fatty acids, as shown in figure 3. You can see that the fatty acids are joined to glycerol by a condensation reaction, and that three molecules of water are removed. Fats and oils made this way are called **triglycerides**, because they are made up of three fatty acids and one glycerol.

Q

2 Triglycerides can be broken down by digestion. Draw a diagram to show the hydrolysis of a triglyceride. (You may need to read page 61.)

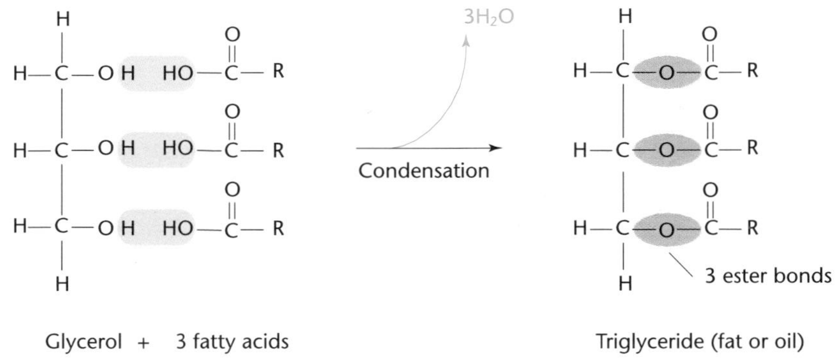

Glycerol + 3 fatty acids $\xrightarrow[\text{Condensation}]{3H_2O}$ Triglyceride (fat or oil)

3 ester bonds

Figure 3 *The formation of a triglyceride.*

Solid or liquid?

Triglycerides that contain long, saturated fatty acids are called **saturated fats**. They tend to form hard fats like lard and butter, which are solid at room temperature. Triglycerides that contain shorter, unsaturated fatty acids are called **unsaturated fats**. They tend to form oils which are liquid at room temperature, like sunflower oil or olive oil. Unsaturated fats have a lower melting point because the double bonds in the fatty acids produce kinks in the carbon chain. This means the molecules cannot lie so close to each other, and this is why unsaturated fats are more fluid.

Looking for lipids

You can test for the presence of lipids in food by using the **emulsion test**, shown in figure 4. Take a solution of the food you are testing and add alcohol (e.g. propan-2-ol). Shake the mixture for one minute, after which two layers will form. Pour the top layer into a test tube and add water. A cloudy white emulsion shows the presence of a lipid.

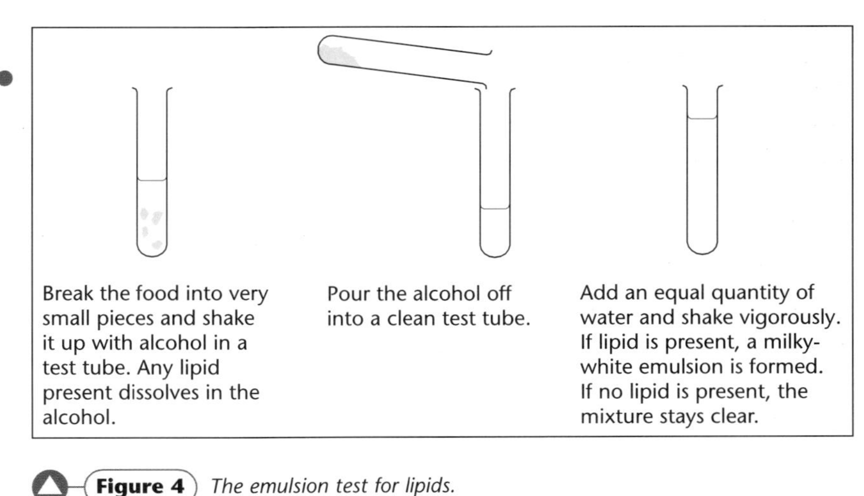

Figure 4 *The emulsion test for lipids.*

Key ideas 70–71

Most fats and oils are triglycerides – they are made up of a glycerol molecule with three fatty acids joined on to it by a condensation reaction.

Saturated fatty acids have R groups in which all the carbon–carbon bonds are single, but unsaturated fatty acids have at least one carbon–carbon double bond.

The emulsion test is used to detect the presence of lipids.

8 Wonderful water

Water is a small molecule that has peculiar properties. These properties probably allowed life as we know it to evolve. A cell contains at least 85% water, and most fluids both inside and outside cells are 90% water. All chemical reactions in cells take place dissolved in water, and most molecules are transported dissolved in water. Water also provides an environment in which many organisms live.

The dissolver – water as a solvent

Look at figure 1 which shows a molecule of water. You can see that the molecule has small positive charges on the hydrogen and a small negative charge on the oxygen. This makes water a **polar** molecule. The polar nature is important to many of the properties of water.

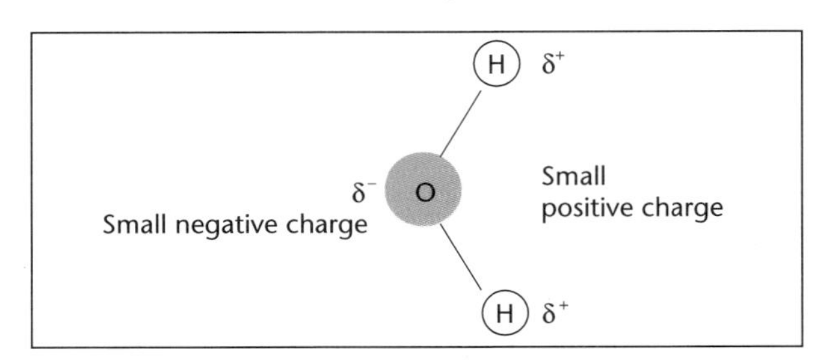

Figure 1 *The polar nature of the water molecule.*

Figure 2 shows what happens when molecules of water are together. The positive charges of hydrogen are attracted to the negative charges of oxygen, and **hydrogen bonds** are formed. Look back to pages 9 and 66 where you met hydrogen bonds in proteins.

Hydrogen bonds make water molecules **cohesive** – they stick to each other. Cohesion holds water molecules together when they move. As a result, water and dissolved substances are easily moved around inside a cell. Transport systems move dissolved substances and water around organisms.

The polar water molecules make water a very good solvent. As you can see in figure 2, water molecules surround charged particles and help them dissolve. All cell reactions occur dissolved in water.

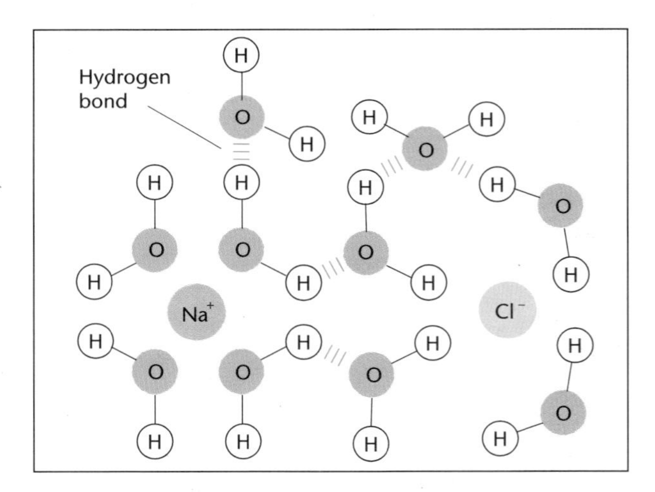

Figure 2 *Hydrogen bonding holds water molecules together. The polar water molecules surround charged substances and help them dissolve.*

The supporter

Water is a liquid at the temperatures and pressures where living organisms survive. Increasing the pressure on water will not make its volume smaller. This allows transport systems in large organisms to pump fluid under pressure. On page 107 you can see how plant cells use water for support.

Some organisms living in water, such as the whale, are very heavy. Their weight is supported by the water around them.

1 Explain why you can float on water but not in air.

On the surface of water, the molecules cohere and form a 'skin' where the water is denser. This is called **surface tension**. In figure 3 you can see how small animals like mosquito larvae use it to support them.

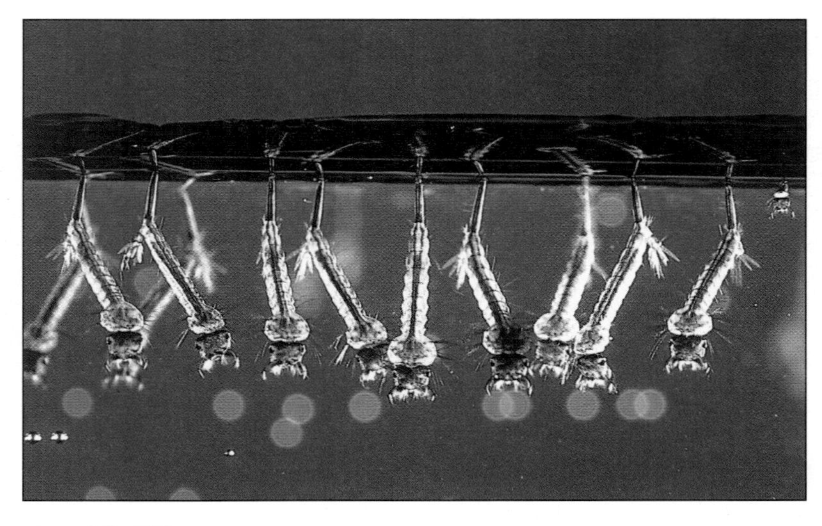

Figure 3 *Surface tension allows mosquito larvae to hang from the surface of the water.*

The heat holder

Water has a high **specific heat capacity**. This means it can absorb a large amount of heat before its temperature changes. As living organisms contain a high proportion of water, the temperature of their cells can remain fairly constant.

A high specific heat capacity gives water two other important properties:

- **High latent heat of vaporisation** – a lot of heat is needed to turn water into water vapour. To lose heat, mammals produce sweat. As the water in sweat evaporates, it takes a lot of heat away from the body.
- **High latent heat of fusion** – water loses a lot of heat before it turns into ice.

As water freezes, it become less dense. In ice, the molecules are held together in a lattice which holds them further apart than in liquid water. This causes ice to float on top of warmer water. It then acts as an insulator, preventing any more heat loss by the water underneath. This allows living organisms to survive in the warmer water under the ice.

Q

2 What advantage do organisms living in water gain from its high specific heat capacity?

3 What is the advantage of a high latent heat of vaporisation for efficient heat loss?

Key ideas 72–3

Living organisms contain a high percentage of water.

Water is the only solvent in living organisms. All reactions in cells take place dissolved in water.

Water is used for support and transport.

The high specific heat capacity of water is important to maintain the temperature of living organisms and their environment.

9 Colour writing

Chromatography comes from a Greek word meaning 'colour writing'. It is a technique used to separate a mixture of substances. It is very useful in biology, because biological samples often contain several different chemicals. Before you can investigate them, you need to separate and identify all the different substances in the mixture. The types of chromatography used by biologists are varied. Here you will find out about paper chromatography and thin layer chromatography, which are very similar.

How it works

Figure 1 shows how **chromatography** works. Spots of a mixture are placed at one end of the paper or thin layer, about 1 cm from the bottom edge. The paper is then stood in a suitable **solvent**, a liquid in which the substances in the mixture dissolve. The solvent moves up through the paper or thin layer. When the solvent reaches the spots of the mixture, the substances in the mixture dissolve in the solvent and are carried with it as it soaks up through the paper or thin layer. The substances will travel different distances up the paper or thin layer, depending on their solubility in the migrating solvent – the more soluble a substance, the further it travels. Once the solvent is nearing the top edge, the paper or thin layer is removed from the solvent. The distance the solvent has travelled is marked.

Some substances are coloured, so the distance travelled by each substance can be measured. If the substances are colourless, the paper or thin layer is treated with a reagent that stains the substances so that they are visible. The end result is a paper or thin layer **chromatogram**. An example is shown in figure 2.

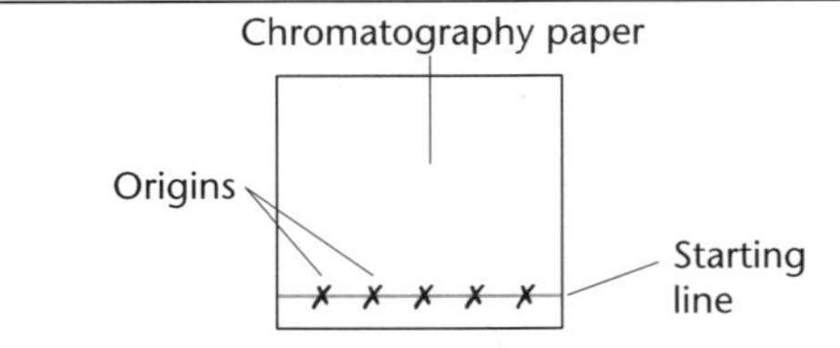

1 A starting line is marked on a piece of chromatography paper (which is very absorbent) using a pencil. Some crosses or **origins** are marked along this line.

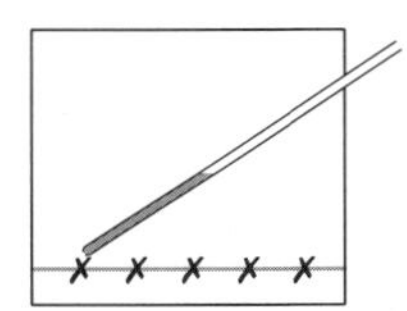

2 A micropipette is used to make a small, concentrated spot of the solution of unknown compounds on the first origin. A spot is applied, allowed to dry, then another spot is applied on top of the first. This is done several times. Solutions of known compounds are then spotted individually on to the other origins.

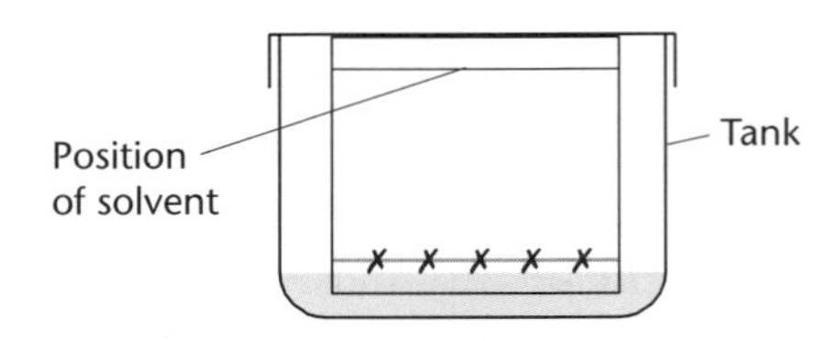

3 The paper is then suspended in a tank of a solvent and left until the solvent is nearly at the top of the paper. The final position of the solvent is marked in pencil. This is called the **solvent front**.

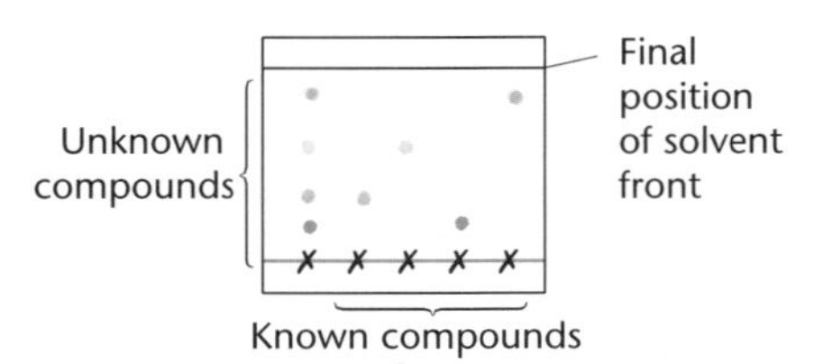

4 The chromatogram is removed from the tank and dried. Sometimes the compounds cannot be seen without adding another chemical called a **locating agent**.

Figure 1 *One-way paper chromatography. Thin layer chromatography is very similar, but instead of paper a glass plate with a thin layer of silica on it is used.*

Finding out about the mixture

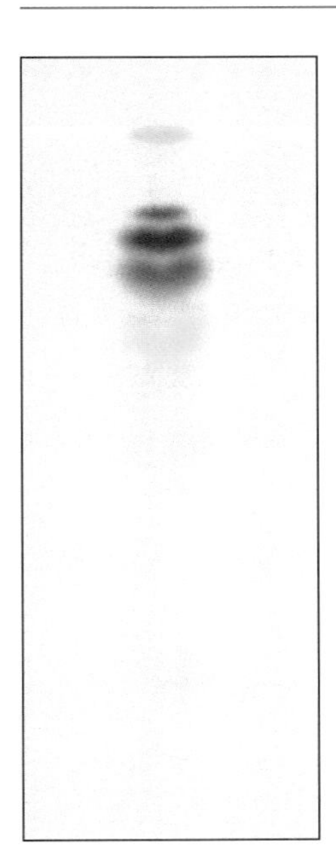

To identify the substances in the mixture, we use a measurement called the **R_f value**. The R_f value for each substance is calculated using the equation:

$$R_f = \frac{\text{distance travelled by the spot (measured at the centre)}}{\text{distance travelled by the solvent}}$$

These R_f values can be compared with R_f values for the same solvents listed in tables, or with R_f values obtained from known samples on the same chromatogram.

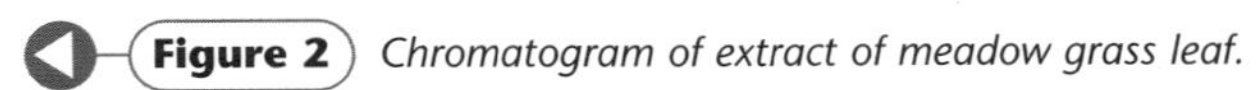
Figure 2 *Chromatogram of extract of meadow grass leaf.*

Two-way chromatography

Sometimes two substances do not separate very well using the technique shown in figure 1, so **two-way chromatography** is used instead. Look at figure 3. After producing the chromatogram using one-way chromatography, a new start line is drawn through the spot. The paper or thin layer is turned through 90° and the chromatogram is run again using a *different* solvent. You can see that what looked like one spot is actually two.

1 Explain why a different solvent is used when the chromatogram is run the second time.

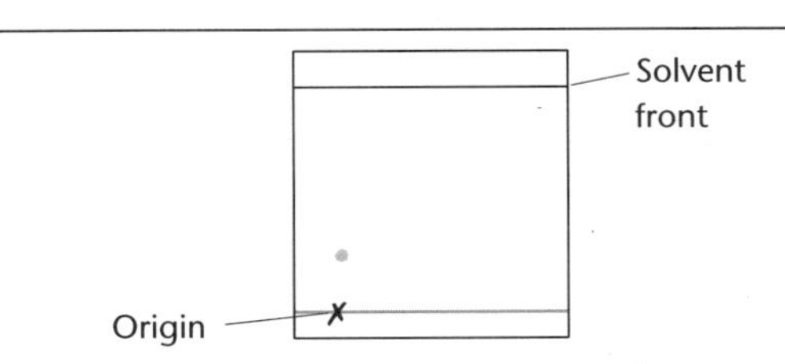

1 After one-way chromatography, this spot has an R_f value of 0.25.

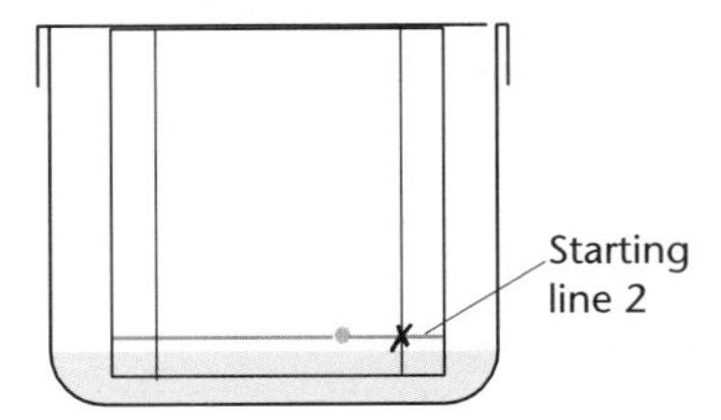

2 A new starting line is drawn through the spot. The paper is turned through 90° and the chromatogram is run again, but using a different solvent this time.

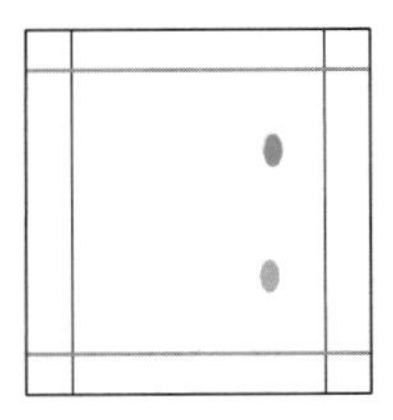

3 After run 2, we find the spot in fact consists of two substances.

Figure 3 *Two-way paper chromatography.*

Key ideas 74–5

Chromatography is used to separate a mixture of substances.

The substances in the mixture can be identified by calculating R_f values and looking them up in a table, or by comparing the positions of the spots with those of known substances.

Two-way chromatography is used to give better separation of substances.

Unit 4 – Questions

10

1) Figure 1 shows the structure of an amino acid.

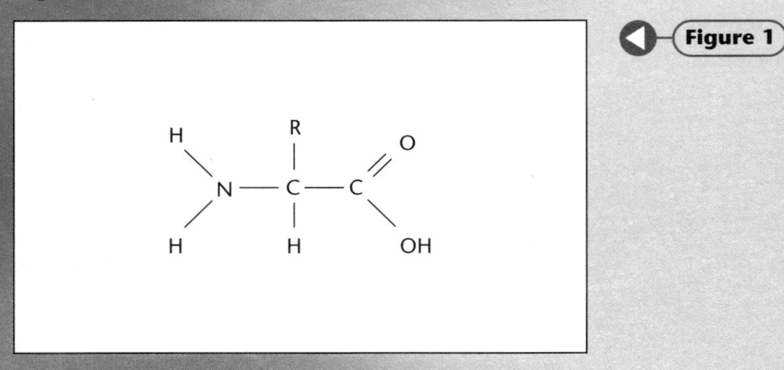

Figure 1

a) Draw a diagram to show how two amino acids join together to form a dipeptide. (2 marks)

b) Protein molecules are described at three different levels. Explain what is meant by:
i) primary structure
ii) secondary structure
iii) tertiary structure. (3 marks)

(Total 5 marks)

2) Copy and complete table 1. Put a tick if the statement is true, or a cross if the statement is false.

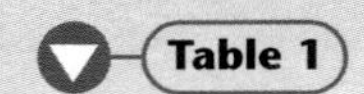
Table 1

Statement	Glucose	Starch	Amino acid	Polypeptide	Protein	Lipid
Contains carbon						
Contains hydrogen						
Contains oxygen						
Contains nitrogen						
May contain sulphur						

(Total 5 marks)

3 Figure 2 represents a triglyceride.

a) Name the parts labelled **A** and **B**. (2 marks)

b) Draw a diagram to show what products are produced when the molecule is hydrolysed. (2 marks)

(Total 4 marks)

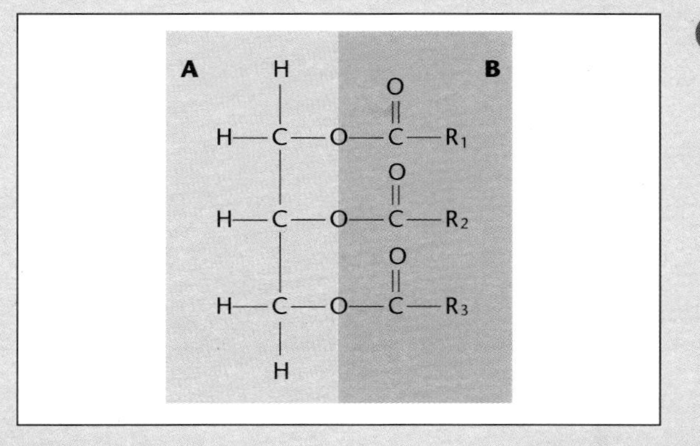

Figure 2

4 a) Name the type of molecule shown in figure 3. (1 mark)

Figure 3

R_1, O, H

H_2N—C—C—N—C—COOH

H, H, R_2

Bond **A**

b) Name the bond labelled **A**. (1 mark)

c) Draw a diagram to show the products made when bond **A** is hydrolysed. (2 marks)

(Total 4 marks)

5 Identify the compounds in figure 4.

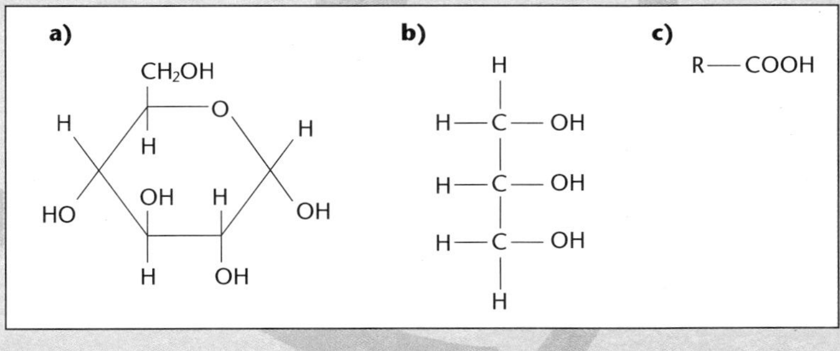

Figure 4

(Total 3 marks)

6 Describe simple biochemical tests that can be used to detect the presence of each of the following molecules:

a) glucose (2 marks)
b) sucrose (2 marks)
c) starch (2 marks)
d) protein (2 marks)
e) lipid. (2 marks)

(Total 10 marks)

1 Boundaries

You will remember from GCSE that each cell has a plasma membrane on its surface, separating it from other cells. The structure of this membrane is the same in all eukaryotic cells. Organelles within a cell have membranes that also share the same structure. Membranes have three main functions:

1. to control the movement of substances into and out of cells
2. to keep the cell contents together and separate from other cells
3. to allow communication between cells.

Keeping apart

Inside an organism there are large numbers of cells packed closely together. The cytoplasm inside the cells is a watery solution in which the organelles move about. Look at figure 1. Between the cells there is liquid called **intercellular fluid**, which is also mainly water. The cell surface membrane keeps these two solutions separate, so the cell contents stay together and substances do not leak into or out of the cell. This helps a cell to function independently of other cells.

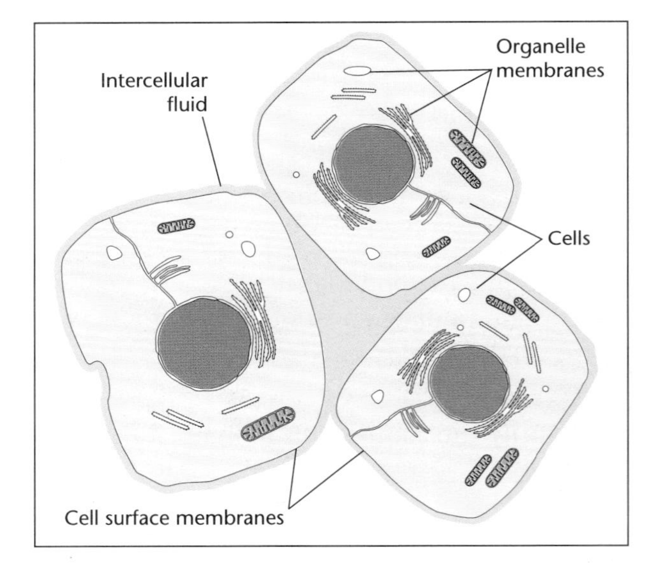

Figure 1 *Cells are separated from each other and from their surroundings by membranes.*

Membranes surround organelles, helping to keep different parts of the cell separate from one another. This keeps all the enzymes needed for one set of reactions together in the organelle that carries them out, which helps reactions to take place more efficiently. Sometimes a membrane is used to hold enzymes in place.

When cells are observed using a microscope, membranes can be seen moving about. Figure 2 shows how parts of the cell surface membrane fold in and form bags called **vesicles**. These vesicles can move through the cytoplasm and join onto other membranes inside a cell.

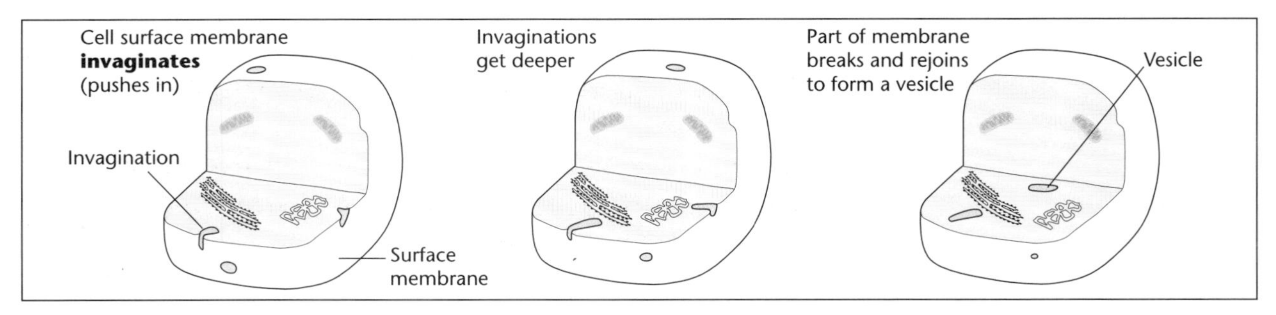

Figure 2 *How vesicles form at the surface of a membrane.*

In and out

Cells use vesicles to carry substances into and out of cells, and to move them around inside the cell. The process of taking in substances using vesicles is called **endocytosis** (endo = inside, cytosis = cell). Look at figure 3 which shows two kinds of endocytosis. In both you can see that the vesicles form from the cell surface membrane and join another membrane inside the cell.

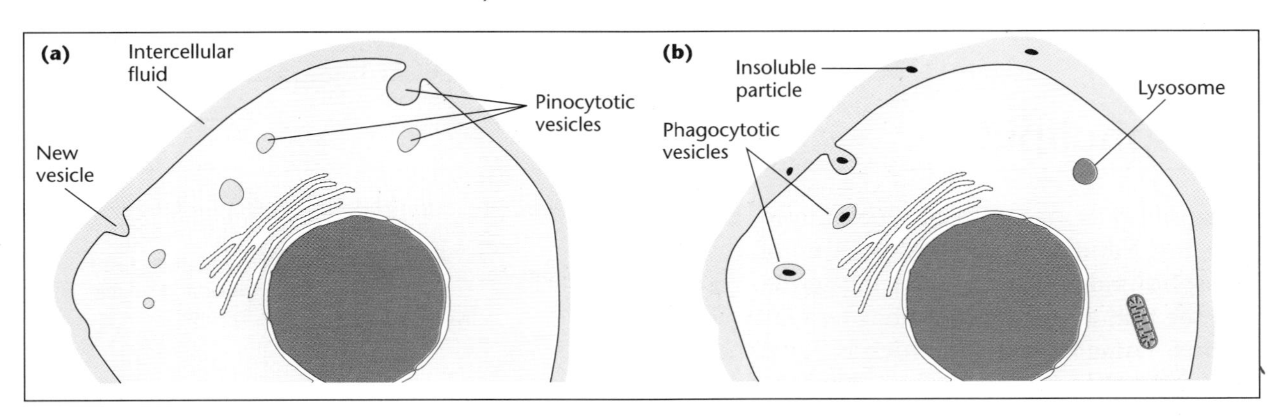

Figure 3 *Vesicles are used for (a) pinocytosis and (b) phagocytosis, two kinds of endocytosis.*

In figure 3 (*a*), soluble molecules are entering the cell. This is called **pinocytosis** – 'cell drinking'. In figure 3 (*b*), insoluble substances are entering the cell. This is **phagocytosis** – 'cell eating'. Unicellular animals feed by phagocytosis, and white blood cells use phagocytosis to remove invading microorganisms. Look again at figure 3 and notice that cell surface membranes carry out pinocytosis and phagocytosis in the same way – it is just the contents of the vesicles that are different.

Vesicles can be used to remove substances from cells. This called **exocytosis** (exo = out, cytosis = cell). Look at figure 4. The vesicle joins the cell surface membrane and its contents leave the cell. Cells use exocytosis to remove useful substances they make from the cell. This is cell **secretion**. The cells of the salivary glands, gastric glands and pancreas secrete the enzymes they produce into ducts by exocytosis.

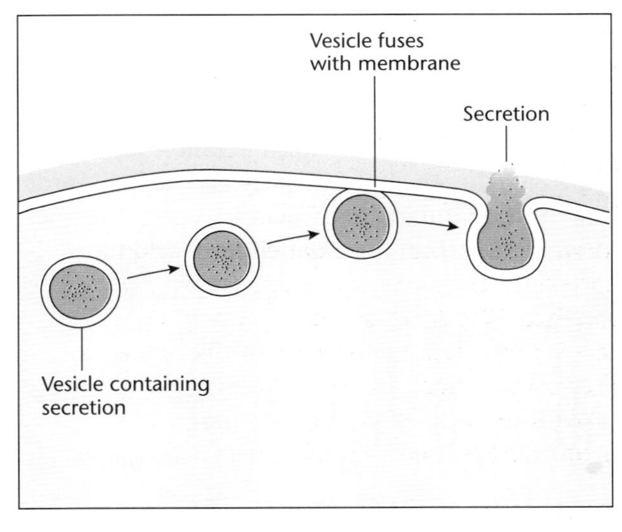

Figure 4 *How cells secrete substances by exocytosis.*

Key ideas 78–9

Membranes separate cells from each other and from their environment.

Membrane vesicles can move substances into and out of cells.

Membrane from the cell surface can be interchanged with membrane from cell organelles.

2 Membrane molecules

A membrane is made up mainly of two sorts of molecule:

1. **phospholipids** forming the bulk of the membrane
2. **proteins** scattered around in the membrane.

Some molecules of **carbohydrates** and **cholesterol** may also be present.

Phospholipids

Phospholipids are a special type of lipid. Look at figure 1 and compare the structure of a phospholipid with that of a triglyceride. You can see that a phospholipid has two fatty acid chains. These form a tail which is **hydrophobic** (hydro = water, phobic = hating). Fatty acid tails do not have a charge, so they are **non-polar** and insoluble in water. The phosphate group is **hydrophilic** (hydro = water, philic = loving) because it has a charge. It is polar and soluble in water.

Phospholipids pack together in a membrane as shown in figure 2. They form a double layer called a **bilayer**, with the fatty acid tails towards the inside. Saturated fatty acid tails pack together more tightly than unsaturated fatty acid tails.

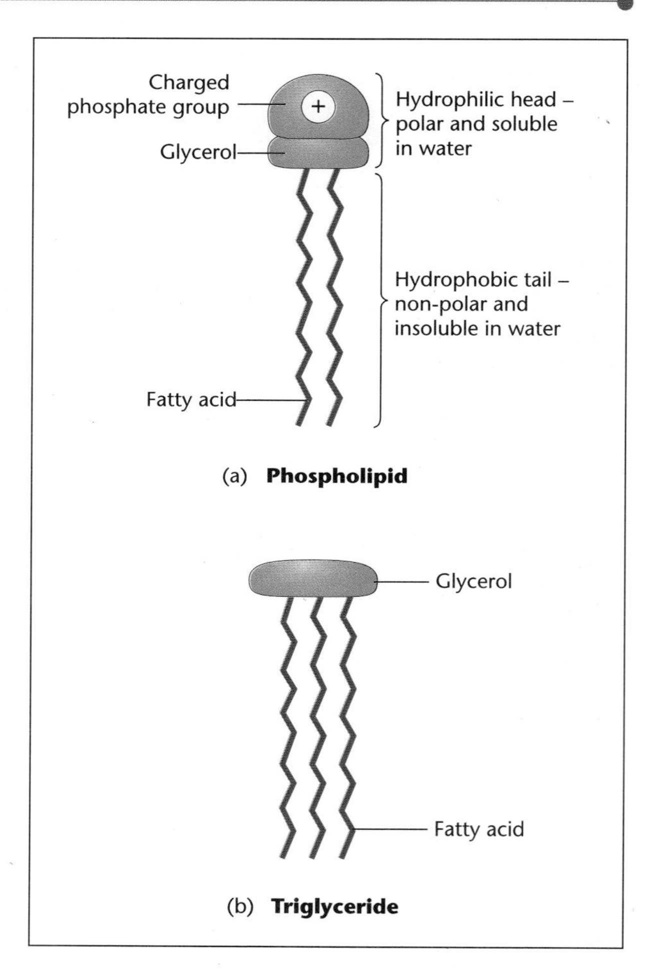

Figure 1 *Simplified structure of (a) a phospholipid and (b) a triglyceride.*

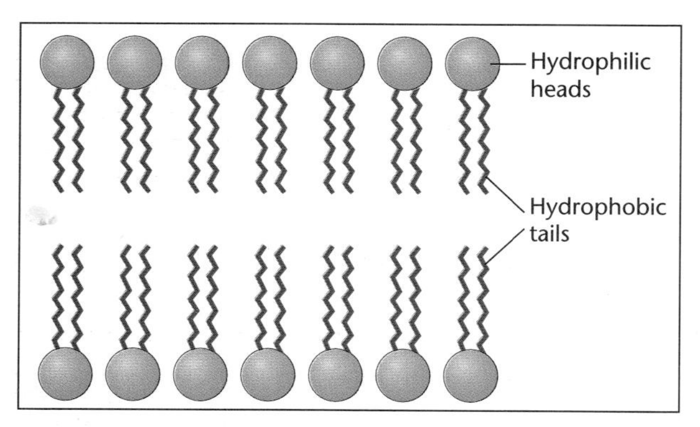

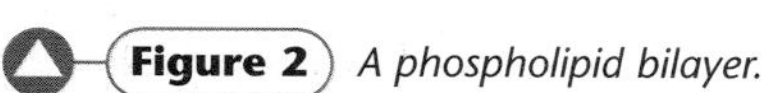
Figure 2 *A phospholipid bilayer.*

1. **What are the differences between a triglyceride and a phospholipid?**
2. **Look at page 70. Suggest why phospholipids with saturated fatty acids pack together more tightly in the membrane than phospholipids with unsaturated fatty acids.**

Proteins

In a membrane there are many different sorts of protein with complex tertiary structures. The proteins are scattered around in the membrane and are always changing their position. There are large proteins which span the whole bilayer, and smaller proteins on just one side of the bilayer. Carbohydrates may be attached to proteins in the membrane, forming **glycoproteins**, or to phospholipids, forming **glycolipids**. In some membranes **cholesterol** lies between the proteins or phospholipids and helps to stabilise their position. Cholesterol is a special type of lipid called a steroid.

Putting a membrane together

The way the molecules in a membrane are organised is described as the **fluid mosaic model** (fluid = moving; mosaic = made of pieces). Look at figure 3 which shows this arrangement. It shows how the proteins are scattered around in the phospholipid bilayer.

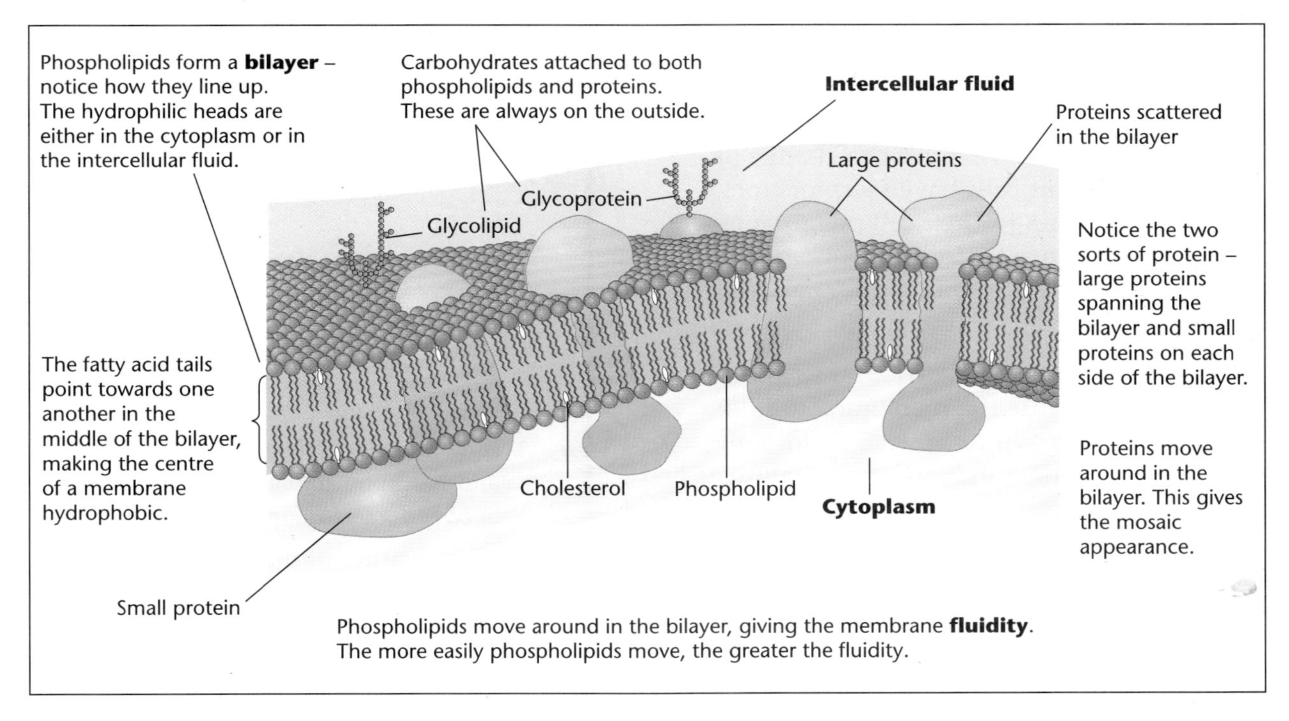

Figure 3 *The fluid mosaic model describes how molecules are arranged in a membrane.*

Key ideas 80–81

Membranes are made up of a bilayer of phospholipids and scattered proteins.

The organisation is called a fluid mosaic which describes the constant movement of the molecules.

Carbohydrates may be attached to proteins and phospholipids on the outer surface of the membrane.

3 Membranes at work

As well as separating the cell contents from the outside environment, membranes have important recognition functions:

1. They recognise other molecules that fit the shape of proteins on the outer side of the membrane.
2. They allow the defence system to recognise foreign cells.

Recognising others

Some membrane proteins on the outside of the bilayer have shapes that are complementary with molecules in the intercellular fluid. These proteins are called membrane **receptors**. Figure 1 shows a receptor protein. You can see there is a specific shape at one part of its molecule. A hormone with a complementary shape binds to the receptor protein. This binding of the hormone sends a chemical signal to a cell, which causes it to change its activities. Different cells have receptors for different hormones in their cell membranes. Viruses, for instance HIV, use membrane receptors to bind onto cells so they can inject their genetic material into the cell.

When some receptor proteins bind to another molecule, they cause the membrane to fold and form an endocytotic vesicle. Lipids are taken into cells like this. Some bacteria use these receptors to get into cells. Some medicinal drugs work by blocking membrane receptors. An example is drugs used in the treatment of stomach ulcers.

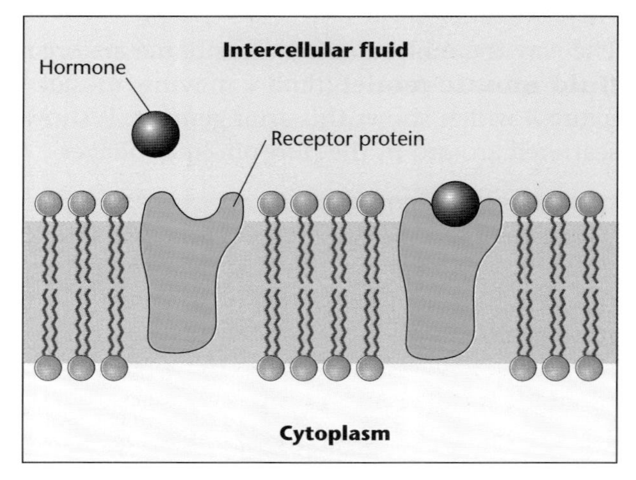

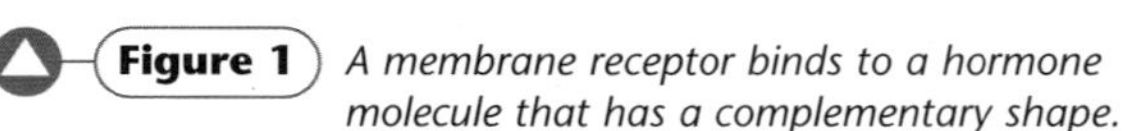
Figure 1 *A membrane receptor binds to a hormone molecule that has a complementary shape.*

1. **How is the reaction of a receptor and hormone similar to the reaction between an enzyme and substrate?**
2. **What feature of proteins makes these reactions possible?**

Acid and ulcers

The gastric glands in the stomach secrete acid, which aids digestion. The stomach is protected from the action of its enzymes and acid by a thick layer of mucus. If stomach acid reaches the mucosa, ulcers develop.

Some people secrete too much acid and develop stomach ulcers. One way that acid secretion is brought about is when a membrane receptor on the mucosa binds with a chemical called **histamine**. The drug **cimetidine** competes with histamine for the receptor, blocking the secretion of acid.

Q 3 **Look at figure 2. Explain why cimetidine can compete with histamine for the receptor.**

$CH_2-CH_2-NH_3^+$ (on imidazole ring HN, N) — Histamine

H_3C, $CH_2-S-CH_2-CH_2-NH-C(=N-C\equiv N)-NH-CH_3$ (on imidazole ring HN, N) — Cimetidine

Figure 2 *Structural formulae of histamine and cimetidine.*

Self-defence

Some membrane proteins are used as a personalised cell label on the outside of the bilayer. These are called **antigens**. Figure 3 shows an antigen in a membrane. The protein has carbohydrate attached, so it is a glycoprotein. Most membrane antigens are glycoproteins.

Your body's defence cells have membrane receptors to recognise the shape of **self-antigens** (your own antigens). Any cell with different antigens is attacked and destroyed by the body's defence cells. This is the main way in which disease-causing organisms are destroyed. Any cell that causes defence cells to attack is called **antigenic**.

Molecules can also be antigenic, for example, toxins in snake venom. The response the body's defence cells makes to antigenic cells or molecules is called the **immune response**.

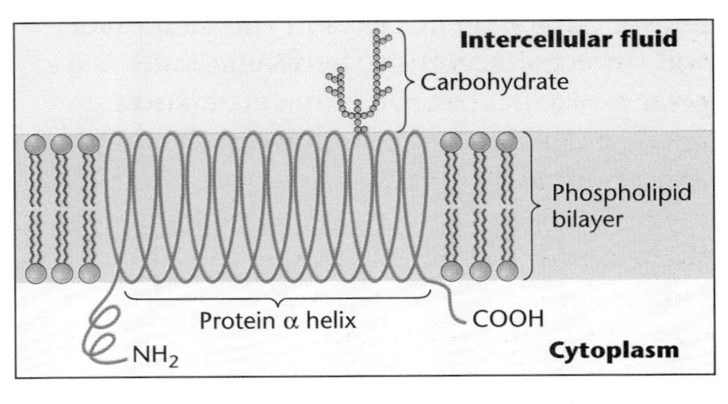

Figure 3 *An antigen (a glycoprotein) in a membrane.*

Reaction and over-reaction

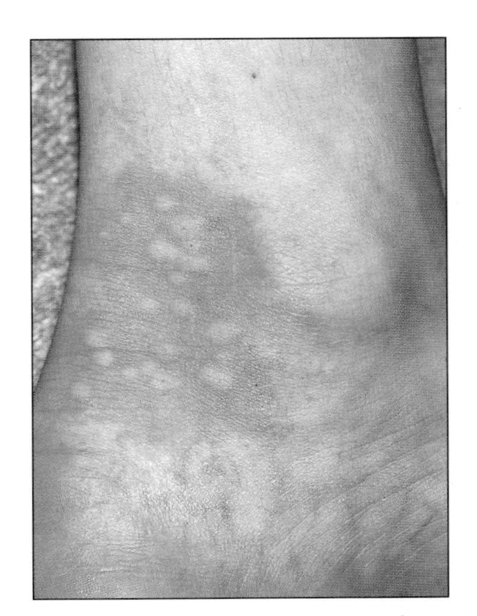

Figure 4 *Nettle rash on an ankle. Nettle rash is a reaction to chemicals in the nettle hairs.*

Look at figure 4. Nettle leaves have hairs with chemicals on them. These chemicals bind to receptors on cells in skin, causing a mild rash, swelling and inflammation.

When an antigen binds to defence cells, it may cause other cells in the body called **mast cells** to release the same chemicals as nettles. The chemicals bind to receptors on other cells, causing inflammation. Sometimes the body over-reacts to a particular antigen, for example insect stings or certain foods. This over-reaction leads to an increased response or an **allergy**.

Key ideas 82–3

Cells recognise other cells and molecules using membrane proteins.

Antigenic cells or molecules bring about an immune response in the body.

4 From side to side

The way a cell membrane is organised makes it partially permeable. This means it lets water and some other molecules pass through in either direction. Whether a molecule can pass through a membrane depends on its size, charge and solubility in water or lipid.

Slipping between the phospholipid gaps

Figure 1 shows how small non-polar and lipid-soluble molecules can pass between the phospholipids. The movement of phospholipids creates gaps in the membrane, and these molecules slip between. Water is a polar molecule, but it is very small, and some water molecules can pass between the moving phospholipids.

1 Look at page 80. Suggest why the hydrophobic inner part of the bilayer limits the movement of water between the phospholipids.

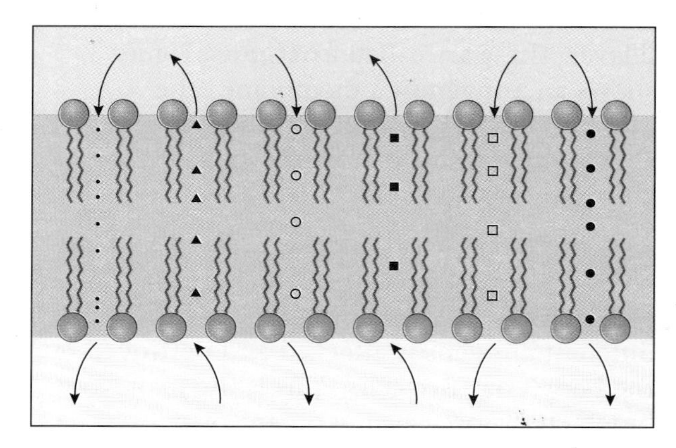

Figure 1 *Small non-polar molecules can slip between the phospholipids in a bilayer.*

Protein passages

Some molecules, such as glucose, are too large to pass between the phospholipids. Substances with a charge, like ions, are pushed away by the polar head of the phospholipids. These larger non-polar molecules and ions pass through proteins to cross the cell membrane.

Figure 2 shows proteins spanning the bilayer. These are **channel proteins** or **pores**. Molecules enter at one side of the protein and pass through to the other side. Each channel protein is specific – it only lets one type of molecule through. Small molecules like water may also pass through these channels.

Two sorts of channel protein are shown. One is permanently open, and the other is **gated**, which means it can be open or closed. The gated channel has a receptor site. When a hormone binds to this receptor site, the channel opens.

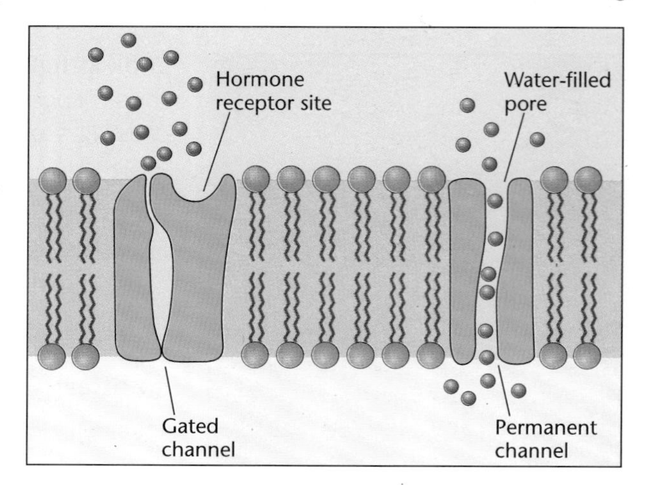

Figure 2 *Two different types of channel protein in membranes.*

2 Suggest how channel proteins can recognise specific molecules.

Glucose uptake – a gated channel in action

Glucose can pass into cells through both permanent and gated channel proteins. When the glucose concentration in blood is in the normal range, only permanent channels are open. When the glucose concentration in the blood rises too high, gated channels open in the cell surface membranes so extra glucose is taken up by cells. Figure 3 shows how this happens.

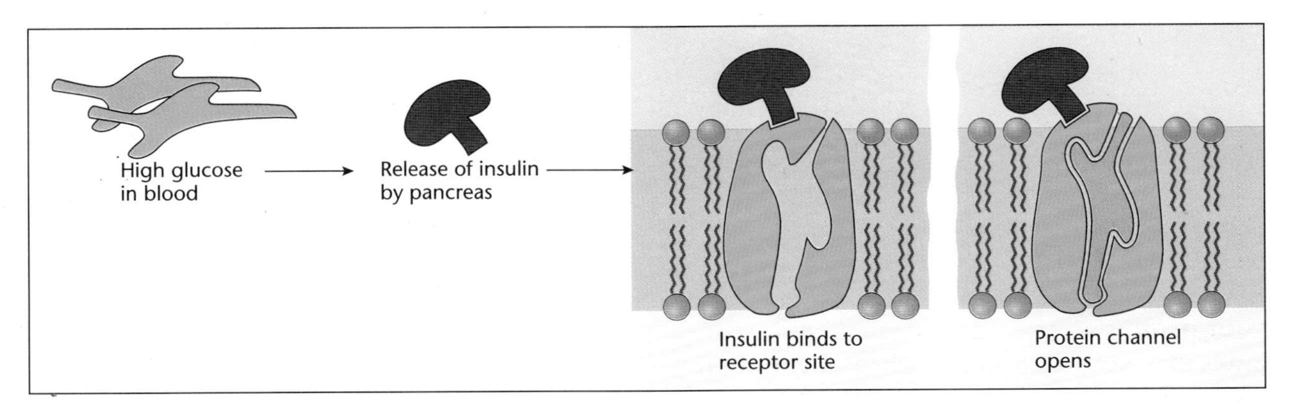

 Figure 3 *Gated glucose channel proteins in membranes are opened when insulin binds to them.*

Energy users – protein carriers

An energy-storing molecule called ATP is produced by respiration. Cells use energy from ATP to carry out reactions. There are proteins called **carrier proteins** in the cell surface membrane that have a specific shape. They carry molecules with a complementary shape across the membrane using energy from ATP.

Figure 4 shows a carrier protein bringing an ion into the cell. Notice that the carrier has a specific site pointing towards the outer side of the membrane. An ion binds to the carrier at this site. ATP is broken down by enzymes linked to the carrier protein. The energy released is used to take the ion across the membrane. The carrier site now points inwards, so the ion is released on the other side of the membrane.

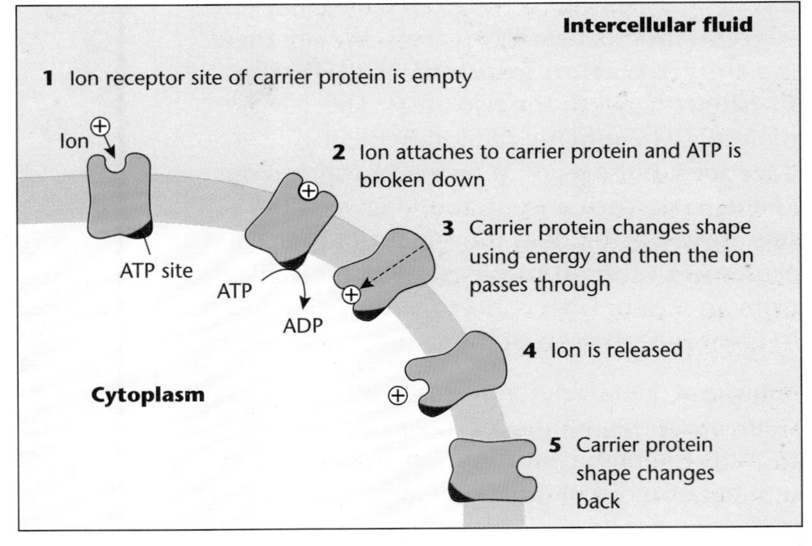

Figure 4 *A carrier protein brings an ion into the cell using energy from the breakdown of ATP.*

Key ideas 84–5

Substances enter and leave a cell by crossing the cell surface membrane.

Most substances cross the membrane through proteins.

5 Molecules on the move

Moving molecules have kinetic energy. Their movement is random. When molecules collide, they change direction. The closer together the molecules are, the more likely are they to hit each other.

How molecules cross cell membranes depends on:

1. their size
2. whether they have a charge
3. their solubility in lipids or water.

Diffusion

Diffusion is an overall movement of molecules from an area of high concentration to an area of lower concentration. When molecules move by diffusion, no energy is used. For this reason diffusion is described as a **passive** process.

Look at figure 1, which shows how diffusion takes place. You can see there is a difference in concentration between two areas. We say there is a **concentration gradient** or **diffusion gradient** between the two areas. The molecules are moving randomly in all directions, but overall, they tend to spread out and equalise the concentration between the two areas. The random movement of molecules causes **net** (overall) **movement** of molecules from an area of high concentration to an area of low concentration of the same molecule.

You can work out net movement by subtracting the number of molecules moving towards the high concentration from the number of molecules moving away from the high concentration. For example, if 50 molecules move towards a high concentration and 300 move away, the net movement is 250 molecules moving away from the high concentration.

The concentration will eventually become the same in each area. This is **equilibrium**. There will be the same net movement in each direction at equilibrium.

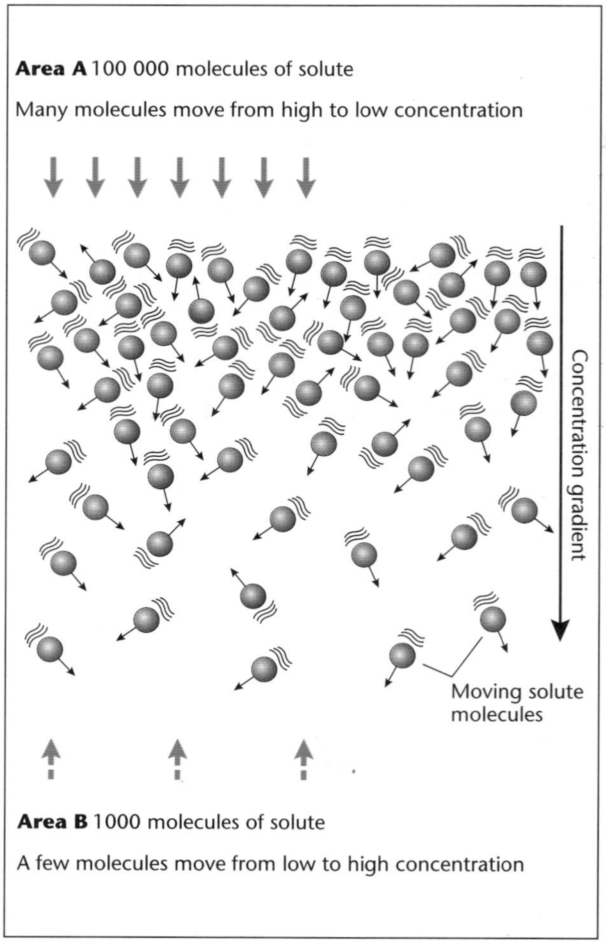

Figure 1 *Diffusion of molecules along a diffusion gradient.*

A helping hand

Molecules that cannot diffuse easily between the phospholipids may be helped through the membrane by channel proteins, as described on page 84. This is **facilitated diffusion** (facilitate = to help). Figure 2 shows facilitated diffusion.

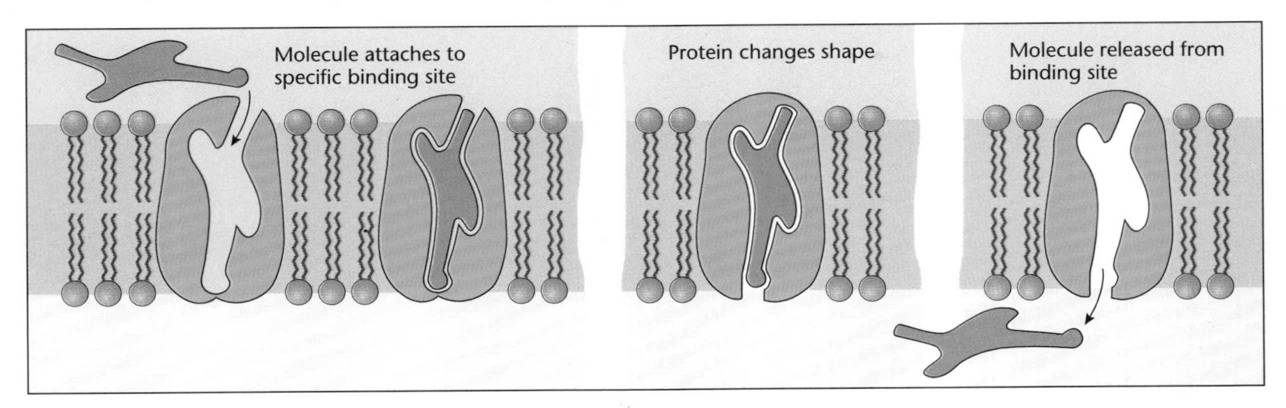

Figure 2 *Facilitated diffusion takes place through channel proteins.*

Active transport

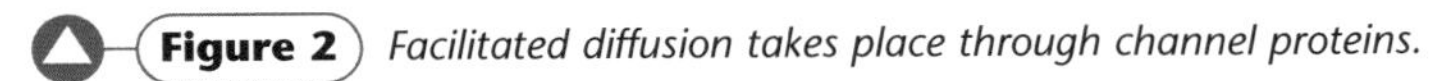

When the concentration of a molecule is higher inside a cell than outside, random movement causes molecules to move down the concentration gradient out of the cell. Energy from ATP may be used by carrier proteins to move molecules into the cell against this gradient. This process is called **active transport** (active = energy-using).

Some carrier proteins are also called **protein pumps**. The pumps act like valves, bringing an ion into the cell and preventing it going back out. Look at figure 3 which shows the two-way sodium (Na^+)/potassium (K^+) pump. You can see that this pump brings potassium into the cell and removes sodium. It is called an **exchange pump**.

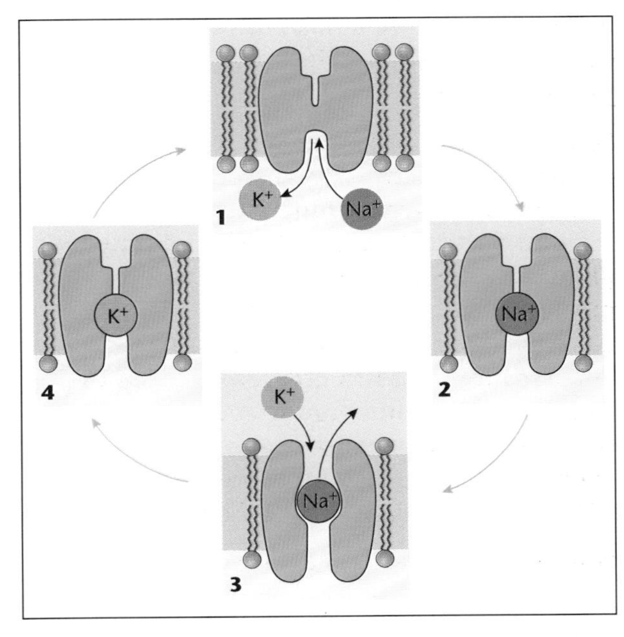

Figure 3 *The Na^+/K^+ pump is a carrier protein.*

Key ideas 86–7

Diffusion occurs down a concentration gradient, from high to low concentration of the same molecule.

Active transport occurs against a concentration gradient, from low to high concentration of the same molecule.

Active transport uses energy from ATP.

Specific membrane proteins are used for facilitated diffusion and for active transport.

Unit 5 – Questions

1) Figure 1 shows the fluid mosaic model of a cell membrane.

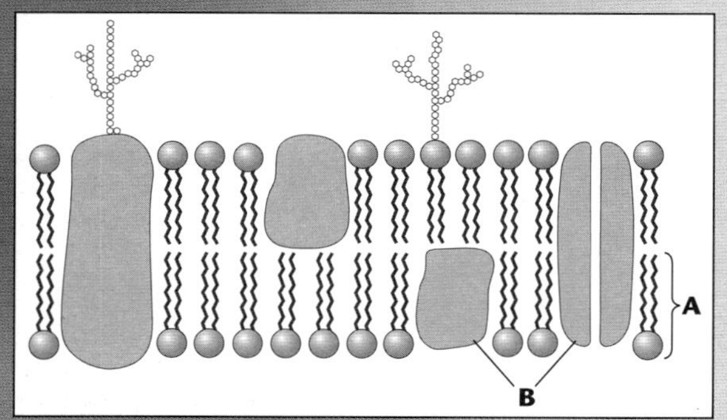

Figure 1

a) Name molecules **A** and **B**. (2 marks)

b) Draw a diagram of molecule **A**. On your diagram label the components and indicate which part is hydrophobic and which part is hydrophilic. (4 marks)

c) Explain why the model is described as being *fluid mosaic*. (2 marks)

d) Give two functions of molecules **B** in the membrane. (2 marks)

e) Sketch the diagram and on your sketch label the outside of the membrane. Give a reason for your answer. (2 marks)

(Total 12 marks)

2) Substances pass across cell membranes in a number of ways.

a) List three ways by which molecules can pass across a cell membrane. (3 marks)

b) The methods you have listed are often described as *active* or *passive*. Identify which of the methods you have listed are:
i) passive
ii) active. (3 marks)

c) Give two differences between an active method and a passive method. (2 marks)

(Total 8 marks)

3) a) What similarity is there between a carrier protein used for active transport and a channel protein used for facilitated diffusion? (1 mark)

b) What are the two differences between active transport and diffusion? (2 marks)

(Total 3 marks)

4) Figure 2 shows some of the main molecules that form the cell membrane.

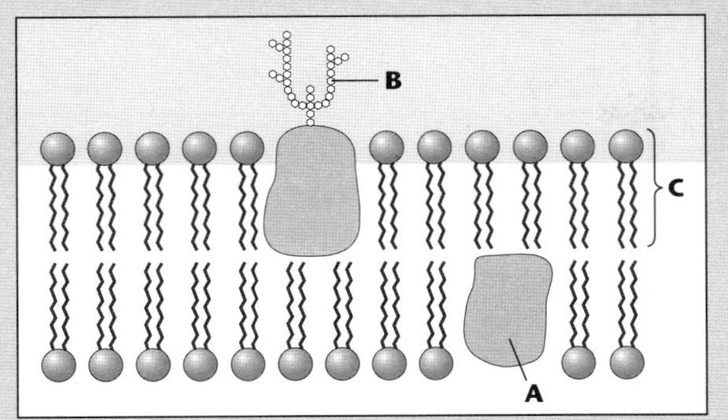

Figure 2

a) Sketch the diagram and use a bracket to identify which part of the membrane is hydrophobic. (1 mark)

b) Identify which molecules, when hydrolysed, would release:
   i) amino acids
   ii) glucose
   iii) fatty acids
   iv) glycerol. (4 marks)

(Total 5 marks)

5) The outer layers of cells in a plant root absorb the mineral ions magnesium, nitrate and phosphate from the soil solution surrounding them.

Figure 3 shows the relative amounts of magnesium, nitrate and phosphate ions in the root cells of a plant and in the soil solution that is in direct contact with the root cells.

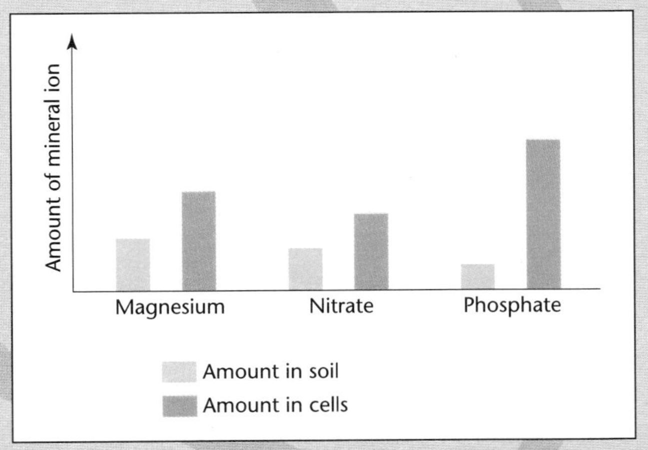

Figure 3

a) Name the process by which the mineral ions move from the soil solution into the cell. Give a reason for your answer. (2 marks)

b) What evidence is there to suggest that the uptake of mineral ions is a selective process? (1 mark)

(Total 3 marks)

1 Supply and demand

All cells need molecules to use in their metabolism. Cells also need to remove waste products and heat produced by metabolism. The more cells an organism has, and the more active the cells, the greater the number of molecules it needs and the more waste products it makes. These molecules are exchanged mainly by diffusion. Heat is exchanged over the same exchange surfaces as molecules. Many organisms have developed special exchange systems, such as:

1. breathing systems to obtain oxygen and remove carbon dioxide
2. digestive systems to obtain food molecules in animals
3. transport systems to carry molecules from place to place.

The bigger you are the harder it is

A unicellular organism can take in molecules all over its surface. However, in a multicellular organism, the cells on the inside cannot exchange materials with the environment. In figure 1, you can see that the cells in the middle are a long way from the outside. It takes too long for diffusion to supply enough molecules to these cells.

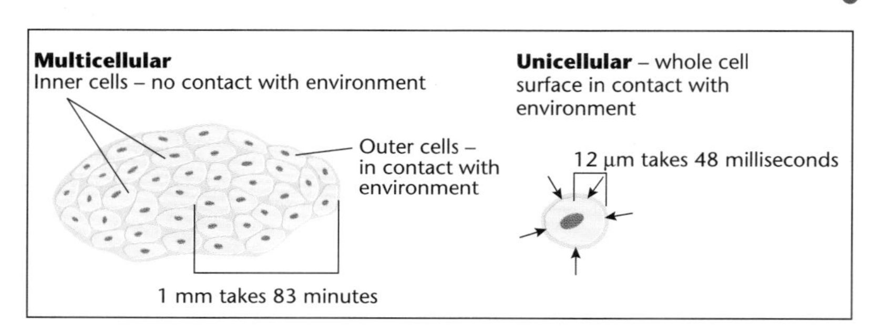

Figure 1 *In a multicellular organism, diffusion cannot supply molecules to the middle cells efficiently.*

Sizing up

The amount of diffusion between a multicellular organism and its environment depends on:

- the total number of cells in contact with the environment – the **surface area**
- the total space occupied by all the cells that need supplying with molecules – the **volume**.

As the number of cells increases, the volume increases. The surface area also increases, but not as much, because some cells are not in contact with the outside. It is useful to work out the proportion of surface area to volume, or the **surface area : volume ratio**.

1 a What is the surface area of each cube in figure 2?
b What is the volume of each cube?
c What is the surface area to volume ratio of each cube?
d Describe how the surface area to volume ratio changes as size increases.

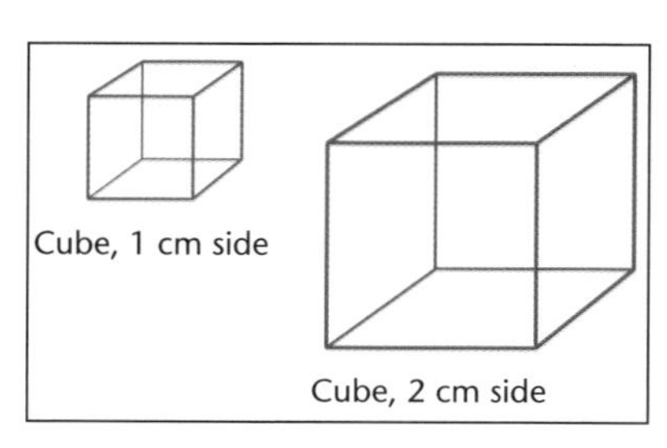

Figure 2

Speeding things up

Unicellular organisms and small multicellular organisms exchange molecules over their whole outer surface, and the whole body shape of smaller organisms can be adapated for exchanging substances. Figure 3 shows an example. In large multicellular animals and plants, molecules and heat often have to pass across layers of cells. These organisms have specialised **exchange surfaces** where molecules and heat are exchanged with the environment. An example is the alveoli in the lungs of a mammal, where gases are exchanged for respiration.

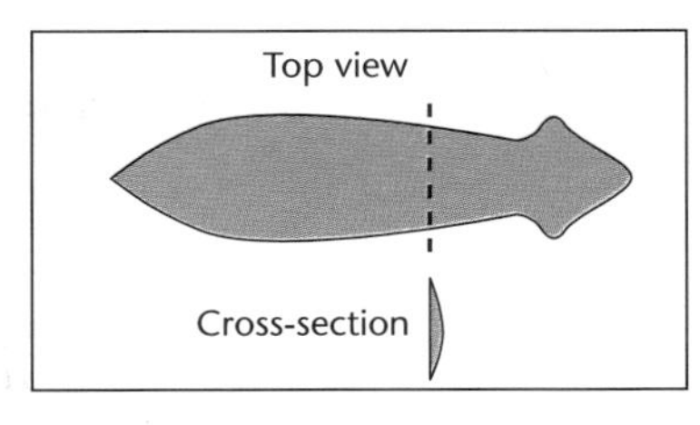

Figure 3 *A flatworm is a small multicellular organism. Its body shape is adapted for exchanging substances with its surroundings.*

(a) Epithelial cell from the small intestine of a mammal

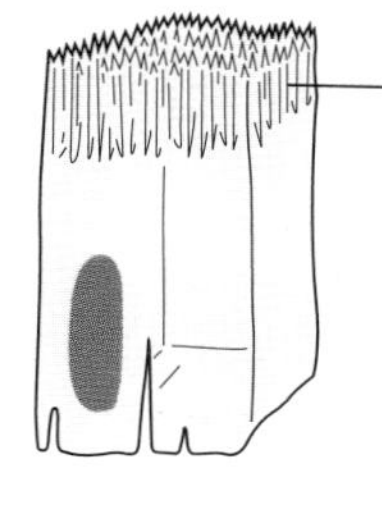

Microvilli – tightly packed finger-like folds of membrane

(b) Epithelial cell from the alveolus of a mammal

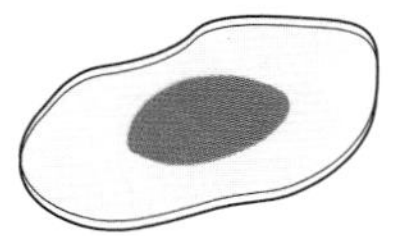

(c) Plant mesophyll cell

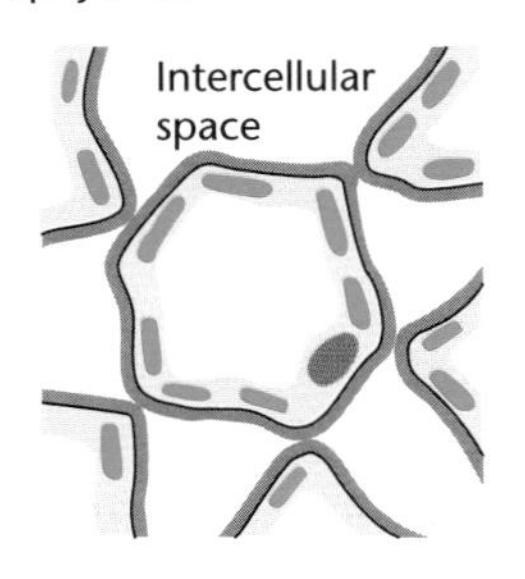

Figure 4 *Cells from different exchange surfaces.*

Good exchange surfaces have:

- a large surface area – this makes the surface area : volume ratio greater, so more molecules can cross the surface per unit time
- a thin surface – there is a shorter distance to travel, so more molecules cross the surface per unit time
- a steep diffusion gradient – a greater difference in concentration increases the rate of diffusion, so more molecules cross the surface per unit time.

Look at figure 4, which show cells from three different exchange surfaces. Although these cells look different, they all have the features of a good exchange surface.

2 Look at figure 4. Describe the adaptations (features) shown by each cell that gives it:
a a large surface area
b a thin surface.

Key ideas 90–91

Exchange of molecules between an organism and the environment occurs mainly by diffusion.

Diffusion over the surface of a large organism is inefficient because of the small surface area : volume ratio.

Larger organisms have specific systems containing exchange surfaces. These are adapted to speed up diffusion.

2 Exchanging gases in mammals

Mammals use oxygen for respiration, and produce carbon dioxide. These gases are part of the air. Lungs inside their bodies contain an exchange surface where oxygen and carbon dioxide are exchanged with the air. You will remember from GCSE that there is a breathing or **ventilation** mechanism to force air in and out of the lungs. The **pulmonary blood system** carries the gases between the lungs and the main blood circulation, which transports them around the body.

The exchanger – the breathing system

Figure 1 shows the lungs. The lungs are inside the **thorax** (chest) and fill most of the **thoracic cavity** (the space inside the chest). You can see that the ribs surround the thoracic cavity, forming a rib cage. At the front the ribs are joined to the sternum (breastbone). There are also joints between the ribs and the vertebral column (backbone). These joints allow the ribs to be moved when you breathe. The **diaphragm** lies across the floor of the thoracic cavity. This separates the thoracic cavity from the **abdominal cavity** underneath.

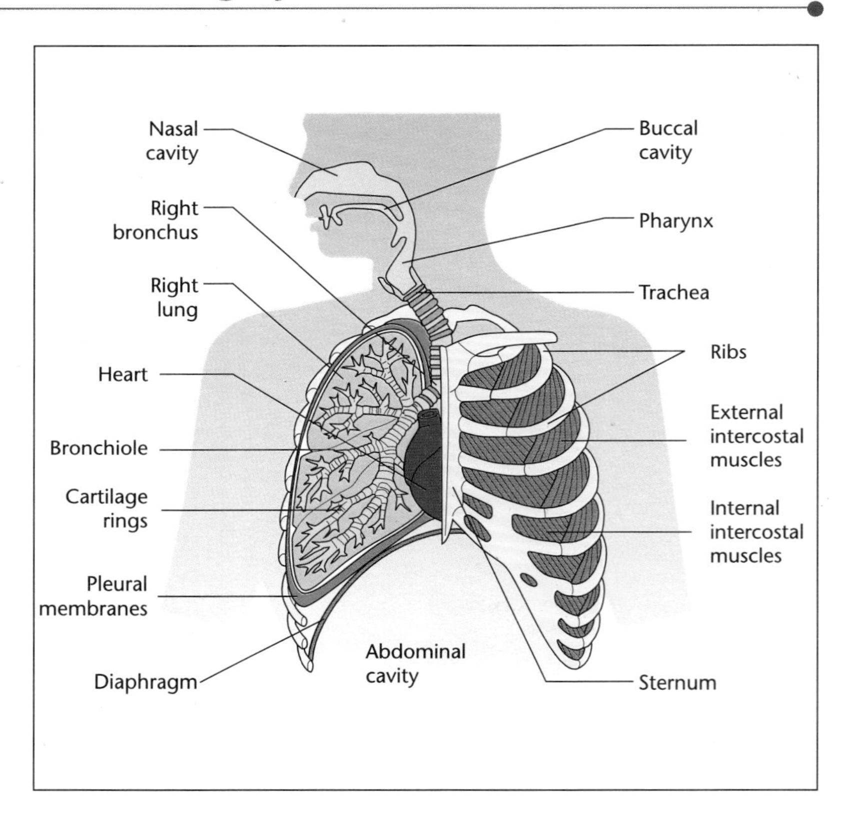

Figure 1 *The mammalian breathing system.*

Connecting up

The exchange surface is inside the lungs, connected to the outside air by a set of tubes. You can see in figure 1 that the **trachea** starts at the back of the mouth, and branches to form two **bronchi**. One bronchus goes into each lung. Inside the lungs, each bronchus branches many times, getting smaller and smaller and forming smaller tubes called **bronchioles**. All of these tubes have cartilage rings supporting them, except the smallest microscopic bronchioles.

Look at figure 2. At the end of the bronchioles are air sacs called **alveoli**. Each alveolus is folded to form a set of interconnected spaces. There are many alveoli, providing a very large surface area for gas exchange. Alongside the alveoli and the bronchioles that carry air in and out of them, there are blood vessels carrying blood to and from the lungs.

The **pulmonary artery** brings deoxygenated blood (blood with low oxygen and high carbon dioxide levels) from the heart to the lungs. The pulmonary artery forms branches inside the lungs, which end as capillaries around each alveolus. These capillaries join to form branches of the **pulmonary vein**, which takes oxygenated blood (blood with high oxygen and low carbon dioxide levels) away from the lungs and back to the heart.

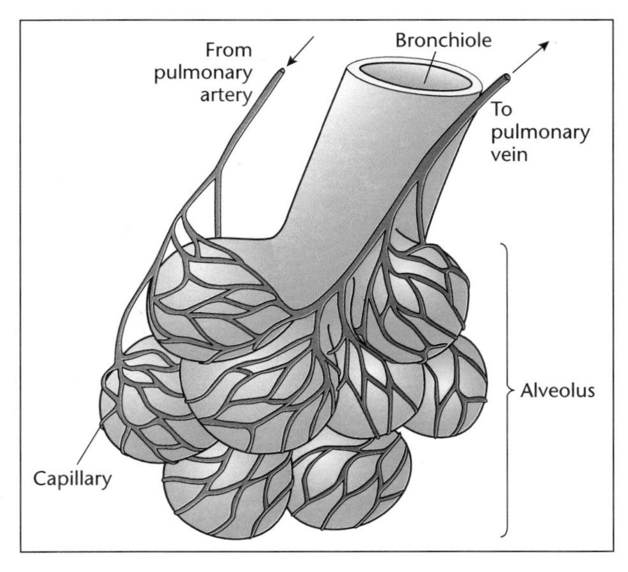

Figure 2 *Each bronchiole ends in a group of alveoli, surrounded by a system of blood vessels.*

Swapping over – gas exchange

On page 91 you looked at a diagram of a cell from an alveolus. In figure 3 you can see how these cells are arranged to form a single layer called an **epithelium**. This is the gas exchange surface. Air with a high concentration of oxygen and a low concentration of carbon dioxide is brought into the alveoli each time you breathe in. Deoxygenated blood flows across the surface of the alveoli all the time. Oxygen from the air dissolves in the layer of liquid on the inside of the alveoli, and diffuses through the epithelium of the alveolus. It then diffuses through the wall of the capillary and into the blood.

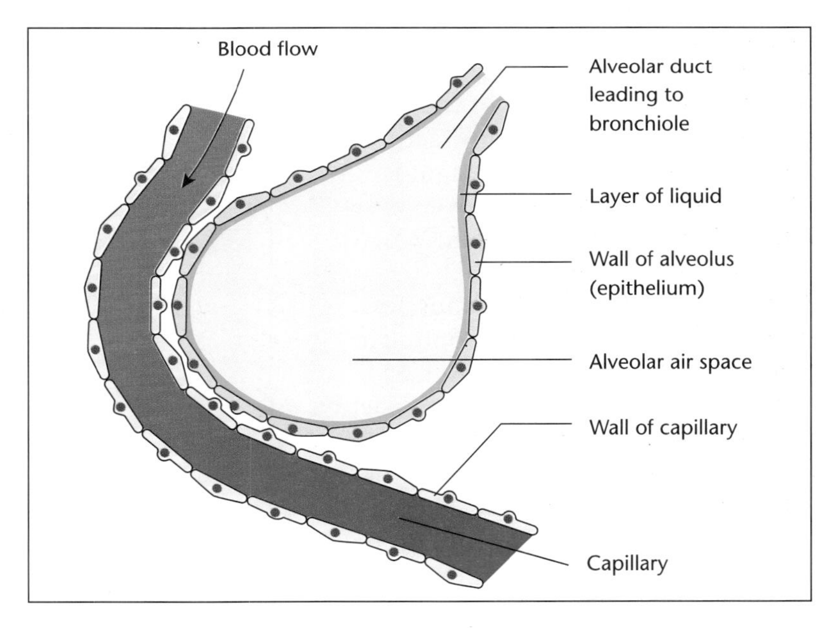

Figure 3 *An alveolus and blood capillary.*

1 Look at figure 3 and the description above of how oxygen diffuses into the blood in the lungs. Describe the diffusion of carbon dioxide from the blood into the air in the lungs.

Key ideas 92–3

Mammals exchange gases with the air through the surfaces of alveoli inside the lungs.

Alveoli are adapted to provide a large thin surface area for diffusion.

A continual blood flow helps to maintain a diffusion gradient by carrying away oxygenated blood from the lungs.

3 Moving air – ventilating the lungs

The air inside the lungs is constantly changed. **Ventilation** causes air to flow in and out of the lungs, so there is a constant circulation of air between the lungs and atmosphere. Mammals change the pressure inside their thorax, and this makes air flow in and out of their lungs. To change the pressure, the **intercostal muscles** and **diaphragm muscles** change the size of the thoracic cavity. The lungs are attached to the inside of the rib cage and diaphragm by the **pleural membranes.** When the thoracic cavity changes size, so do the lungs.

Power providers

The **external intercostal muscles** are on the outside of the rib cage, between the ribs. They are attached at an angle so when they contract, the ribs are pulled up. The **diaphragm muscles** are at the edge of the diaphragm. When they contract, the centre of the domed diaphragm is pulled flatter. These two movements happen when you breathe in. When you breathe out, the external intercostal and diaphragm muscles relax, so the rib cage and diaphragm return to their starting positions. Breathing in (**inspiration**) is an active process because the muscles contract and use energy from ATP. Breathing out (**expiration**) is a passive process because the muscles relax and do not use ATP. Look at figure 1 showing the main events during one breath.

When there is a high demand for oxygen, for example during exercise, another set of muscles on the inside of the rib cage can be used to pull the ribs inwards. These are the **internal intercostal muscles**. When they contract, the rib cage squashes the lungs so more air is forced out during expiration. Abdominal muscles also contract and help to push air out of the lungs. As a result, during the next breath in, the lungs can take in extra air.

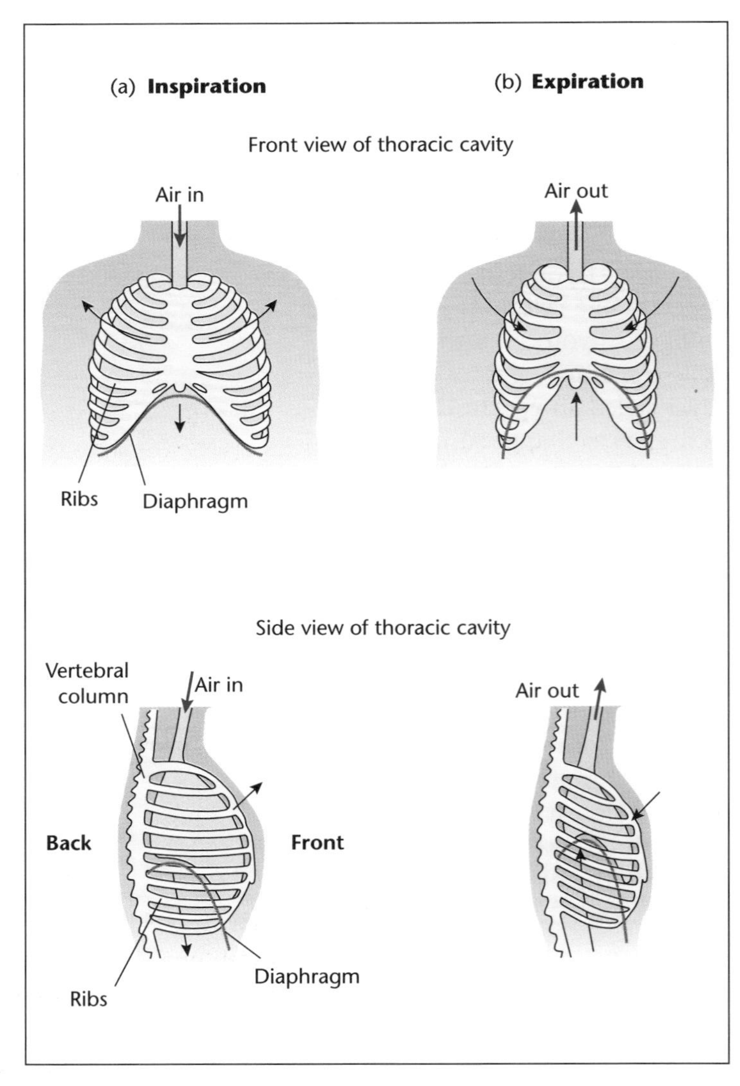

Figure 1 *The events taking place during inspiration and expiration.*

Air flow

There is only one set of tubes between the alveoli and the outside, so air enters and leaves along the same path. The nasal (nose) passages and mouth both link to the pharynx, so air can enter the trachea from either of these. It is better to breathe in through your nose because the nasal passage has a lining of mucus, which traps pathogens on the way to the lungs.

1 Look back at the structure of the lungs on page 92. Copy and complete the flow chart showing the path of air into the lungs in figure 2.

Air is pushed through the tube system by differences in pressure between the atmosphere and the lungs. Cartilage rings hold the wide tubes of the breathing system open, and prevent them collapsing when the pressure inside them falls. If you press the skin on the outside of your throat gently, you can feel the rings of cartilage. Take care not to press too hard.

2 Cartilage is more elastic than bone. Suggest why the breathing tubes are supported by cartilage instead of bone.

Problems breathing

Asthma is a disease of the lungs. Its symptoms include coughing, wheezing and tightness in the chest. Asthma cannot be cured, although it can be controlled. During an asthma attack the airways become narrowed, inflamed and swollen, making it difficult to breathe. Asthma is caused by over-sensitivity in the airways that can be triggered by many things, such as cigarette smoke, pollen or cold air.

3 What effect will asthma have on gas exchange? Explain your answer.

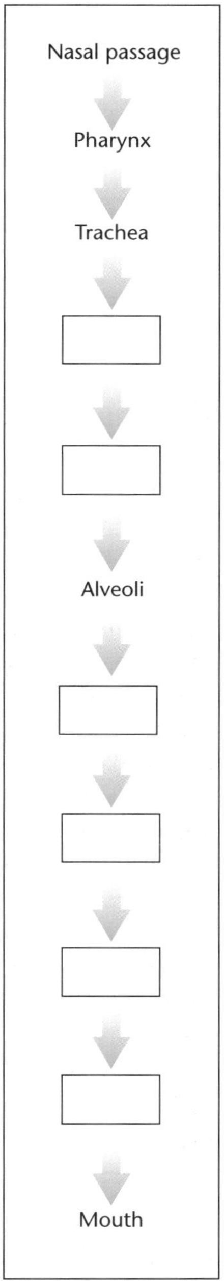

Nasal passage
↓
Pharynx
↓
Trachea
↓
[ ]
↓
[ ]
↓
Alveoli
↓
[ ]
↓
[ ]
↓
[ ]
↓
[ ]
↓
Mouth

Figure 2 *Flow chart of the path of air into the lungs.*

Key ideas 94–5

Ventilation helps to maintain an oxygen diffusion gradient between the blood and the air in the alveoli. It does this by bringing oxygen-rich air into the lungs.

The diffusion gradient for carbon dioxide is maintained in the same way, by removing carbon dioxide-rich air from the lungs.

4 Exchanging gases in bony fish

Fish use gases that are dissolved in the water, instead of exchanging gases with the air. **Gills** inside their body form an exchange surface for oxygen and carbon dioxide. Their ventilation system forces water in and out of the body, keeping water flowing over the gills. The blood system carries gases between the gills and the cells in the rest of the body.

The exchanger – the gills

Look at figure 1. The gills of a fish are found just behind the head, in the pharynx. There are four pairs of gills in a space called the **opercular cavity**. The flap you can see over the gills on each side of the fish is called the **operculum**. There is a valve in the operculum. When it opens, it lets water out of the opercular cavity.

Figure 1 *The position of the gills in a fish.*

Figure 2 shows a magnified part of a gill. Each gill is made from many of these structures. The diagram shows you the function of each part of the gill.

The **afferent blood vessel** brings blood to the gill. A branch of it goes from the gill arch along the inside of each lamella towards the tip. The **efferent blood vessel** carries blood away from the gill. A branch of the efferent blood vessel goes from the tip along the outside of each lamella back to the gill arch. Blood flows along the afferent vessel, across the gill plates and into the capillaries inside the gill plates. These capillaries eventually flow into the efferent vessel.

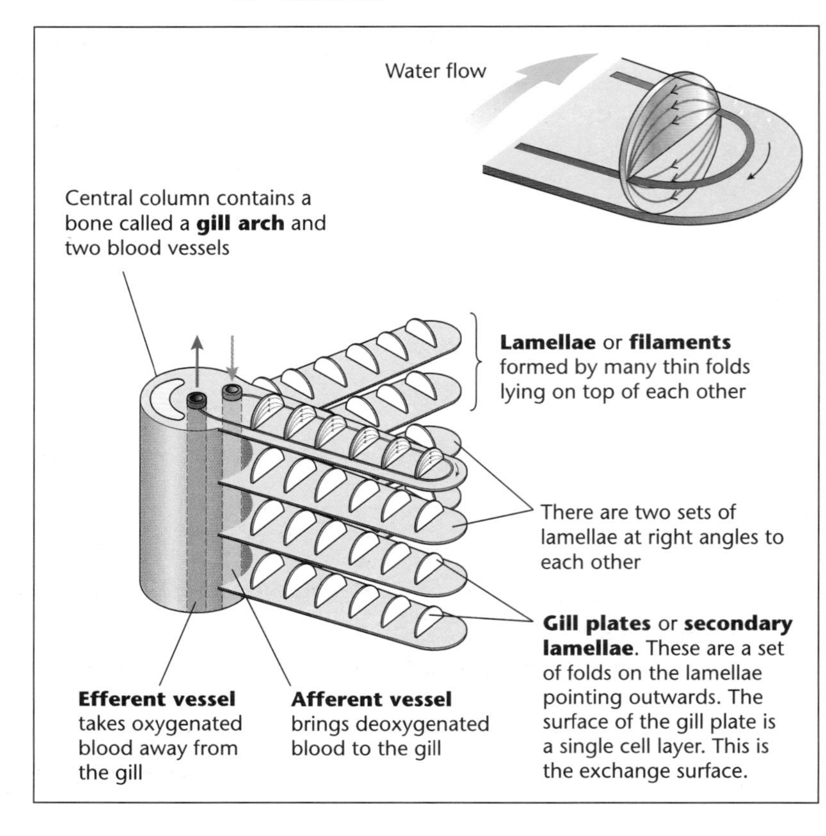

Figure 2 *The structure of part of a gill.*

Swapping over – gas exchange

Figure 3 shows the blood and water flow in gills. Notice that water with a moderate oxygen concentration and a low carbon dioxide concentration flows across the gills all the time. Blood with a low oxygen concentration and a high carbon dioxide concentration also flows through the gills all the time. Oxygen dissolved in the water diffuses through the surface of the gill plates, through the capillary walls and into the blood. Carbon dioxide in the blood diffuses through the capillary walls and the surface of the gill plates into the water.

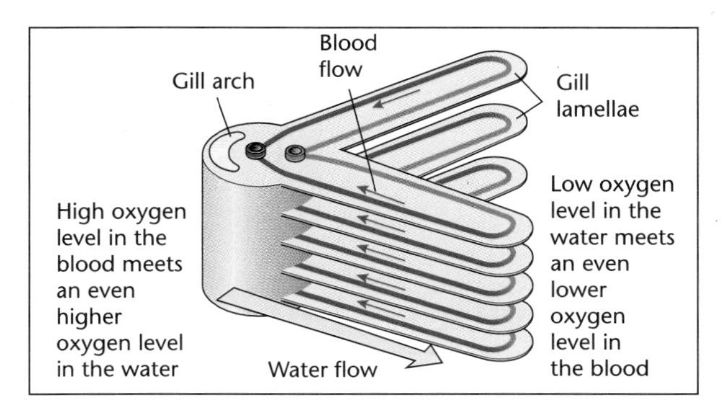

Figure 3 *The flow of blood and water in a gill lamella.*

Improving the odds – countercurrent flow

Water has a much lower concentration of oxygen than air does. To help fish obtain as much oxygen as possible, a **countercurrent flow** mechanism is used. This means that the blood and water flow in opposite directions. You can see this on figure 3.

Figure 4 shows how the countercurrent flow in a gill helps to maintain a diffusion gradient all the way along the gill. As a result, more oxygen can diffuse from the water into the blood. The same is also true for the diffusion of carbon dioxide from the blood to the water.

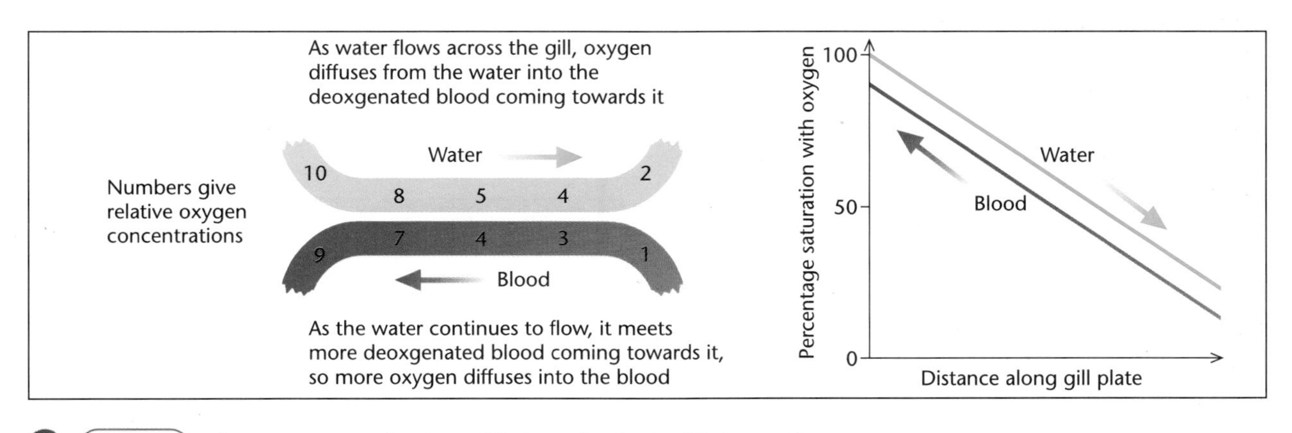

Figure 4 *The countercurrent flow in a gill helps maintain the diffusion gradient.*

Key ideas 96–7

Fish exchange gases through gill plates on the surface of gills.

Gills are adapted to provide a large thin surface area for diffusion.

A continual blood flow helps to maintain a diffusion gradient by carrying away oxygenated blood from the gills.

Blood and water flow through the gills in opposite directions. This countercurrent flow increases the efficiency of gas exchange.

5 Moving water – ventilating the gills

A fish changes the pressure inside its body to make water flow across the gills. Muscles in the buccal cavity (the mouth) change the size of the mouth. Muscles in the **operculum** change the size of the opercular cavity.

Two cavities – buccal cavity and opercular cavity

Figure 1 shows how the gills are arranged inside the opercular cavity. You can also see the operculum valve. There are muscles in the walls of the buccal cavity and operculum, which make the opercular cavity smaller when they contract.

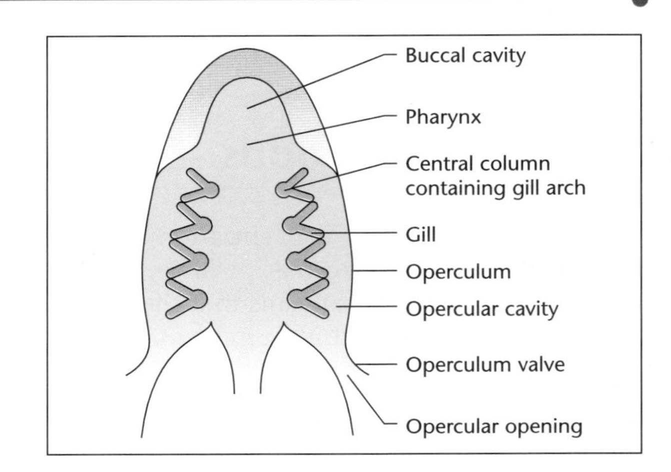

Figure 1 *A section of a fish head showing position of the gills.*

Power providers – ventilation movements

Now look at figures 2 and 3 showing the ventilation of the gills. The processes correspond to one breath in a mammal, so the terms inspiration and expiration are used.

During **inspiration** water is taken in:

- The mouth is open and the operculum valve is closed. The buccal cavity expands.
- The expansion of the buccal cavity causes the pressure in the mouth to fall below the pressure of the water outside.
- Water enters the mouth down the pressure gradient.
- The operculum expands so the pressure in the opercular cavity falls.
- The mouth closes and the buccal cavity contracts so the pressure in the buccal cavity rises.
- The pressure in the buccal cavity is higher than the pressure in the opercular cavity.
- The water now enters the opercular cavity down the pressure gradient.

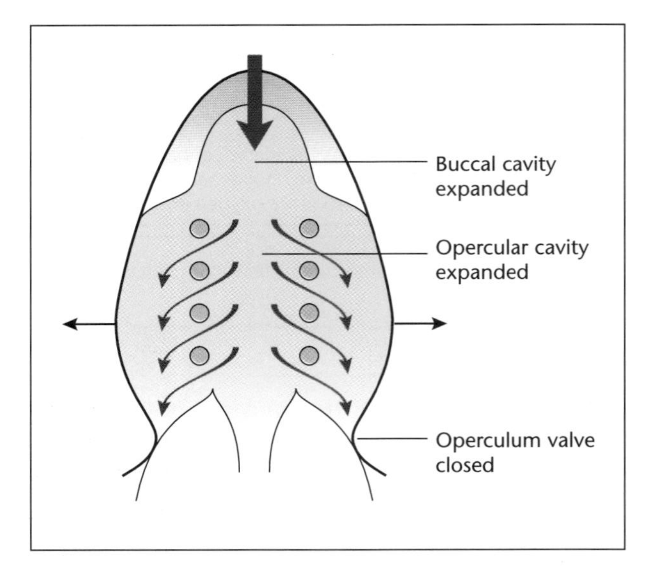

Figure 2 *The events during inspiration in a fish.*

In **expiration**, the water is forced out. Look at figure 3 to see how this occurs.

- The mouth is closed and the operculum valve is open.
- The operculum contracts further so the pressure rises above the pressure of the water outside.
- The buccal cavity contracts so the pressure rises even higher.
- Water is forced to leave through the operculum valve, down the pressure gradient.

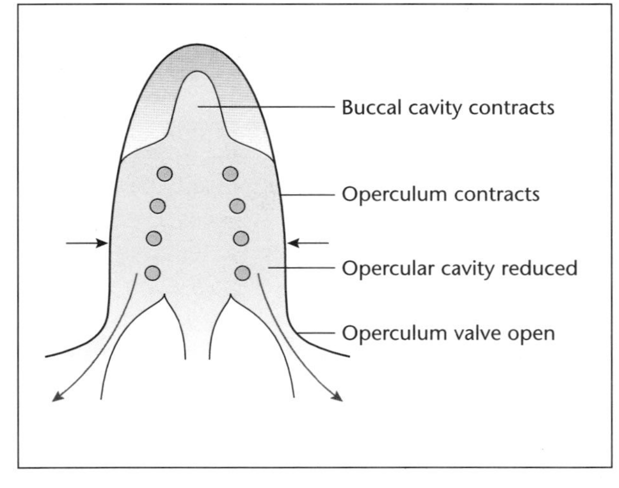

Figure 3 *The events during expiration in a fish.*

Water flow

The ventilation system of fish causes a one-way flow of water. Water flows into the opercular cavity from the mouth. It leaves the opercular cavity through the operculum valve.

Compared with air, water is very dense. The mass of 100 cm^3 of water is much greater than the mass of 100 cm^3 of air. A two-way flow as in mammals would be inefficient, as a dense substance is harder to move in opposite directions. Water supports the gill lamellae, and a one-way flow lets water move across both sides of the lamellae, allowing maximum gas exchange.

1 Use figures 2 and 3 to explain the pressure changes that cause water to:
a enter the mouth
b enter the opercular cavity
c leave the opercular cavity.

2 A fish out of water dies of lack of oxygen, even though air contains more oxygen than water does. Suggest why gills cannot obtain enough oxygen from air.

Key ideas 98–9

Ventilation helps to maintain an oxygen diffusion gradient between the blood and the water in the gills. It does this by carrying oxygen-rich water across the gills.

The diffusion gradient for carbon dioxide is maintained in the same way, by removing carbon dioxide-rich water from the gills.

6 Exchanging gases in plants

Like animals, plants use gases from the atmosphere. You will remember from GCSE that plants use their leaves to obtain gases from the air. The leaves are adapted to increase gas exchange. All the cells inside a leaf exchange gases with the air in spaces between cells, called **intercellular spaces.** Air in the intercellular spaces is in contact with the atmosphere through small pores called **stomata** in the leaf surface. Unlike mammals and fish, there is no method of ventilation or transport of gases to other parts of the plant.

The exchanger – leaves

The number of leaves varies with the size of the plant – bigger plants have more leaves. Look at figure 1. You can see that the leaf has a central vein, with branches forming a network over the whole leaf. This vein pattern is found in the leaves of all **dicotyledonous** plants. The name 'dicotyledon' describes the number of storage leaves in the seed (di = two, cotyledon = storage leaf).

Figure 1 *The structure of a dicotyledonous leaf.*

Now look at figure 2. There is a single-celled layer forming the outside surface of the leaf. This is the **epidermis**. On the outside of the epidermis you can see a covering over all of the cells. This is the **cuticle**. The cuticle prevents water loss because it contains a waterproof wax called suberin. You can also see that most of the inside of a leaf is made of loosely packed cells with large intercellular spaces. This is the **mesophyll**. There is a thin layer of water on the surface of the mesophyll cells.

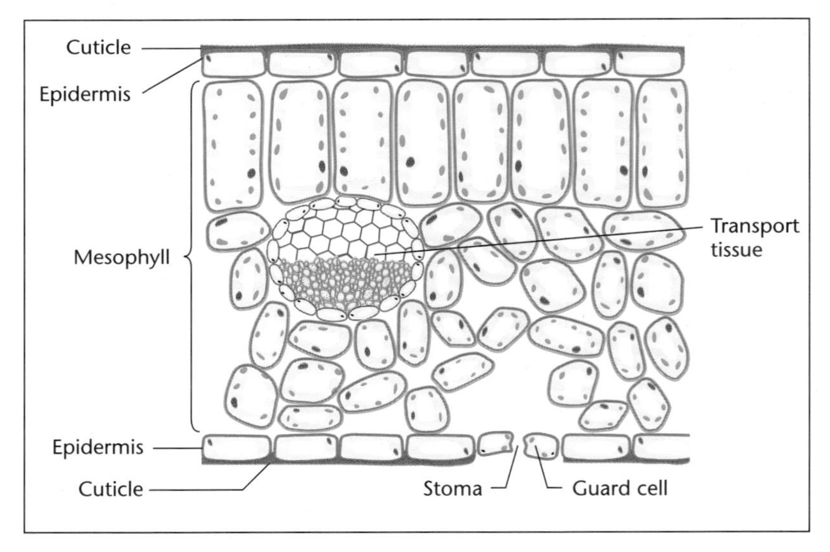

Figure 2 *A section through a leaf showing how the cells are arranged.*

Connecting up

There are openings or pores on the outside of the leaf, which allow gases to move in and out of the leaf. These openings are called **stomata**. Each stoma lies between a pair of cells called **guard cells**.

Figure 3 shows two different views of a stoma. You can see in diagram (a) that guard cells have a different shape from other epidermis cells. They can change shape and close the stomata to reduce water loss.

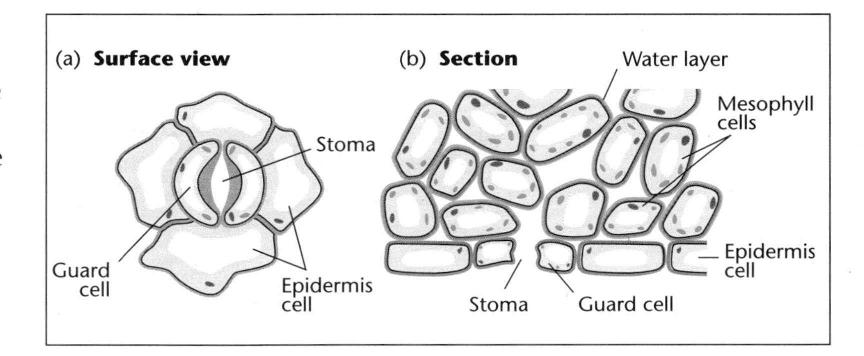

(a) A stoma in the leaf surface. (b) Section of a leaf.

Swapping over – gas exchange

Figure 2 shows that the leaf is very thin, so that its centre is quite close to the outside. Also, the large intercellular spaces mean that air can move easily between the cells. Therefore diffusion is fast enough to supply gases to all the cells. The gases diffuse through the epidermis and stomata into the intercellular air spaces. Here they dissolve in the water layer and diffuse into the mesophyll cells through the cell wall and cell membrane.

Day and night – different exchange

The main function of leaves is photosynthesis, which takes place in light. Look at figure 4 showing the overall reaction in photosynthesis.

Plants also carry out respiration all the time. Look at figure 5 showing the overall reaction in respiration.

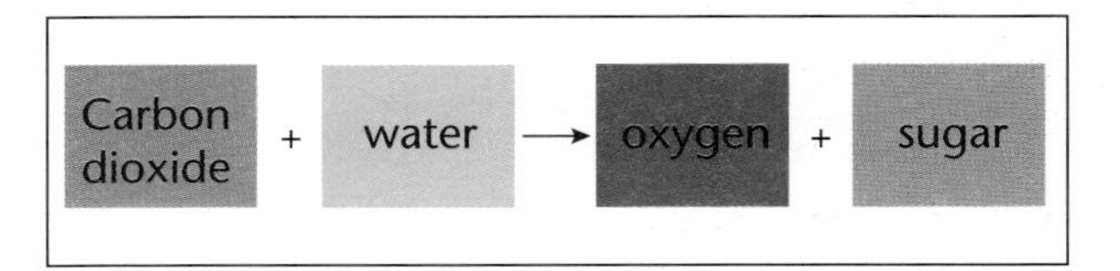

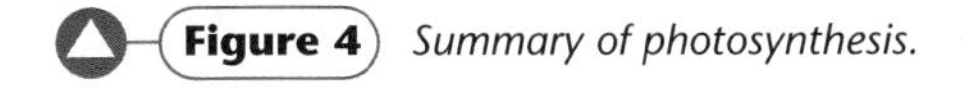

Summary of photosynthesis.

1. **Which gases will be exchanged by a leaf during light?**
2. **How will a diffusion gradient be maintained?**
3. **How will a plant obtain the gas it needs for respiration during light?**
4. **Describe how a plant will carry out gas exchange for respiration during the night.**

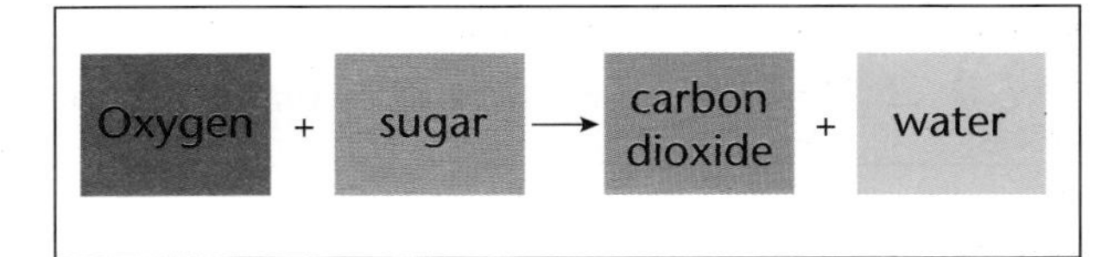

Summary of respiration.

Key ideas 100–101

Plants exchange gases through the surface of mesophyll cells inside the leaf.

Leaves are so thin that there is no need for a special method of ventilation or gas transport.

In plants, gas exchange is different in the presence of light and at night.

7 Efficient exchange surfaces

The exchange surfaces of living organisms show adaptations that allow them to function as efficiently as possible. The alveoli of mammals, the gills of fish and the leaves of plants all look very different, but they all have the common features of exchange surfaces. They are different because these common features have developed in different ways.

Meeting their needs – mammals

Mammals are large and need a good exchange surface so that gases can diffuse efficiently. Even so, the lungs can only remove about 5 per cent of the total oxygen in the air. Alveoli provide a good gas exchange surface because of a number of factors, which are listed below.

- A large surface area:
  - The bronchioles are highly branched, giving a large number of pathways for air to enter and leave.
  - There are millions of alveoli in each lung.
  - Each alveolus is folded, giving an even greater surface.
- A thin permeable surface.
- A diffusion gradient:
  - Blood circulation carries oxygenated blood away from the alveoli in the pulmonary vein, and brings deoxygenated blood to the alveoli in the pulmonary artery.
  - Ventilation brings in air rich in oxygen into the alveoli, and takes air with increased carbon dioxide away from alveoli.

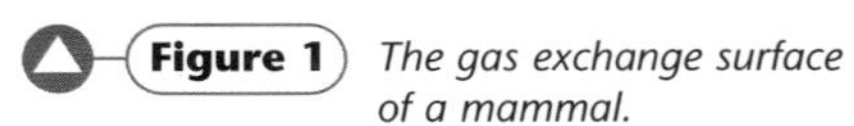

Figure 1 *The gas exchange surface of a mammal.*

1 Write your own list of the features of alveoli that provide a thin permeable surface.

Meeting their needs – fish

Since fish live in water, they have different needs from land animals.

The gas exchange surface of a fish is the gill plates on the lamellae. They also have a number of features that make them ideal gas exchange surfaces, listed on the next page.

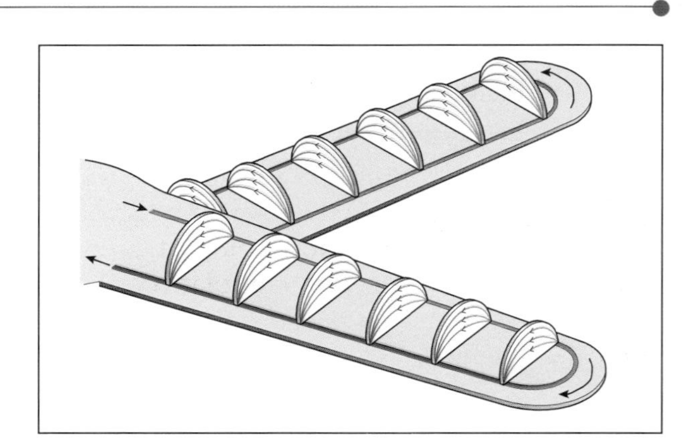

Figure 2 *The gas exchange surface of a fish.*

- A large surface area.
- A thin permeable surface:
  - The surface of the gill plates is an epithelium. The cells in the epithelium are flattened.
  - The capillary wall is also made up of flattened cells.
  - The two surfaces are next to each other so the total distance for diffusion is only 0.5 µm.
- A diffusion gradient:
  - Blood circulation carries oxygenated blood away from the gill plates, and brings deoxygenated blood to the gill plates.
  - Ventilation brings water relatively high in oxygen to the gill plates, and carries water with increased carbon dioxide away.
  - The lamellae are held apart by water so the water can circulate over the whole surface of the gills.

2 Make a list of the features of gills that give a large surface area.

3 List the similarities between a fish and a mammal in the way in which a diffusion gradient is maintained.

4 How do fish differ from mammals in the organisation of the gas exchange surface and the blood circulation?

Meeting their needs – plants

Each plant has a large number of leaves which all contribute to the gas exchange surface.

- A large surface area:
  - Each leaf is flat, and leaves are spread out so they cover a large area.
  - The mesophyll cells inside the leaf are separated and there are large spaces between them in which gases can move.
  - Most of the cell surface of each mesophyll cell has air around it.
- A thin permeable surface:
  - There are rarely more than 10 cell layers from top to bottom of a leaf.
  - To enter the cells, gases have only to cross a cell wall and cell surface membrane.
- A diffusion gradient.

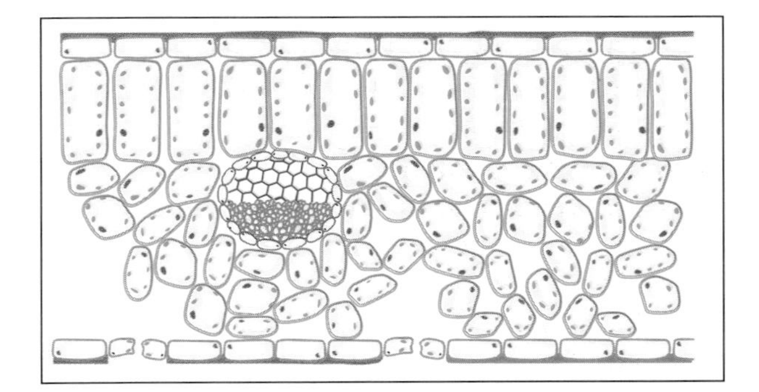

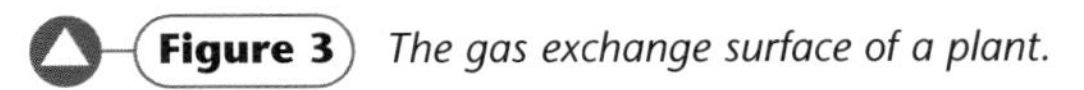

Figure 3 *The gas exchange surface of a plant.*

5 How do plants maintain a diffusion gradient in the light?

Being different

Plants have adapted in a different way to animals. Plants do not move from place to place and so some plants are much larger than animals. Animals have more compact bodies and they use more energy than plants because they move about. This increases the demand on their gas exchange surfaces.

Key ideas 102–3

All gas exchange surfaces share the same features of a large surface area, a thin surface and a diffusion gradient.

Different organisms have different structures to enable them to exchange gases.

8 Waterways – osmosis

On pages 86–7 you saw the different ways in which molecules can move across membranes. Water crosses membranes using a special form of diffusion called **osmosis**. Because it is diffusion, it is a passive process. The direction in which water molecules move depends on the **water potential** of different regions. The water potential measures the energy of water molecules in a solution, and their ability to move freely. The more water is present, the higher the water potential and the more freely the molecules can move.

Moving by osmosis

Look back to the diagram on page 86 showing how diffusion takes place. Compare it with figure 1 opposite showing osmosis. You can see that in both diffusion and osmosis, there is a difference in concentration of a substance in two regions. What makes osmosis special is the partially permeable membrane you can see separating the two regions. The difference in concentration of water molecules between the two regions is called the **water potential gradient**.

The water molecules in figure 1 have kinetic energy so they move randomly. This random movement causes net movement of water molecules down the water potential gradient from a region of high water potential to a region of lower water potential. This is **osmosis.** When there is the same water potential on each side of the membrane, an **equilibrium** has been reached. Water molecules then pass equally in both directions across the membrane. You can see that osmosis is different from diffusion because it only occurs across a partially permeable membrane. Diffusion takes place through any surface.

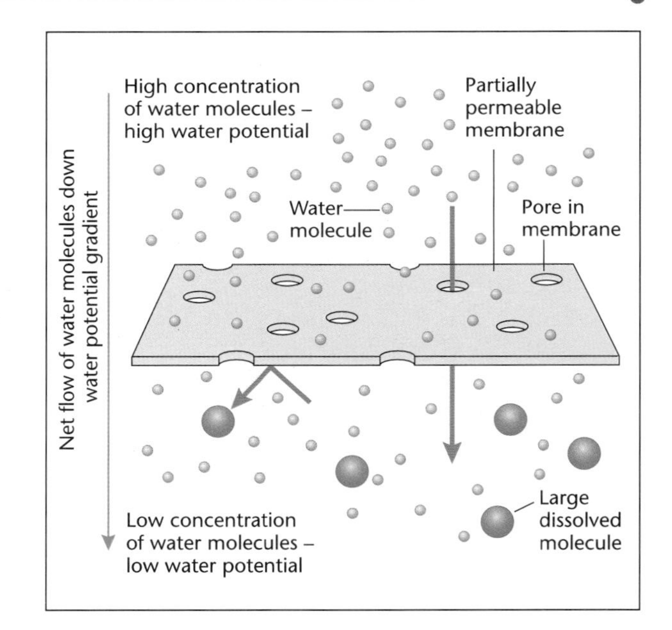

Figure 1 *Osmosis is the diffusion of water through a partially permeable membrane.*

1 List the similarities and differences between diffusion and osmosis.

Getting to grips with water potential

Water potential is represented by the symbol Ψ, the Greek letter 'psi' which is pronounced 'sigh'. As water molecules move, they collide with the partially permeable membrane, generating a pressure. This pressure is measured in units called kilopascals, kPa. The water potential of pure water at standard temperature and pressure is zero ($\Psi = 0$ kPa). When substances are dissolved in water, the solutes make the water potential lower, so the value becomes negative. In osmosis, water molecules move to the region with the lowest water potential (the greatest negative value).

Look at figure 2 showing three cells **A**, **B** and **C** and their water potentials.

2 In which direction will osmosis occur in these cells?

3 Between which cells will the net movement of water be the greatest? Explain why.

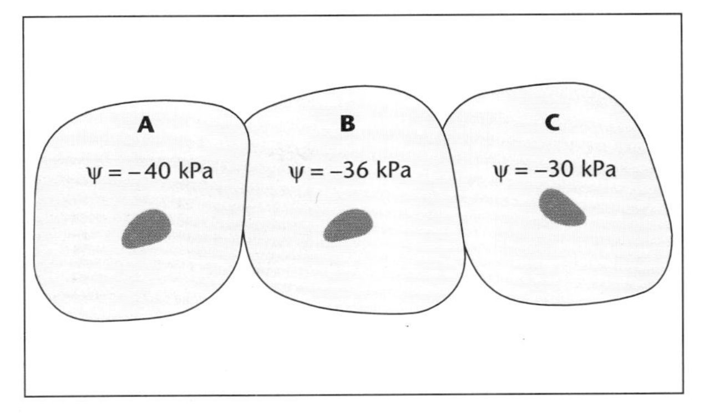

Figure 2 *Three adjacent cells and their water potentials.*

Now look at the three cells **D**, **E** and **F** in figure 3. Their water potentials and the water potentials of the surrounding solutions are shown.

4 Which cell in figure 3 has the highest water potential?

5 Which surrounding solution has the highest concentration of solutes in it?

6 Copy figure 3. Draw arrows to show the net movement of water between each cell and its surrounding solution.

7 Which cell will not show any osmosis?

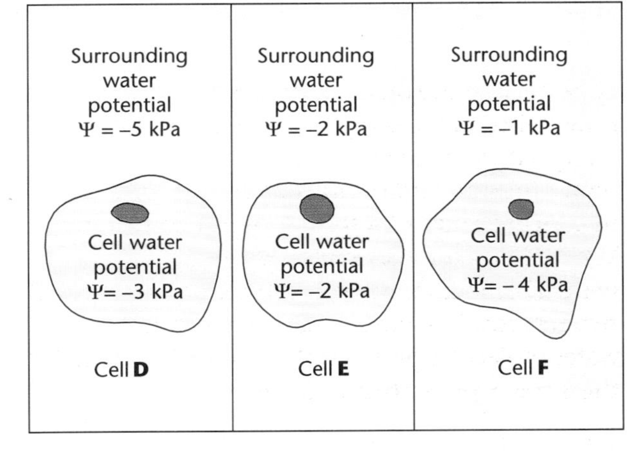

Figure 3 *Three cells in different solutions.*

Cells and solutions – what's in a name?

To study osmosis, animal cells may be placed in solutions of known concentrations. The concentration of these solutions may be described in comparison to the concentration of the animal cell contents:

- A **hypotonic** solution has a lower (hypo) concentration of dissolved solutes than the cell contents.
- A **hypertonic** solution has a higher (hyper) concentration of dissolved solutes than the cell contents.
- An **isotonic** solution has the same (iso) concentration of dissolved solutes as the cell contents.

8 Look again at figure 3. Compared with the contents of the cell in it, which solution is:
a hypotonic b hypertonic
c isotonic?

Key ideas 104–5

Osmosis is a special type of diffusion, in which water diffuses through a partially permeable membrane.

Osmosis is the net movement of water down a water potential gradient.

Water potential is a measure of the amount of water in a solution. The more water molecules there are, the higher the water potential.

9 Cells and osmosis

The main differences between animal cells and plant cells is that a plant cell has a cell wall and a central vacuole. These two features have a great effect on osmosis in the cell.

Soft surfaces – animal cells

The surface of an animal cell is a membrane consisting of protein and phospholipids. This allows it to stretch a little before breaking apart. Look at table 1 and figure 1. These show the results of an investigation using red blood cells. Look carefully at the appearance and size of the cells before and after they have been left in different solutions.

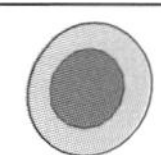
(a) A red blood cell as it appears in blood

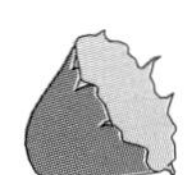
(b) A red blood cell after being in a hypotonic solution

(c) A red blood cell after being in a hypertonic solution

Figure 1 *Results of an investigation into osmosis.*

Solution used	Diameter of cell/μm	
	At start of investigation	At end of investigation
Isotonic	8	8
Hypotonic	8	10
Hypertonic	8	6

Table 1

1. **Use your knowledge of osmosis to explain:**
   a **the results shown in the table in terms of water potential**
   b **the effect of a hypotonic solution on the red blood cell**
   c **the effect of a hypertonic solution on the cell membrane.**
2. **Explain why animals keep the water potential of their blood within a very narrow range.**

Stiff surfaces – plant cells

In the investigation using red blood cells, you can see that animal cells increase in size as water enters them by osmosis. In plant cells, the cell wall exerts a pressure against the cell membrane, stopping it from stretching. This occurs because the cellulose forming the wall does not stretch very much. Look at figure 2 showing a plant cell, and notice the effects of the cell wall and vacuole on osmosis.

If there is room for a plant cell vacuole to expand, then water can enter the cell by osmosis. This happens when the cell's water potential is lower than the water potential of the surrounding solution.

As water enters the cell, the water potential becomes less negative. At the same time, the cell wall starts to prevent the vacuole expanding. Eventually the vacuole cannot expand any more because the cell wall is stopping it. We say that the cell is **turgid**. **Turgor pressure** gives a plant cell its shape and stops it being squashed.

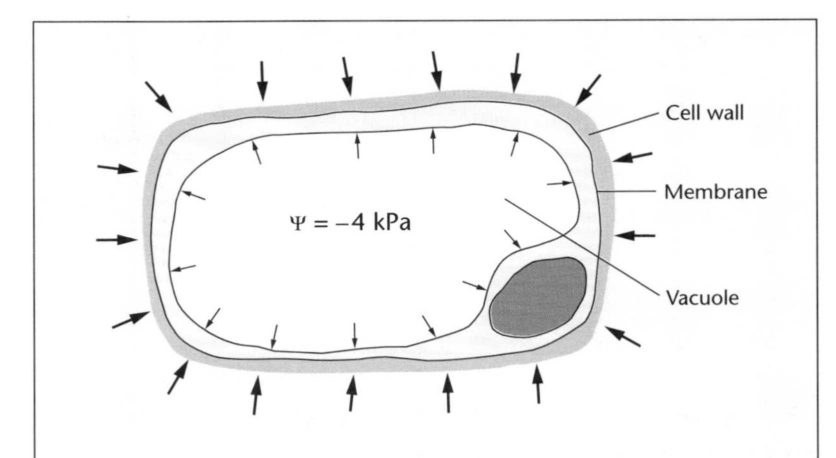

→ Pressure caused by the wall pushing inwards. It acts in the opposite direction to water potential.

→ Turgor pressure caused by the solution in the cell vacuole. It pushes the cytoplasm and membrane against the cell wall.

The effect of the cell wall and vacuole of a plant cell on osmosis.

3 As water enters a plant cell:
  a Why does the water potential become less negative?
  b Why does the pressure of the cell wall increase?

4 When a plant cell is left in a solution with a high solute concentration, the vacuole shrinks and the cell becomes soft. Explain why this happens.

5 A plant cell can use active transport to keep high concentrations of ions inside the cell. For example, plant cells take up potassium ions. This helps them to keep their cells turgid. Explain how high concentrations of ions inside the cell help keep plant cells turgid.

6 The gas exchange surface of a leaf is wet, as all the mesophyll cells have a layer of water on their surface. The air outside the leaf is usually drier, so water can very quickly diffuse out of a leaf.
  a Explain, in terms of diffusion gradients, why leaves lose water.
  b A plant wilts as the cells in its leaves become soft, which makes the leaf droop. Explain why the loss of water from leaves causes wilting.

Key ideas 106–7

Animals control the water potential of their blood to control osmosis in their cells.

In plant cells, the cell wall limits the entry of water by osmosis.

Water supports plant cells, making them turgid.

Unit 6 – Questions

1. Figure 1 shows part of the gill of a fish.

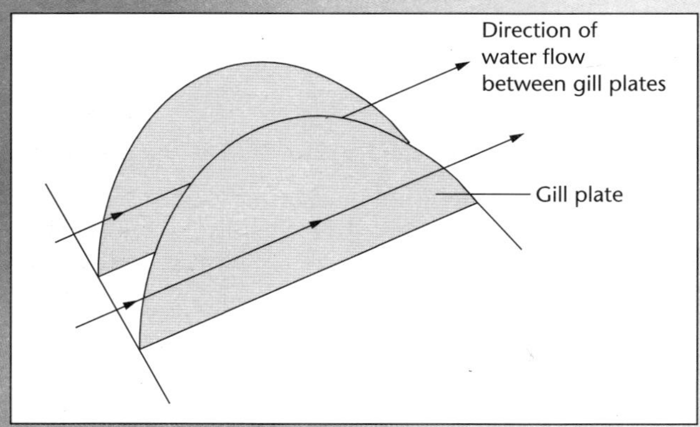

Figure 1

a) Sketch the diagram and on your sketch draw an arrow to show the direction of blood flow in the gill plate. (1 mark)

b) Explain how the direction of the flow of blood and the flow of water increase the efficiency of the gill plate as an exchange surface. (3 marks)

Table 1 shows some features of gills in several species of fish.

Table 1

Fish species	Thickness of gill plates/ μm	Number of gill plates per cm	Distance between gill plates/μm	Distance between blood and water/μm	Activity
Ice fish	33	80	75	6	Slow moving
Bullhead	25	140	45	10	Slow moving
Trout	15	200	40	3	Active
Herring	7	320	20	<1	Very active
Mackerel	5	320	20	<1	Very active

c) Use the table to explain two ways in which the structure of the gills is related to the activity of the fish. (4 marks)

(Total 8 marks)

2. Describe the mechanisms used for ventilating the gas exchange systems of:

a) mammals (8 marks)

b) bony fish. (6 marks)

(Total 14 marks)

(3) Figure 2 shows part of the lung.

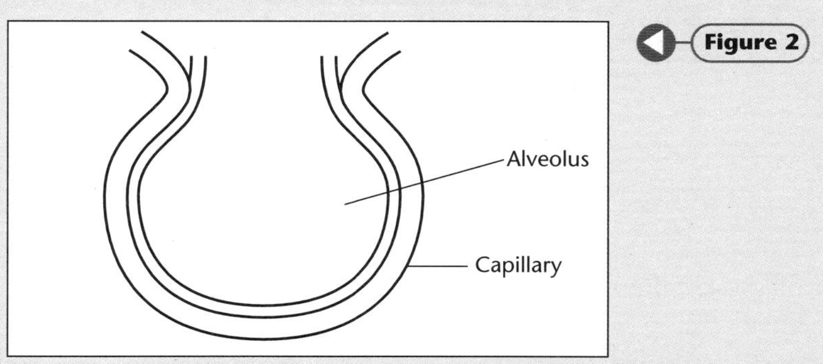

Figure 2

a) Name the process by which oxygen passes from the alveolus to the capillary. (1 mark)
b) Give two features of the alveolus that allow efficient gas exchange. (2 marks)
c) Describe the process of gas exchange between the alveolus and the capillary. (4 marks)

(Total 7 marks)

(4) Figure 3 shows a section through a leaf.

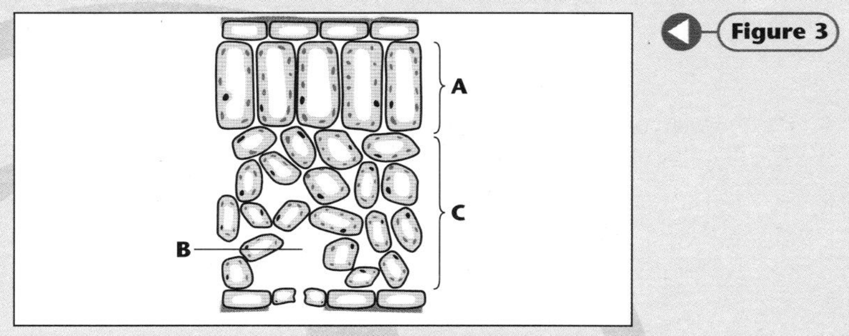

Figure 3

a) i) Name the features labelled **A**, **B** and **C**. (3 marks)
ii) Sketch the diagram and draw two sets of arrows to show the movement of gases between the air and the gas exchange surface. (2 marks)
iii) Label the gases that are moving. (1 mark)
b) What is the function of stomata in gas exchange in leaves? (2 marks)

(Total 8 marks)

(5) a) Water moves by osmosis. Describe osmosis in terms of water potential. (2 marks)

Figure 4 shows cells from the root of a plant. Cells **A**, **B** and **C** are next to each other. Cell **A** has a water potential of −340 kPa, cell **B** has a water potential of −350 kPa and cell **C** has a water potential of −360 kPa.

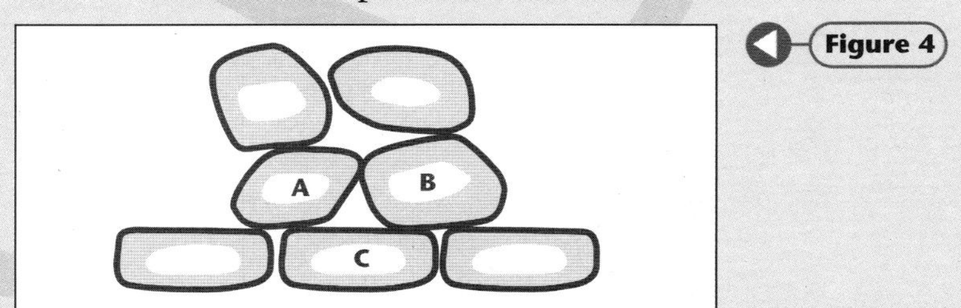

Figure 4

b) Predict the direction of water movement between the three cells. Give a reason for your answer. (4 marks)

(Total 6 marks)

Module 1 – Test yourself

1. Figure 1 shows how ribosomes, nuclei and mitochondria were separated from liver tissue.

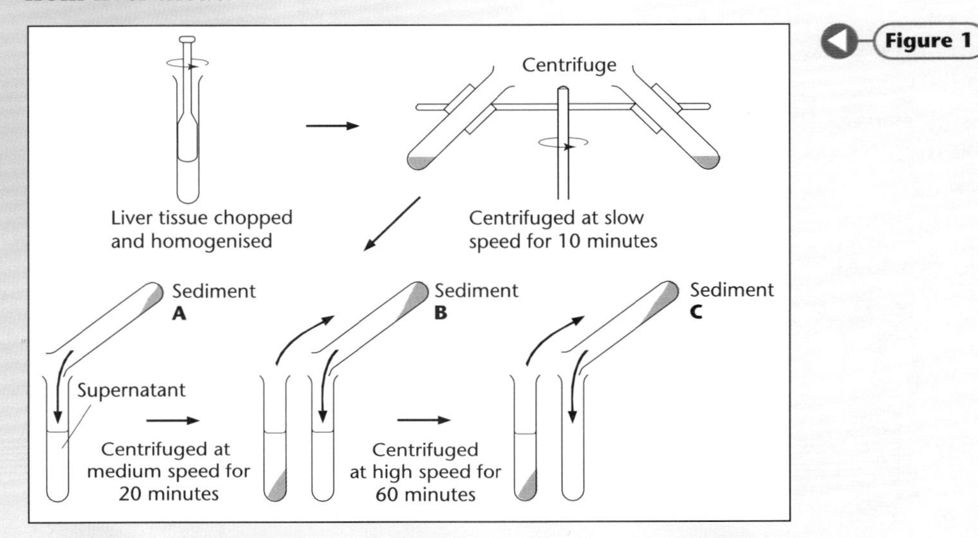

Figure 1

a) The liver tissue was placed in an ice-cold, isotonic buffer solution before it was homogenised. Suggest why the solution was:
i) ice-cold ii) isotonic iii) buffered. (3 marks)

b) Each sediment contains a different organelle. Say in which sediment you would expect to find each of the following organelles. Give a reason for your answer.
i) ribosomes ii) nuclei iii) mitochondria (4 marks)

(Total 7 marks)

2. Figure 2 shows three plant cells with different water potentials. They were placed in pure water.

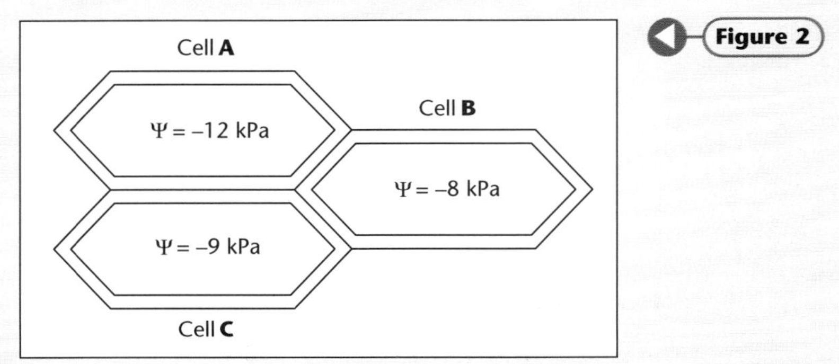

Figure 2

a) Sketch the diagram and draw arrows on your sketch to show the direction of water movement between each cell and its surroundings. (3 marks)

b) If the water potential of cell **A** changed to -7 kPa, what effect would this have on the rate of water movement between cells **A** and **B**? (1 mark)

c) Give two differences between osmosis and active transport. (2 marks)

(Total 6 marks)

3 Equal volumes of four different concentrations of fat suspension were placed into four test tubes labelled **A** to **D**. 1 cm^3 of an enzyme was added to each test tube. The contents of each tube were mixed and the time noted. The pH in each tube was measured using a pH meter. In each tube the pH fell to a constant level. The time taken for the pH to reach this level was recorded.

a) Name the type of enzyme used. (1 mark)

b) Explain why:

i) the pH fell in each tube (1 mark)

ii) the pH reached a constant level in each tube. (1 mark)

c) The results from this experiment are shown in figure 3.

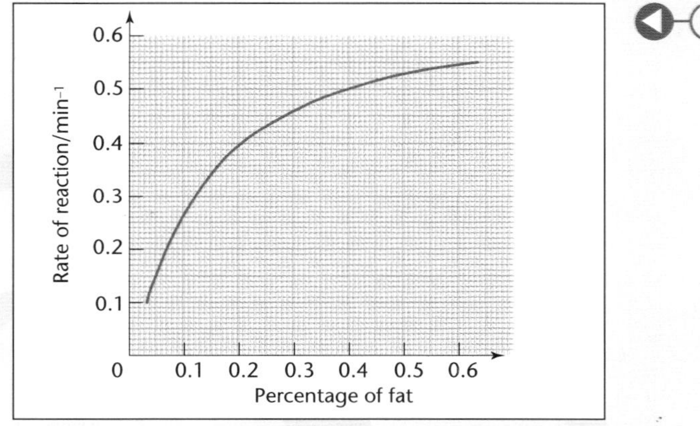

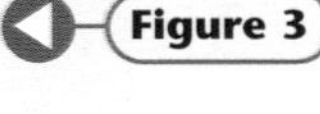

i) Explain how the rate of the reaction was calculated. (2 marks)

ii) Use the graph to predict the rate of the reaction for a 0.3% fat suspension. (1 mark)

iii) Suggest a suitable control for this experiment. (1 mark)

(Total 7 marks)

4 Equal amounts of four different moulds were placed on the surface of a starch–agar plate. After 48 hours some iodine solution was poured over the plate. The result is shown in figure 4.

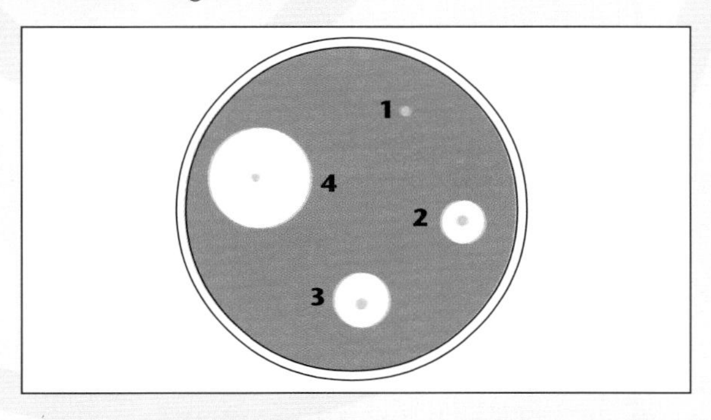

a) Explain the difference in size of the clear zones around three of the moulds.

b) Suggest why there is no clear zone around one of the moulds.

(Total 4 marks)

Module 1 – Test yourself

2

(5) Figure 5 shows the structure of a molecule of glucose.

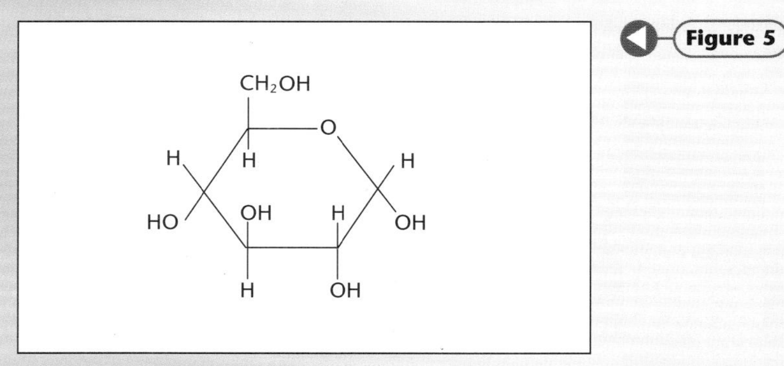

Figure 5

a) Draw a sketch to show how two glucose molecules join together to form a disaccharide. (3 marks)

b) Describe a simple biochemical test which you could use to distinguish between a solution of sucrose and a solution of glucose. (3 marks)

Figure 6 shows the relationship between substrate concentration and the rate of an enzyme-controlled reaction under different conditions.

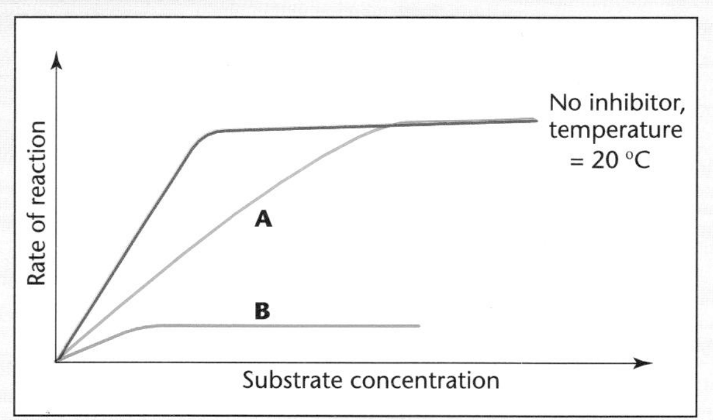

Figure 6

c) Lines **A** and **B** show the rate of reaction in the presence of two different types of inhibitor. Explain with a reason the type of inhibitor used in:

i) **A**

ii) **B**. (4 marks)

d) Copy figure 6 and draw in a line to show the rate of reaction when the temperature was increased by 10 °C. (2 marks)

(Total 12 marks)

6 One feature of a gas exchange surface is a steep diffusion gradient.

a) What is a diffusion gradient? (1 mark)

b) Explain how a diffusion gradient is achieved in:

i) a mammal (2 marks)

ii) a leaf. (2 marks)

(Total 5 marks)

7 Figure 7 shows a villus.

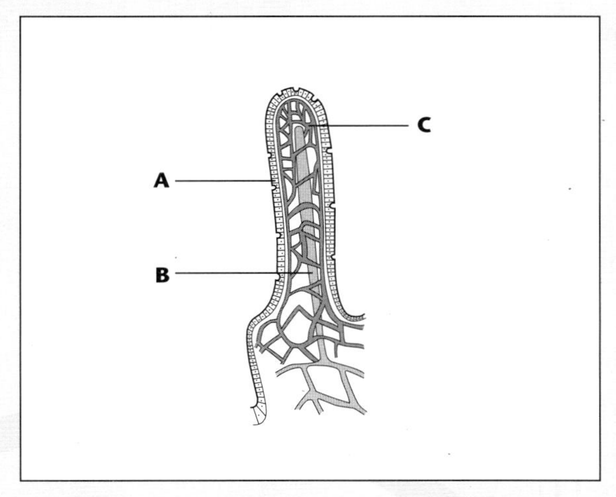

Figure 7

a) Name the structures labelled **A**, **B** and **C** and state the function of each in the absorption of food. (6 marks)

Figure 8 shows a cell from a region of the human gut.

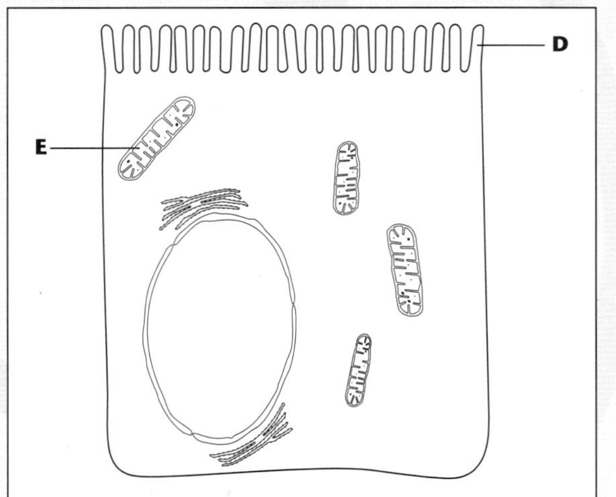

b) i) Name the cell and say in which region of the gut it is found. (2 marks)

ii) Name parts **D** and **E**. (2 marks)

iii) Explain why **D** and **E** increase the rate of absorption. (2 marks)

(Total 12 marks)

Module 2

Genes and Genetic Engineering

This module looks more closely at how living things inherit, store and use coded information to carry out all the chemical reactions in their bodies.

Unit 7 is about DNA, the molecule that stores the coded information used by cells. The organisation of the molecule, how it stores information and how the cell uses this information are revealed in this unit.

Unit 8 considers the different ways living organisms pass on DNA from one cell to another, and from one generation to another. This unit also looks at the ways humans have made use of the cell's ability to copy its stored DNA.

Unit 9 focuses on genetic engineering, another way in which humans use the central role of DNA in cells and adapt it for our own purposes. The various techniques used to transfer genes from one organism to another are described in this unit. The unit also raises ethical issues concerned with genetic engineering.

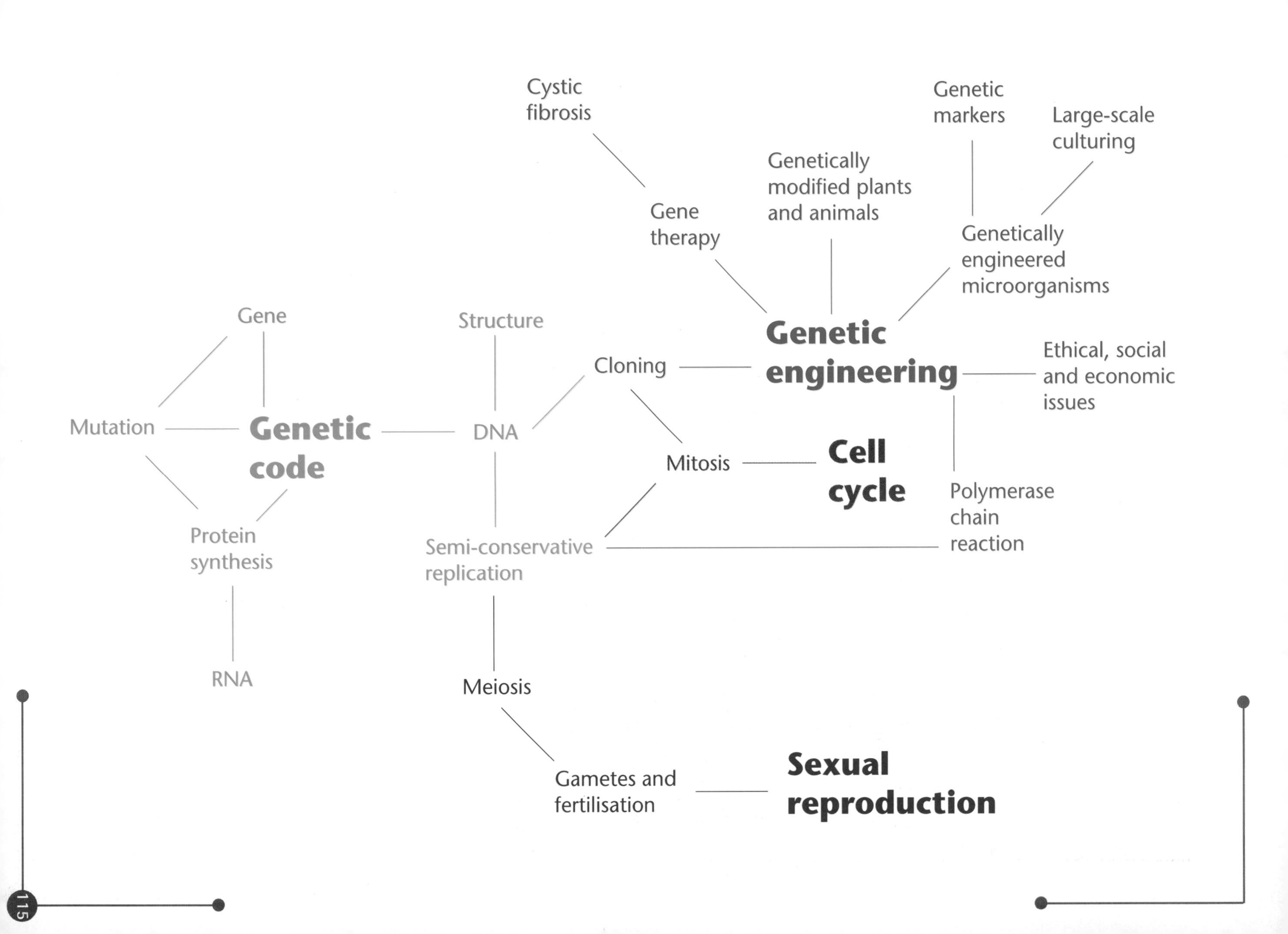
Cystic fibrosis
Gene therapy
Genetically modified plants and animals
Genetic markers
Large-scale culturing
Genetically engineered microorganisms
Gene
Structure
Cloning
Genetic engineering
Ethical, social and economic issues
Mutation
Genetic code
DNA
Mitosis
Cell cycle
Polymerase chain reaction
Protein synthesis
Semi-conservative replication
RNA
Meiosis
Gametes and fertilisation
Sexual reproduction

1 Looking similar

You inherit your physical appearance and other characteristics from your parents. **Genes** are passed from one generation to the next, carrying all the information needed to make a functioning organism. You receive one set of genes from your father and one set from your mother. Each person has their own unique combination of genes (except for identical twins). Some characteristics are not only inherited but are also influenced by where and how you were brought up. For example, height is partly inherited and partly influenced by the food a person eats when growing up.

Passing on the code

The nucleus of each human cell contains 46 structures called **chromosomes**. In figure 1 you can see pictures of the 46 chromosomes found in each human cell. They are arranged in 23 pairs. You inherit 23 chromosomes from each parent, one of each pair from your father and the other from your mother. Sperm cells and egg cells are the only cells in the body that do not have 46 chromosomes – they have 23. When a sperm cell fertilises an egg cell and they fuse, the chromosomes from each cell pair up to form a full set of 46 chromosomes.

Figure 1 shows the number and structure of the chromosomes present in the nuclei of two different cells. Pictures like these are called **karyotypes**. The chromosomes in each cell have been paired up. Doctors use karyotypes to determine the sex of a baby before it is born, and also to see if the individual has inherited a genetic condition such as Down's syndrome. Look carefully at each photograph. Figure 1(a) shows the karyotype of a male. In the last pair, called the **sex chromosomes**, the chromosomes are different sizes. There is one X chromosome and one Y chromosome. The X chromosome has been inherited from the mother and the Y chromosome has been inherited from the father. Figure 1(b) is a karyotype of a female – there are two X chromosomes instead of an X and a Y.

Down's syndrome is an inherited disorder that can arise when a person has not two but three copies of one chromosome. Figure 1(b) shows the karyotype of a female with Down's syndrome.

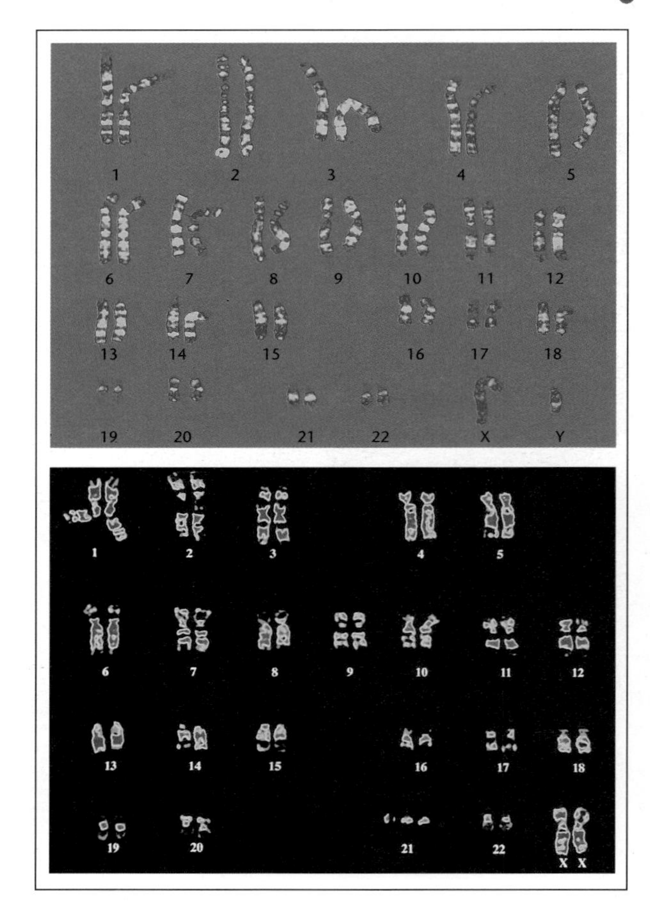

Figure 1 *The chromosomes present in a human cell.*
(a) A normal male.
(b) A female with Down's syndrome.

1 Give the number of the chromosome that has three copies in figure 1(b).

Coded information

Chromosomes are made of a chemical called **DNA**, which stands for **d**eoxyribo**n**ucleic **a**cid. DNA is a polymer made up of monomers called **nucleotides**. The nucleotides are arranged in many different orders to form coded instructions, the **genes**. There are millions of genes in each cell and each gene determines a different characteristic, such as the colour of your eyes. All the instructions a cell needs to function are contained in the cell's genes.

Chromosomes can be seen using a light microscope. They look like a rod or a thread. Figure 2 shows a pair of human chromosomes. The chromosomes have been stained with special dyes that fluoresce when combined chemically with DNA. When the chromosomes are viewed using high magnification, you can see that they have a banding pattern which is different for each chromosome in a pair. The bands show the position, the **locus**, of the genes on the chromosomes.

Genes can exist in different forms, called **alleles**. Look at the pair of fruit fly chromosomes in figure 3. Along the length of each chromosome there are a number of genes. The gene for eye colour in fruit flies is shown. You can see that there are two forms of the gene for fruit fly eye colour, the allele for red eyes and the allele for white eyes. Both alleles are found at the same locus.

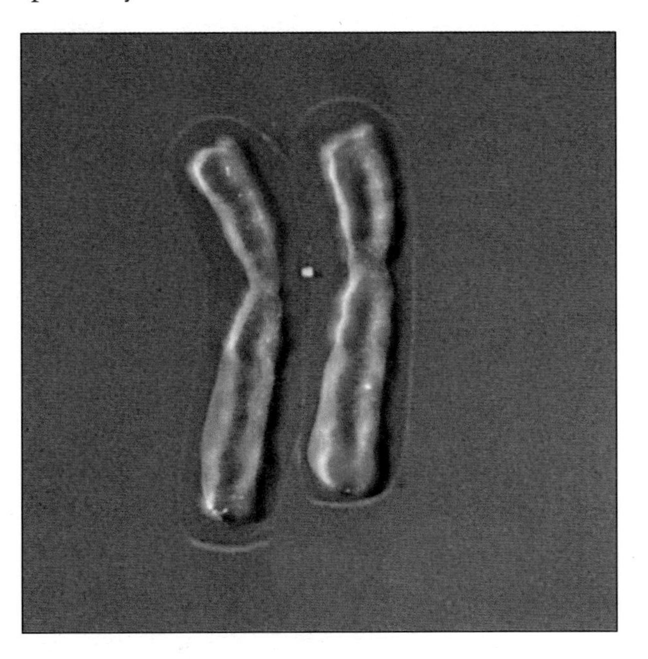

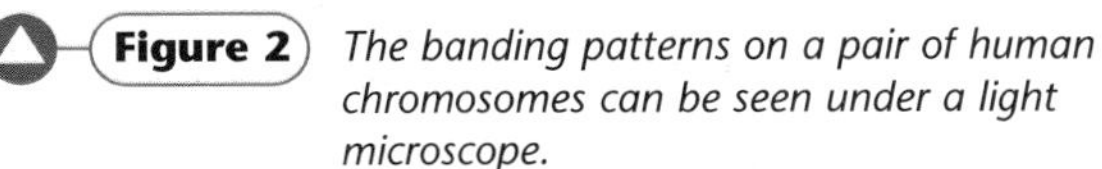

Figure 2 *The banding patterns on a pair of human chromosomes can be seen under a light microscope.*

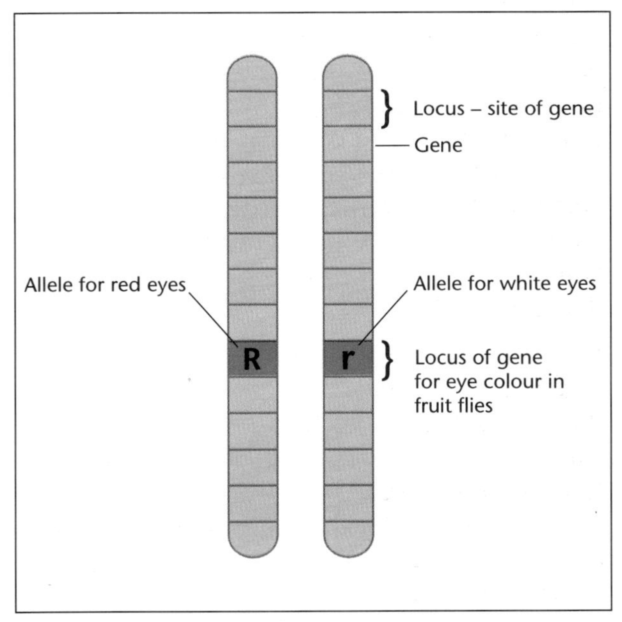

Figure 3 *Genes and alleles. (This diagram is not drawn to scale – there are many more genes on a chromosome than are shown here.)*

Key ideas 116–17

Genes are sections of DNA, which are inherited and carry coded information about an organism.

Alleles are alternative forms of a gene.

Alleles of genes occupy the same locus on each chromosome in a pair.

2

Storing information

Enzymes control all the processes going on in cells. Enzymes determine which chemicals are made in a cell, and what sort of cell it is – for example, whether it is a kidney cell, a nerve cell or a blood cell. The information about which enzymes to make has to be permanently stored in a cell, so it can be used when necessary. The store has to be organised so that the different cells can use the parts that they need and can ignore the rest.

Memory molecules

Molecules of **nucleic acid** carry the information a cell needs in order to make enzymes. The storage molecule is **DNA** or **deoxyribonucleic acid**, which is contained in the chromosomes in the nucleus of the cell. To use the stored information, another type of molecule, **RNA** or **ribonucleic acid**, is needed. DNA and RNA are both nucleic acids.

Building blocks of nucleic acids

DNA and RNA are both polymers made up of monomers called **nucleotides**. The nucleotides in DNA and RNA are very similar.

A nucleotide is made up of three parts:

- a five-carbon sugar called a **pentose**
- a nitrogen-containing **base**
- a **phosphate** group.

The pentose sugar is slightly different in DNA and RNA. In RNA the sugar is called **ribose** and in DNA the sugar is called **deoxyribose**.

Nucleotides may contain two types of nitrogen-containing base – **purines** and **pyrimidines**. Purine have two rings in their structure, and pyrimidines have only one.

- In DNA the purine bases are **adenine** (A) and **guanine** (G), and the pyrimidine bases are **cytosine** (C) and **thymine** (T).
- In RNA the purine bases are the same as in DNA, but the pyrimidine bases are cytosine (C) and **uracil** (U).

As well as a pentose sugar and a purine or pyrimidine base, each nucleotide has an inorganic phosphate group.

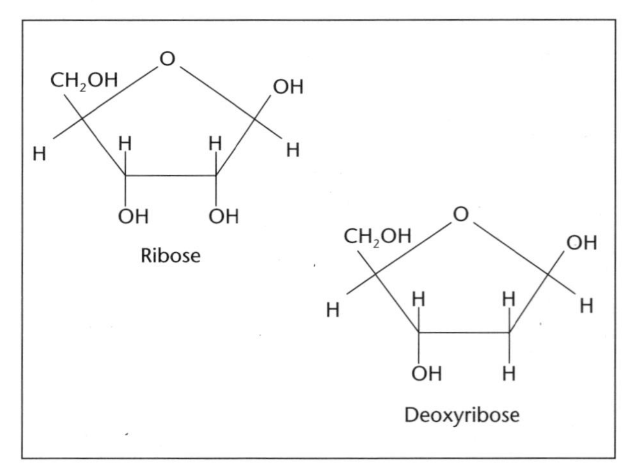

Figure 1 *The structural formulae of ribose and deoxyribose.*

Q

1 What is:
a a polymer
b a monomer?

2 Look at figure 1 showing the structure of ribose and deoxyribose. See if you can explain their names by looking at the difference between them.

> **Q** 3 Copy and complete table 1 to show the similarities and differences between DNA and RNA. Use a red pen for similarities and a blue pen for differences.

	DNA	RNA
Sugar		
Purine bases		
Pyrimidine bases		
Inorganic component		

Putting it together

The sugar, base and phosphate groups join by condensation reactions to form a nucleotide.

To make DNA, deoxyribose nucleotides containing the bases A, C, G and T join together to form long chains with a sugar–phosphate backbone. In RNA, ribose nucleotides containing A, C, G and U join together in the same way. The long chains of nucleotides in DNA and RNA are called **polynucleotide strands**. However, the way these nucleotides fit together to form a three-dimensional structure is different in DNA and RNA.

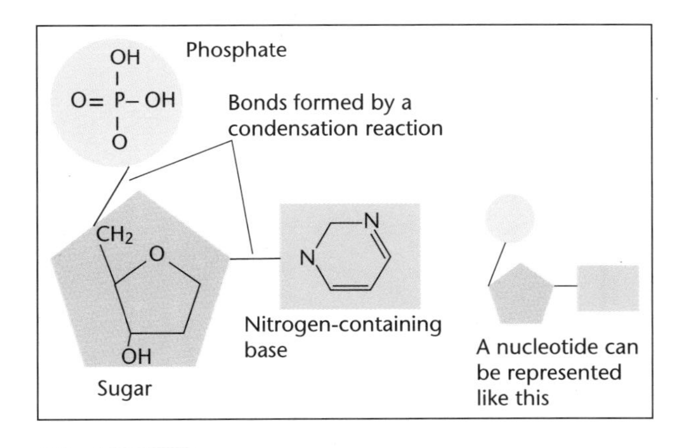

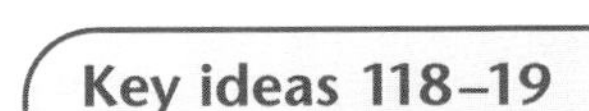

How a nucleotide is formed.

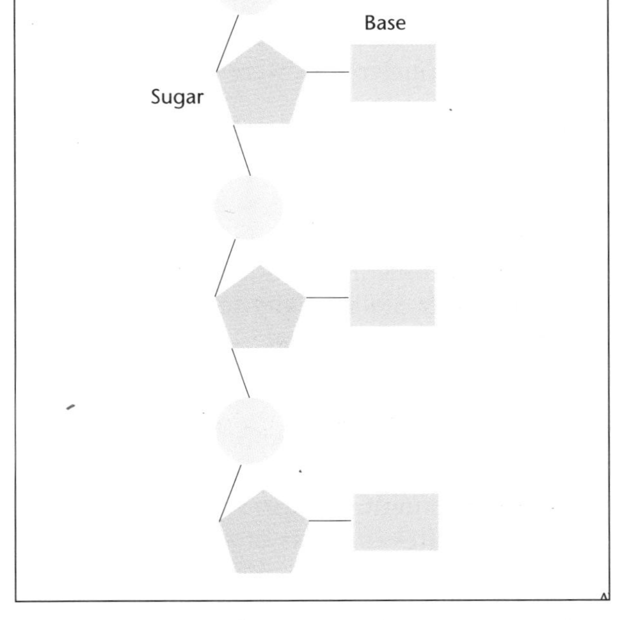

Figure 3 *The diagram shows a chain of nucleotides – a polynucleotide strand. This is how the nucleic acids DNA and RNA are formed.*

> **Q** 4 What is a condensation reaction?

Key ideas 118–19

DNA and RNA are both nucleic acids, and they store and use genetic information.

Nucleic acids are polynucleotide strands (polymers made up of nucleotides). Each nucleotide contains a pentose sugar, a nitrogen-containing base and a phosphate group.

There are two kinds of base – purines and pyrimidines. Adenine and guanine are purines, while cytosine, thymine and uracil are pyrimidines.

3 DNA structure

The importance of DNA in inheritance was known a long time before its structure was worked out. The molecule is very large and, until recently, difficult to obtain from cells.

Working out the puzzle

James Watson and Francis Crick worked out the structure of DNA in the early 1950s at Cambridge University. It was known that DNA was made of nucleotides, but how the nucleotides were arranged was unknown. However, other scientists in London had found out information about DNA. Maurice Wilkins and Rosalind Franklin had used a technique called X-ray crystallography to show that DNA is a helical molecule. Also, an Austrian chemist called Erwin Chargaff had shown that the pyrimidine content of DNA always equalled the purine content. He also showed that the amounts of A and T were always equal, and so were the amounts of C and G. Table 1 shows some of Chargaff's ratios.

Using a combination of inspiration and persistence, Watson and Crick tried to make a model of DNA which fitted with all this data, and succeeded. Maurice Wilkins, James Watson and Francis Crick were awarded a Nobel Prize in 1962. Unfortunately, Rosalind Franklin died in 1958, and Nobel Prizes are not awarded posthumously.

Figure 1 *Francis Crick and James Watson with their model of DNA.*

Table 1 *Chargaff's ratios of bases in several organisms.*

Organism	Adenine	Guanine	Cytosine	Thymine
Human (sperm)	31.0	19.1	18.4	31.5
Cattle (sperm)	28.6	22.2	22.0	27.2
Salmon	29.7	20.8	20.4	29.1
Wheat	27.3	22.7	22.8	27.2
Yeast	31.3	18.7	?	?

The double helix

DNA consists of two strands of nucleotides, one running the opposite way to the other, forming a double helix. The nitrogen-containing bases in each strand are held together by hydrogen bonding. As you can see in figure 2, there are 10 base pairs per turn of the double helix.

To form the 'rungs' of the DNA 'ladder', a purine base always pairs with a pyrimidine base. Look at figure 2. You can see that adenine always pairs with thymine and guanine always pairs with cytosine. This is called **base pairing**. Adenine forms *two* hydrogen bonds with thymine, while cytosine forms *three* hydrogen bonds with guanine. This makes sure that adenine and thymine pair specifically with each other, and cytosine and guanine pair specifically. Bases that pair with each other are called **complementary** bases, so adenine is complementary to thymine, and cytosine is complementary to guanine.

1. **If one strand of a DNA molecule contained a sequence of bases reading ATGCCAGTC, what bases would the other strand have?**
2. **A sample of DNA was analysed and 15 per cent of the nucleotides contained adenine. What percentage of the nucleotides would you expect to contain guanine?**
3. **Copy and complete table 1, filling in the missing values to the nearest whole number.**

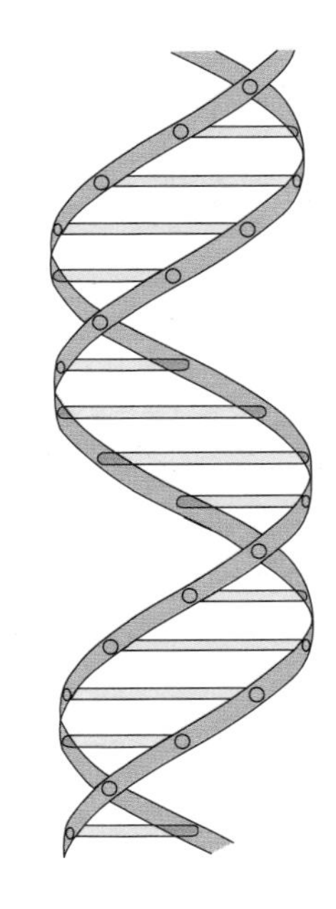

DNA is a double helix held together by hydrogen bonds between complementary base pairs. There are 10 base pairs for every complete turn of the helix.

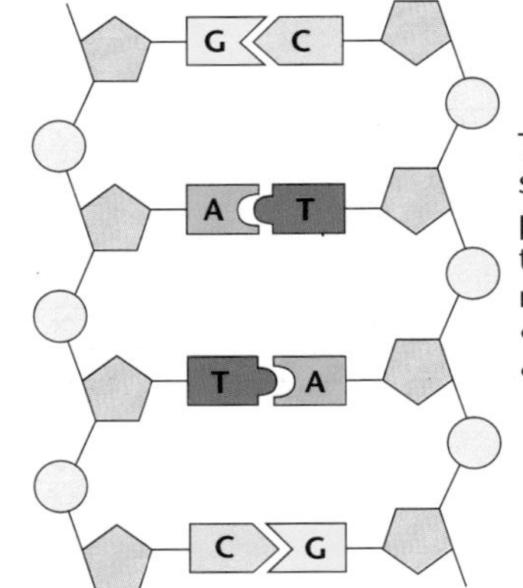

The two nucleotide strands fit together perfectly as long as the base-pairing rules are followed:
- **G** pairs with **C**
- **A** pairs with **T**.

Figure 2 *The structure of DNA.*

Key ideas 120–21

The DNA molecule is a double helix shape, with two polynucleotide strands held together by hydrogen bonds between the nitrogen-containing bases.

The nitrogen-containing bases show specific base pairing: C will only pair with G and A will only pair with T.

4 Copying DNA

Since DNA carries the information that enables a cell to make the enzymes it needs, it is very important that DNA can copy itself accurately whenever a cell divides. Every daughter cell must have a complete set of genes. If this did not happen properly, organisms would not be able to grow normally and reproduce.

Zipping away

DNA copies itself by a mechanism called **semi-conservative replication**. The double helix unwinds, and the hydrogen bonds between the bases break. It is rather like a zip-fastener being opened, as you can see in figure 1. Each exposed strand of DNA can now act as a template for the formation of a new strand. New DNA nucleotides line up along the exposed strands, following the base-pairing rules. These new nucleotides are joined together by an enzyme called **DNA polymerase**. DNA polymerase joins the nucleotides together in short pieces. Another enzyme, **DNA ligase**, is needed to join the short pieces together. You can see in the diagram that the newly formed strands of DNA are identical with the original strands of DNA.

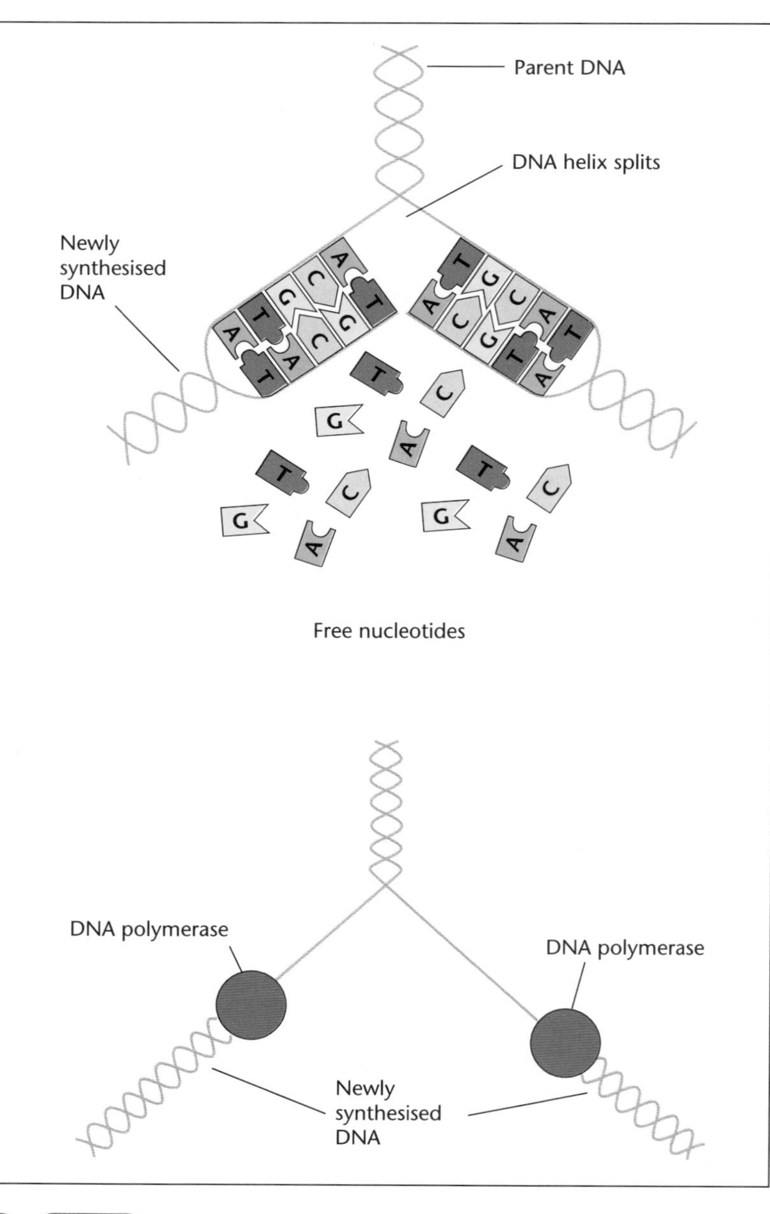

Figure 1 *The semi-conservative replication of DNA.*

1 Why do you think that this method of DNA replication is called 'semi-conservative'?

The way that DNA replicates is described as 'semi-conservative' because half of the original molecule is kept (or conserved) and the other half is newly synthesised.

Making DNA

Now that the structure of DNA is known, it is possible to make artificial DNA in a DNA-synthesising machine. You can see one of these in figure 2. Artificial DNA has many applications, some of which you will learn about later in this module.

Figure 2 *A DNA-synthesising machine.*

The structure of DNA is well suited to its function

To carry out its job properly, DNA must be able to copy itself accurately and remain stable, so that the information it carries is unchanged. The structure of DNA makes it very suitable for this, because:

- It is a very stable molecule, held by strong covalent bonds which are not easily broken down.
- It is able to copy itself accurately because of the specific base pairing.
- The long DNA molecule is capable of folding itself up, so a great deal of information can be stored in a small volume, in the chromosomes inside the nucleus.
- It carries information coded in the order of bases, which can easily be copied.

Key ideas 122–3

DNA replicates semi-conservatively. This involves the DNA 'unzipping' and new nucleotides joining on by specific base pairing.

DNA is well suited to its function because it is very stable, compact, can copy itself accurately and carries information for making proteins in its base sequence.

5 How genes work

Proteins are the key to the genetic code. Almost all enzymes are proteins, and enzymes control all the chemical processes going on inside cells. DNA carries the instructions for the cell in the form of codes to make particular proteins.

You will remember that proteins are made up of **amino acids**. There are 20 different types of amino acid that occur in proteins, but because they can join together in different combinations the range of proteins that can be built from them is virtually limitless. The **genetic code** determines which amino acids are put together, and the order in which they are arranged.

Cracking the code

The code in the DNA is a **triplet code**. This means that three bases code for one amino acid. Each sequence of three bases is called a **codon**. There are 64 (or 4^3) different codons. Most of these codons code for different amino acids, though a few are 'nonsense' codons serving as punctuation marks – they signal the beginning or end of a gene. Since there are 20 different types of amino acid making up proteins, 64 codons is more than enough to code for them. The genetic code has now been worked out, so scientists know what all the codons mean.

Carrying the message

To make a protein, the information in the DNA has to get into the cytoplasm of the cell, because that is where proteins are made. DNA is too large to leave the nucleus. A copy of the information in the gene is made in the form of a smaller molecule called **messenger RNA** (mRNA). Study figure 1.

mRNA is small enough to leave the nucleus and enter the cytoplasm. You can see that the sequence of bases in the mRNA is complementary to the base sequence in the DNA. A list of mRNA codons is shown in table 1 on the opposite page. Notice how some amino acids have several different codons, while others have only one or two. You can also see that three of the codons are **stop codons**. These do not code for an amino acid, but are rather like a full stop, marking the end of the piece of code.

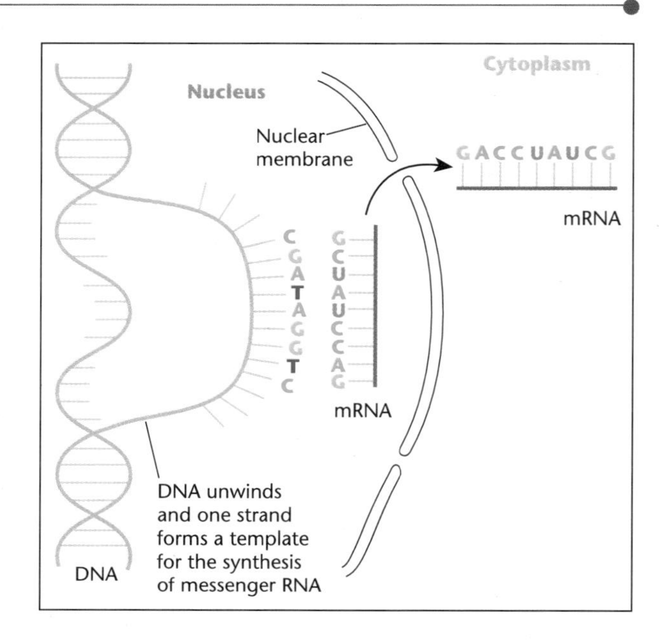

Figure 1 *How mRNA carries the genetic code from the nucleus to the cytoplasm.*

The mRNA codons (purple) and the amino acids they code for (green).
** stands for a stop codon.*

First base	Second base U	Second base C	Second base A	Second base G	Third base
U	UUU } Phenylalanine (Phe)	UCU } Serine (Ser)	UAU } Tyrosine (Tyr)	UGU } Cysteine (Cys)	U
	UUC	UCC	UAC	UGC	C
	UUA } Leucine (Leu)	UCA	UAA*	UGA*	A
	UUG	UCG	UAG*	UGG Tryptophan (Trp)	G
C	CUU } Leucine (Leu)	CCU } Proline (Pro)	CAU } Histidine (His)	CGU } Arginine (Arg)	U
	CUC	CCC	CAC	CGC	C
	CUA	CCA	CAA } Glutamine (Gln)	CGA	A
	CUG	CCG	CAG	CGG	G
A	AUU } Isoleucine (Ile)	ACU } Threonine (Thr)	AAU } Asparagine (Asn)	AGU } Serine (Ser)	U
	AUC	ACC	AAC	AGC	C
	AUA	ACA	AAA } Lysine (Lys)	AGA } Arginine (Arg)	A
	AUG Methionine (Met)	ACG	AAG	AGG	G
G	GUU } Valine (Val)	GCU } Alanine (Ala)	GAU } Aspartic acid (Asp)	GGU } Glycine (Gly)	U
	GUC	GCC	GAC	GGC	C
	GUA	GCA	GAA } Glutamic acid (Glu)	GGA	A
	GUG	GCG	GAG	GGG	G

1 Three bases code for an amino acid in the genetic code. This gives 64 different codons. How many different codons would there be if:
a 2 bases coded for an amino acid
b 4 bases coded for an amino acid?

2 Why do you think DNA has a triplet code, rather than pairs or fours?

3 Give the sequence of amino acids coded for by a piece of mRNA with the following order of bases:
CAGAAUGUCUUUUGG.

Key ideas 124–5

Genes code for proteins.

The code in the DNA is copied in the form of a molecule of messenger RNA.

The DNA code is a triplet code – three bases code for one amino acid.

The sequence of three bases is called a codon.

6 Copying the code

RNA, as you have already seen, is closely related to DNA. However, it has a different sugar, ribose, and instead of the base thymine it has uracil. In addition, it forms a single strand and its molecules are smaller and less complex than those of DNA.

The instructions for making proteins are coded in the DNA inside the nucleus, but proteins are made in the cytoplasm of the cell. RNA:

1. copies the information coded in the DNA inside the nucleus and carries it to the ribosomes where the proteins will be made
2. collects specific amino acids from the cytoplasm and carries them to the ribosomes
3. makes up most of the ribosomes themselves.

Copying the code

The information in the DNA is copied, or **transcribed**, on to a smaller mRNA molecule. This process is called **transcription**. The mRNA molecule is small enough to pass through the pores in the nuclear membrane into the cytoplasm.

The piece of DNA that is copied is called a **gene**. A gene carries the code for a polypeptide, called a **gene product**. Before DNA can be copied it has to unwind so the code can be read. Look at figure 1 of DNA being transcribed. You can see that part of the DNA molecule is unwound and the two strands have separated, exposing the DNA base sequence. Enzymes control this process. The enzyme RNA polymerase attaches to the DNA at a specific sequence of bases called a 'start' code.

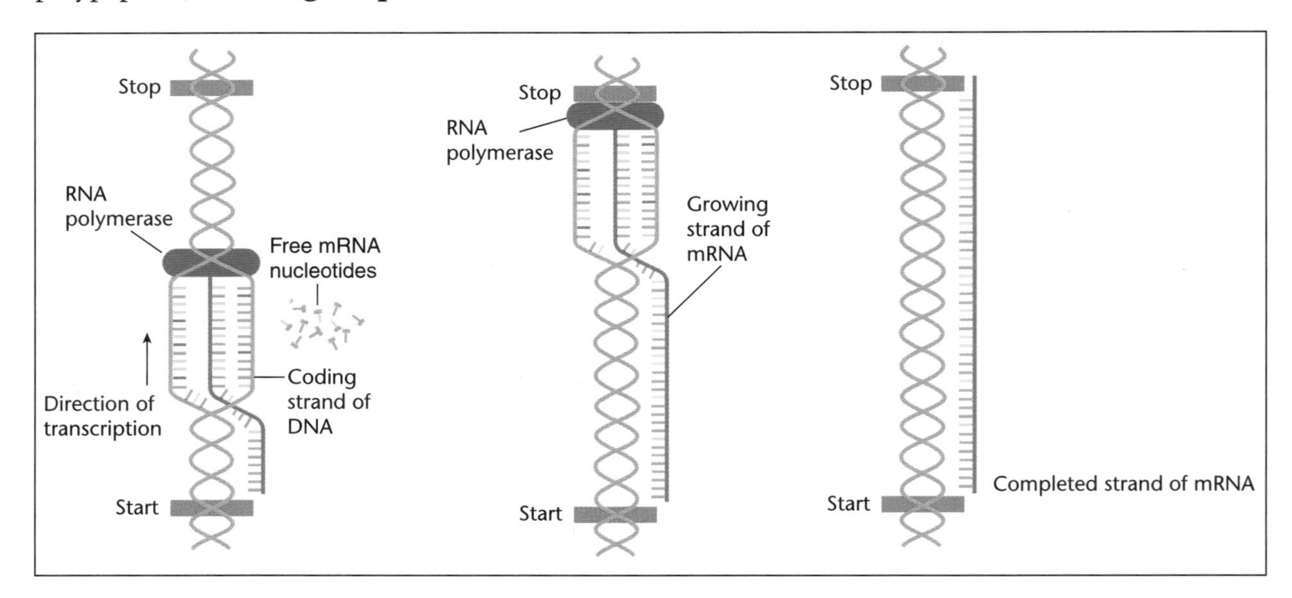

Figure 1 *Transcription – the code is copied from DNA to mRNA in the nucleus.*

Once the RNA polymerase enzyme is in the right place, it moves along the gene. As the enzyme moves, the DNA unzips and complementary mRNA nucleotides are matched with the exposed bases of one of the DNA strands. This strand is the **coding strand**. A complementary copy of this DNA strand is made in the form of an mRNA molecule. Once the coding strand has been copied, the DNA strands rewind. At the end of the gene there is a 'stop' code. When the enzyme reaches this, the enzyme falls away from the DNA. The mRNA is released and leaves the nucleus through a nuclear pore.

1. **Name the type of bond that must be broken for the DNA helix to come apart.**
2. **Explain why the enzyme needs a start signal.**
3. **Explain why the DNA needs to unwind to be copied.**
4. **If the base sequence on the DNA coding strand is ATTGCCAAG, what will the sequence of bases in the mRNA be?**

Material movers

On page 64 you saw how amino acids are used to build proteins. These amino acids have to be in the right place at the right time so that they can be joined in the right order. Another kind of RNA is used to carry amino acids to the right place, called **transfer RNA** or **tRNA**.

In figure 2 you can see that tRNA has a specific shape, like a clover leaf. The middle leaf shape has three unpaired bases, called the **anticodon**. It is the anticodon that determines which amino acid the tRNA carries. The anticodon makes a tRNA molecule specific – it can only carry a particular amino acid. At the opposite end of the tRNA molecule is another set of unpaired bases. This is the site where an amino acid joins on to the tRNA molecule, to be carried.

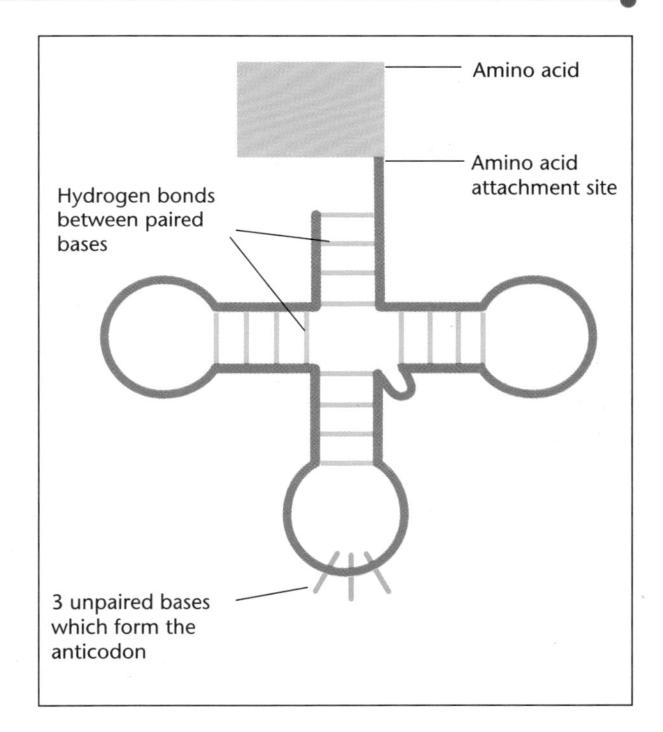

Figure 2 *Transfer RNA is made up of a single polynucleotide chain folded back on itself. Each type of tRNA carries its own specific amino acid to the ribosome.*

5. **There are 20 different types of amino acid that are used to make proteins. How many different tRNA molecules will be needed?**

Key ideas 126–7

In transcription, a DNA sequence is copied as mRNA.

The mRNA carries the coded information from the nucleus to the cytoplasm for protein synthesis.

tRNA molecules carry specific amino acids to the place where proteins are made.

7 Reading the message

You have seen on page 126 how the code in DNA is copied as messenger RNA (mRNA), which moves into out of the nucleus into the cytoplasm. You have also seen how another type of RNA, transfer RNA (tRNA), joins and forms a complex with specific amino acids. In the cytoplasm these different molecules are all used to synthesise proteins.

Needing the message

Translation happens when the code in the mRNA is used to assemble a polypeptide. Translation takes place on ribosomes, as shown in figure 1.

1 mRNA moves into cytoplasm and a ribosome attaches to the mRNA strand. Three bases on the mRNA make a codon, which carries the code for one amino acid.

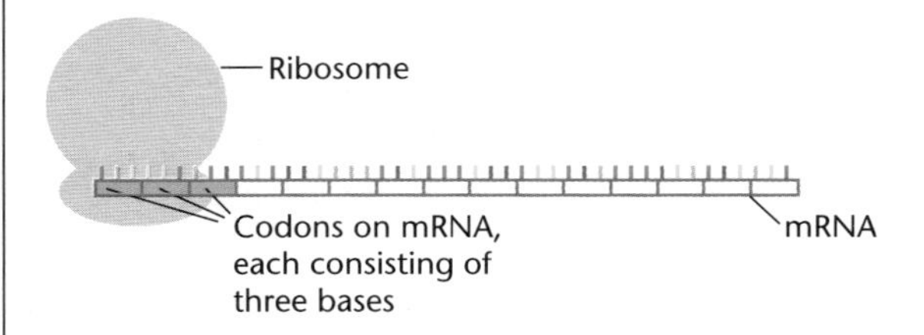

2 When the ribosome attaches to the mRNA, there are two codons inside the ribosome. Two tRNA molecules that have anticodons complementary to these codons enter the ribosome. They pair with the codons, bringing the amino acids that they are carrying very close together.

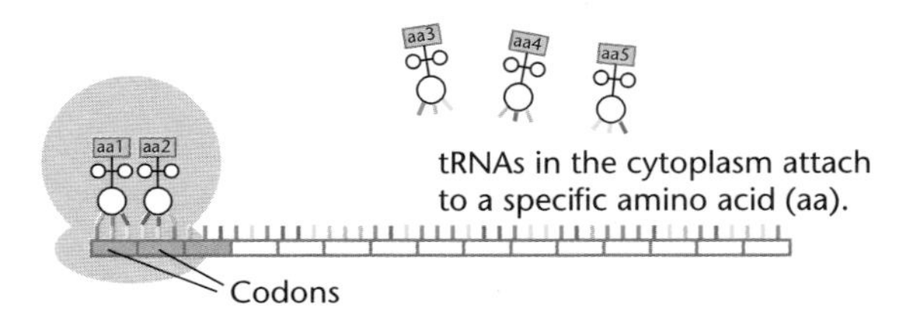

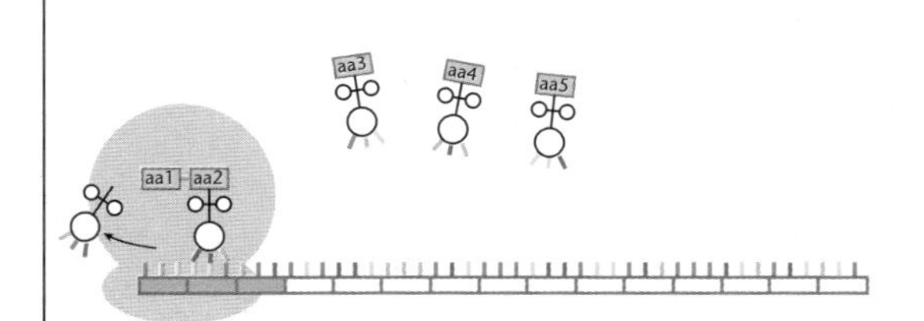

3 The two amino acids join by a peptide bond. The first tRNA molecule can leave the ribosome and combine with a new amino acid. The ribosome moves along the mRNA, and a new tRNA can enter the ribosome.

Polypeptide chain

4 This sequence continues. When the ribosome reaches the end of the mRNA there is a 'stop' codon and the polypeptide is released into the cytoplasm.

Figure 1 *Translation – amino acids are brought by tRNA and built up into a polypeptide according to the code on mRNA.*

In this way, ribosomes use mRNA and tRNA carrying amino acids to translate the sequence of nucleotides into an order of amino acids in a polypeptide. You saw on page 66 that the order of amino acids is the primary structure of a protein.

1 If the codon on the mRNA is UAG, what will the anticodon on the correct tRNA molecule be?

Multiple conversions

Once a ribosome has worked its way along the first part of an mRNA, another ribosome can attach itself to the beginning of the mRNA. Each ribosome will then make a separate polypeptide. Several ribosomes working their way along a single mRNA molecule are called a **polysome**. Polysomes speed up protein synthesis, as one mRNA template can be used again and again.

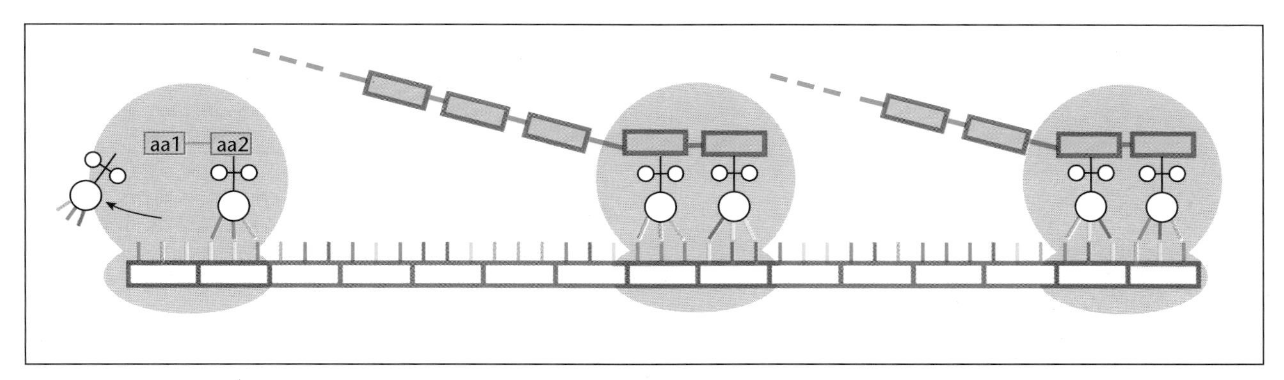

Figure 2 *Polysomes make several polypeptides at once from the same mRNA.*

2 How is the structure of RNA related to its functions?

3 Why do you think it is more efficient to have polysomes on one strand of mRNA rather than to have several strands of mRNA being translated by one ribosome?

Key ideas 128–9

In translation, a ribosome attaches to the messenger RNA (mRNA).

Transfer RNA (tRNA) molecules bring specific amino acids to the ribosome, so that the tRNA anticodon is complementary to the mRNA codon.

The DNA code is translated into a polypeptide.

In a polysome, several ribosomes work their way along the mRNA at the same time, which speeds up protein synthesis.

8 Changed codes

A gene is a section of DNA, which carries coded information to make a protein. Sometimes genes can become changed by a mutation.

Alternative alleles

DNA in most eukaryotic organisms is packaged in the form of chromosomes. Most organisms that reproduce sexually have paired sets of chromosomes, one set coming from each parent. The matching pair of chromosomes is called a **homologous pair**. They contain equivalent sets of genes on them, but each chromosome may have a different version of the gene. These different versions are called **alleles**.

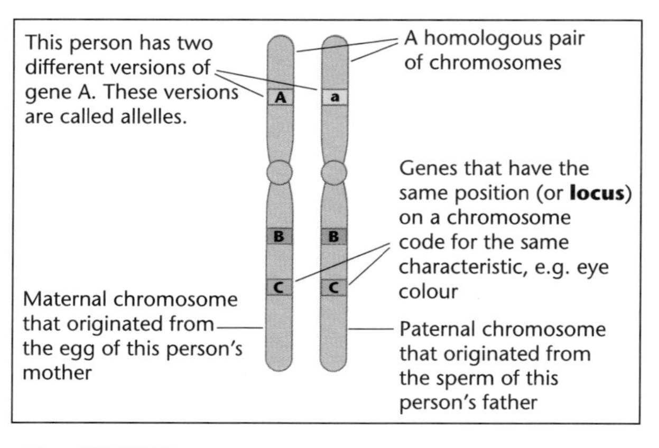

Figure 1 *A homologous pair of chromosomes. Each chromosome may carry different alleles of the same gene.*

Changing genes

A gene **mutation** is a change in the nucleotide sequence of a gene. Remember that DNA is a very stable molecule, and it copies itself very accurately. However, sometimes there is a spontaneous change in the nucleotides. It may be a very small change affecting only one base pair, or a large change affecting many base pairs. If the base sequence is changed, this will change at least one codon and therefore may change the amino acid sequence in the protein. Just one 'wrong' amino acid in a protein sequence might change the way the protein folds. If the mutation codes for a protein that will not work, this makes the gene 'useless' and it may be lethal for the organism.

> **Q**
> 1 **Most genes code for proteins, which are enzymes. Explain why just one 'wrong' amino acid might produce an enzyme that will not work.**

Small changes can have big effects

Look at figure 2 showing some different ways in which a DNA sequence might alter. You can see that in all of them only one base pair is changed. These are called **point mutations**.

When a **substitution** occurs, one base pair is removed and replaced by a different base pair. An **addition** places an extra base pair in the DNA sequence, while a **deletion** means that a base pair is lost.

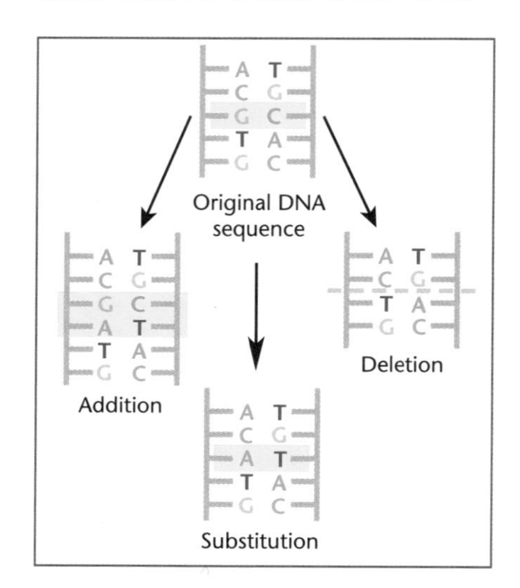

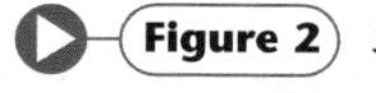
Figure 2 *Some of the ways in which DNA can change.*

Opposite is a DNA sequence and its complementary mRNA copy. The amino acid sequence that the DNA codes for has been worked out using the table on page 125.

Normal DNA sequence:	TAC GGGAATTCG
mRNA copy:	AUGCCCUUAAGC
Amino acid sequence:	Met–Pro–Leu–Ser

When a mutation occurs, the DNA sequence changes. This affects the mRNA and amino acid sequence, as shown opposite.

Normal DNA sequence:	TAC GGGAA**A**TCG	
mRNA copy:	AUGCCCUUUAGC	Substitution
Amino acid sequence:	Met–Pro–**Phe**–Ser	

The example above shows a substitution. One T in the normal DNA sequence has been substituted by an A in the mutated sequence. Only one codon is affected by the substitution.

Now let us look at a different mutation in the same DNA. This time, it changes from the original sequence shown above to the one shown opposite.

Normal DNA sequence:	TAC GGG**T**AATTCG	
mRNA copy:	AUGCCCAUUAAGC	Addition
Amino acid sequence:	Met–Pro–**Ile**–**Lys**	

In this example a single base pair addition has occurred. An addition can affect many codons, and cause extensive changes to the amino acid sequence. A single base pair deletion can also affect many codons.

You can see that a substitution has a less damaging effect than an addition or a deletion because it affects only one codon. It is possible that a substitution will not change the amino acid coded for at all, since most amino acids can be specified by several alternative codons. However, even if only one amino acid is changed, it may make a very different protein. Deletion and addition mutations change all the codons following the point at which they occur. They usually cause very big changes in the protein being made, so the protein is likely to be non-functional.

The new DNA sequence produced by a mutation is a new allele, but it is rarely an improvement. However, occasionally new alleles arise by mutation which are beneficial, and they increase the **variation** in the population.

Speeding up changes

The rate at which genes mutate varies from gene to gene. However, the rate of mutation is greatly increased by environmental factors called **mutagens**. Examples of mutagens include ultraviolet light, X-rays, radiation from radioactive substances, and chemicals in cigarette smoke and in caffeine.

Key ideas 130–31

New forms of alleles arise from changes (mutations) in existing alleles.

Mutations change the sequence of bases in the DNA. Types of mutation include substitution, addition and deletion.

As a result of mutation, enzymes may function less efficiently or not at all.

Mutations occur naturally and the rate of mutation may be increased by mutagens.

9 Altered genes

Many of the proteins synthesised in cells are enzymes that control metabolic pathways such as respiration. If one of these enzymes is faulty, then the pathway may not be able to function and the individual is said to have a **genetic disorder**. An example of this type of genetic disorder is **phenylketonuria**. Proteins have many functions therefore mutations can have many different effects.

Abnormal red blood cells

Thalassaemia is a genetic disorder which prevents the formation of normal haemoglobin in red blood cells. There are two types of thalassaemia – **thalassaemia minor** and **thalassaemia major**. In thalassaemia minor, the sufferer has inherited a normal allele from one parent and the abnormal allele from the other parent. In the more severe thalassaemia major, the sufferer has inherited the abnormal allele from both parents.

Compare the normal red blood cells in figure 1(a) with those showing thalassaemia major in figure 1(b). The red blood cells in figure 1(b) are small and pale.

Instead of normal haemoglobin, the cells contain another form of haemoglobin. This folds differently from normal haemoglobin, so it is less efficient at carrying oxygen. However, not enough of this is made and so there are fewer red blood cells than normal. These cells are also destroyed more quickly than cells containing normal haemoglobin, which leads to severe anaemia. The symptoms of thalassaemia include paleness, tiredness, weakness, breathlessness and palpitations (increased heart activity).

People with thalassaemia minor do not usually show any symptoms. For those with thalassaemia major, repeated blood transfusions are needed to treat the anaemia.

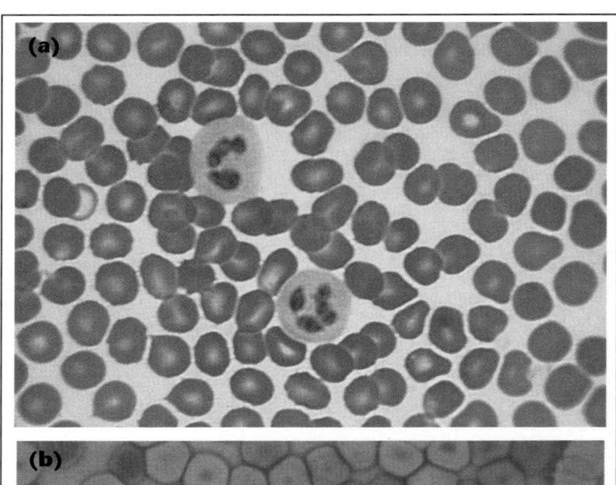

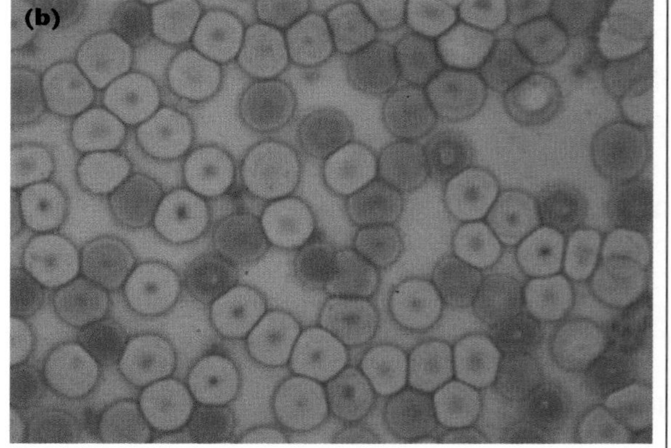

Figure 1 *(a) Photomicrograph showing normal red blood cells (× 770).*
(b) Photomicrograph showing abnormal red blood cells from an embryo with thalassaemia major (× 770). As well as the abnormal haemoglobin, you can also see the nucleus in these developing cells (see page 46).

Unsound hip joints

The effect of some mutations can be modified by environmental factors. **Hip dysplasia** is an inherited disorder common in pedigree dogs, which can lead to severe lameness and disability. The term 'hip dysplasia' means the abnormal formation of the hip joint. It is a disease that develops in young dogs of many different breeds, but is especially common in giant, large and medium-sized breeds. Genetic and environmental factors both influence the development of hip dysplasia and affect the final degree of lameness.

Signs of hip dysplasia cannot be detected in the newborn puppy, but usually appear in the rapid growth period of between four and nine months of age. The only accurate way of finding out the condition of the hip joint is by X-ray examination.

Figure 2(a) shows that in a normal hip joint, the head of the femur fits snugly into the socket in the pelvis. In a dog with hip dysplasia, figure 2(b), the head of the femur fits too loosely into the socket. When the dog walks, the femur head rubs unevenly against the rim of the pelvic socket, causing excessive wear. The joint lining becomes inflamed and painful and results in the bones becoming deformed.

Even though hip dysplasia is a genetic disorder, the severity of the condition can be made worse by environmental factors, particularly:

- overfeeding, resulting in an overweight puppy
- over-exercise of dogs with unstable joints.

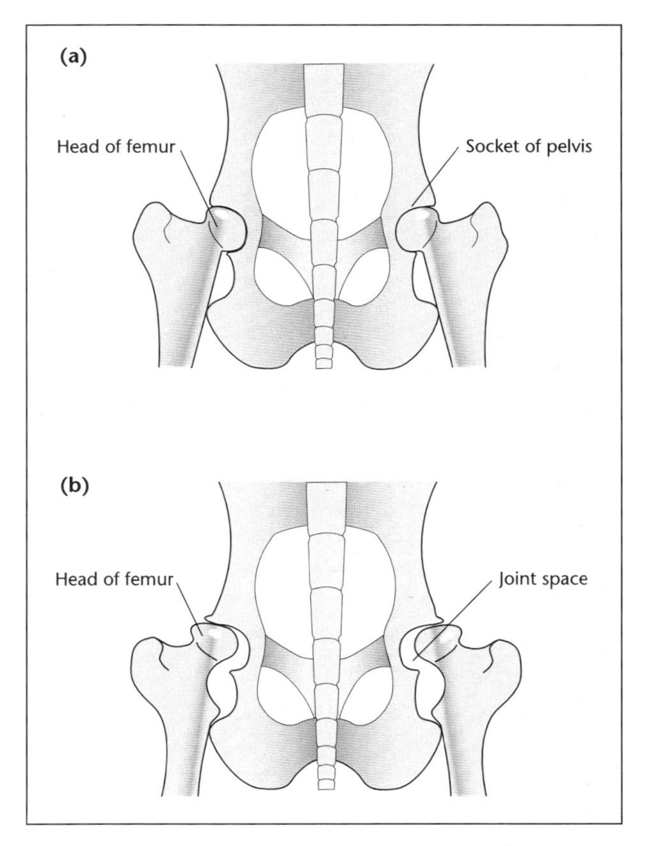

Figure 2 *(a) Normal canine hips. The head of the femur fits snugly into the socket of the pelvis. (b) Hip dysplasia. The head of the femur fits too loosely into the socket.*

Key ideas 132–3

A mutation can produce an enzyme that functions less efficiently or not at all.

A mutation can cause a block in a metabolic pathway.

The effect of some mutations can be modified by environmental factors.

Unit 7 – Questions

10

1. **A** and **B** are two enzymes, both made of 136 amino acids joined together in a single chain. They both catalyse the same reaction, but enzyme **A** works more efficiently than enzyme **B**. Their amino acid sequences were worked out, and it was found that they both had the same sequence of amino acids, except for one small part of the molecules. The amino acid sequence of this part of enzyme **A** is shown below and the corresponding DNA base sequence.

Amino acid sequence for enzyme A:	Lys–Ser–Pro–Ser–Leu–Asn–Ala–Ala
DNA sequence for enzyme A:	TTTTCAGGTAGTGAATTACGACGA

a) Write down the appropriate mRNA sequence for this part of enzyme **A**. (1 mark)

It was found that enzyme **B** was the result of two mutations in the DNA coding for enzyme **A**. In the first mutation, a single nucleotide was deleted (lost) from the DNA. In the second mutation, a single nucleotide was inserted (added) to the DNA.

The amino acid sequence of the corresponding part of enzyme **B** is shown below:

Amino acid sequence for enzyme B:	Lys–Val–His–His–Leu–Met–Ala–Ala

Amino acid	Codons that can be used
Lys	AAA
Ser	AGU or UCA
Pro	CCA
Leu	CUU or UUA
Asn	AAU
Ala	GCU
Val	GUC
His	CAU or CAC
Met	AUG

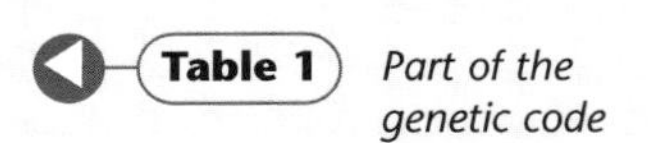
Table 1 *Part of the genetic code*

b) Use table 1 to work out, as accurately as you can:
   i) the sequence of bases in the mRNA coding for enzyme **B** (2 marks)
   ii) the base (nucleotide) deleted in the first mutation (1 mark)
   iii) the base (nucleotide) inserted in the second mutation. (1 mark)

c) Suggest a reason why enzyme **B** is not as efficient an enzyme as enzyme **A**. (2 marks)

(Total 7 marks)

2) Some scientists visited the distant planet Gromos and found some living organisms. They had proteins very much like those on Earth. However, their genetic material (DNA) had a double helix of nucleotides like DNA on Earth, but contained six different bases, which they called **H**, **I**, **J**, **K**, **L** and **M**. **J**, **L** and **M** were found to be pyrimidine bases. When the scientists studied the DNA, they obtained the results shown in table 2.

Ratio of bases in Gromos DNA	Numerical value
H/J	1.00
(H + I)/(J + M)	1.02
(H + K)/(J + M)	1.14
(H + K)/(J + L)	1.01

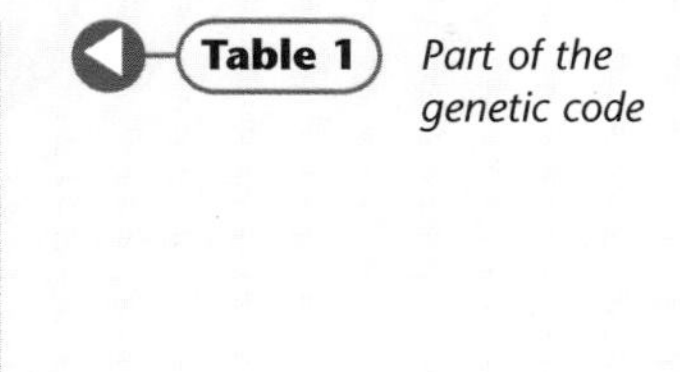

Part of the genetic code

a) Assuming that base-pairing rules similar to those in Earth DNA apply, what can be concluded from these data? (3 marks)

The scientists investigating the DNA from Gromos found a sequence of bases in one gene which coded for a small protein containing seven amino acids. The sequence of bases is shown below:

H–H–J–K–J–L–K–J–L–L–M–J–L–M–J–K–J–L–L–L–M

The scientists investigated the protein and found it contained four different amino acids, in the proportions shown in table 3. They also worked out that y was the first amino acid in the sequence.

Amino acid	Number of amino acids per protein
w	3
x	2
y	1
z	1

b) i) How many bases are present in a codon of the Gromos DNA coding for one amino acid? Explain your answer. (3 marks)

ii) Work out the actual sequence of amino acids in the protein and write them in the correct order. (3 marks)

(Total 9 marks)

3) The DNA of a sea urchin contains 17.5% cytosine nucleotides.

a) i) What percentage of the nucleotides would you expect to contain thymine? (1 mark)

ii) The percentage of cytosine nucleotides is very similar in yeast and in sea urchins. Explain why organisms with the same proportion of cytosine can be as different from each other as sea urchins and yeast. (2 marks)

b) A piece of DNA was extracted from a sea urchin and found to be 249 base pairs long. What is the maximum number of amino acids for which this section of DNA could code? (1 marks)

(Total 4 marks)

1 Understanding cell division

Each day between one and two per cent of an adult's cells die. To replace these cells, existing cells divide repeatedly by the process known as **mitosis.** In mitosis the DNA in the dividing or **parent cell** replicates, and this DNA is distributed equally to each of two new **daughter cells.** These processes must occur accurately so that the DNA is handed on unchanged from one generation of cells to the next.

The 'blue-print'

DNA is found in the nucleus of a cell, where it is supported by proteins, forming **chromosomes**. Chromosomes can only be seen during cell division using a light or electron microscope. As you have seen, a molecule of DNA consists of a double polynucleotide strand. In a chromosome this DNA molecule is attached to proteins. Before a cell divides, the DNA is replicated and the new double strands are attached to proteins. When the cell is about to divide, these two daughter copies of the chromosome become visible, attached to each other. The two copies are called **chromatids** and they are attached to each other at a region called the **centromere**.

In non-dividing cells the chromosomes are extremely long and thin and are dispersed throughout the nucleus. The individual chromosomes cannot be seen, although **chromatin**, the chromosomal material, can be stained with certain dyes. Chromatin is seen as densely staining grains in the typical nucleus.

1 DNA is a polynucleotide. Name the components of DNA nucleotides, and draw a simple diagram showing the structure of DNA.

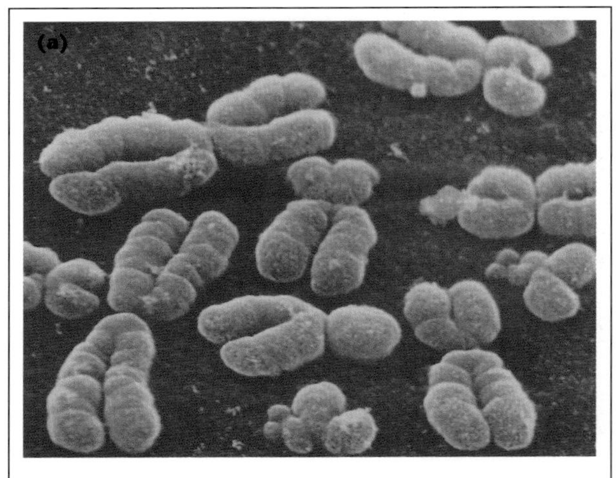

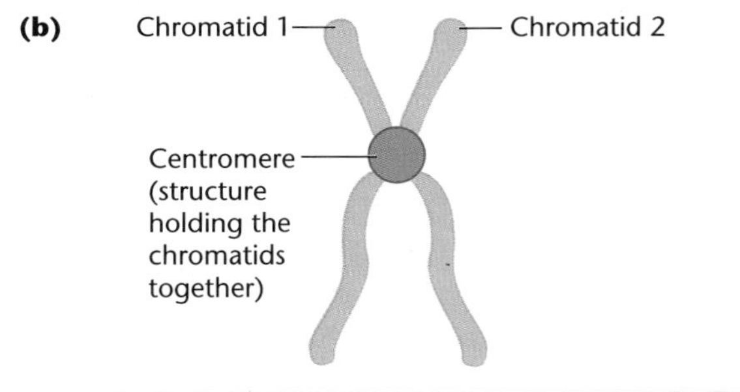

Figure 1 *(a) False-colour scanning electron micrograph of a group of human chromosomes.*
(b) Simplified diagram of the structure of a chromosome, showing identical chromatids and the centromere.

The chromosome number

The number of chromosomes varies from one species to another. However, in an individual organism all the cells have the same number of chromosomes, as do the cells of all other normal individuals of the same species. In human cells there are 46 chromosomes, occurring in pairs, and a copy of all 46 must be given to each daughter cell in mitosis.

The cell cycle

The sequence of events that takes place from the formation of an individual cell until it divides to form daughter cells is called the **cell cycle**. This cycle is usually split into three stages: **interphase**, **mitosis** and division of the cytoplasm (**cytokinesis**).

Figure 2 shows the relative duration of each stage in the cell cycle. Interphase is longer than the other two stages. The actual length of the cycle depends on the type of cell and external factors such as temperature. The cell cycle typically lasts from 8 to 24 hours in humans, with mitosis – the nuclear division – occupying about 10 per cent of the time.

Interphase is divided into three phases: **first growth phase (G1)**, **synthesis phase (S)** and **second growth phase (G2)**. Mitosis is split into four stages: **prophase**, **metaphase**, **anaphase** and **telophase**. Table 1 summarises the events that occur in the cell during each phase of the cell cycle.

2 During the synthesis phase, DNA replicates. Describe the semi-conservative mechanism of DNA replication, including the role of DNA polymerase.

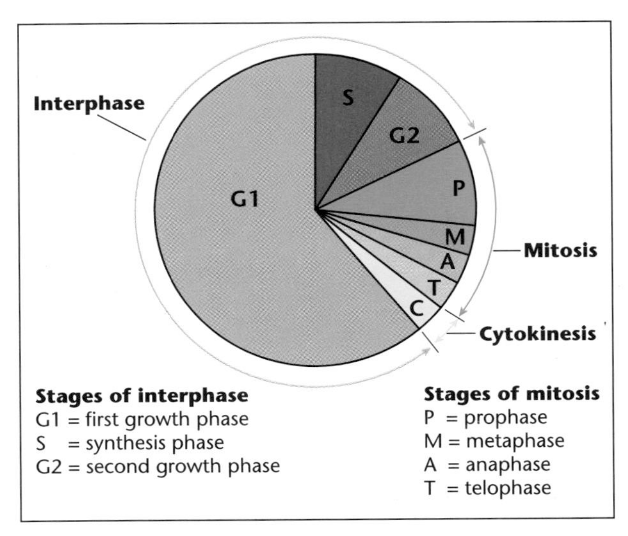

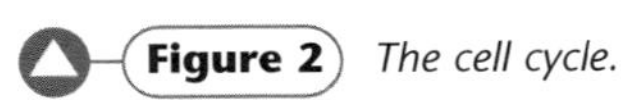

Figure 2 *The cell cycle.*

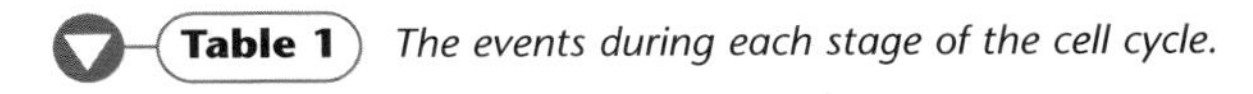

Table 1 *The events during each stage of the cell cycle.*

Phase		Events within the cell
Interphase	G1	Organelle synthesis Cell growth Protein synthesis
	S	DNA replication – each chromosome made of two chromatids
	G2	Cell growth ATP production Chromosomes start to condense
Mitosis		Nuclear division
Cytokinesis		Equal distribution of organelles and cytoplasm into daughter cells

Key ideas 136–7

Cells are replaced by mitosis.

In mitosis, the DNA is copied and then equally distributed to each of two new daughter cells.

DNA exists as chromosomes in the cell nucleus. Before cell division, each chromosome is made of two identical chromatids lying side by side, attached to each other at the centromere.

The number of chromosomes varies from one species to another but is always the same for normal individuals of one species.

Cells undergo a regular pattern of events known as the cell cycle.

2 Making copies

The chromosomes change and move during the cell cycle, and this can be observed in cells that have been fixed and stained using a microscope. Interphase, prophase, metaphase, anaphase, telophase and the division of the cytoplasm can be seen.

Business as usual – interphase

During **interphase** the cell carries out all its routine metabolic activities. Mitosis follows interphase, and during interphase the cell prepares for division in a number of ways. First the cell grows rapidly and cell organelles are synthesised. Then DNA replication occurs and finally the cell enters a second growth period during which energy stores (levels of ATP) increase.

Look at figure 1. The chromosomes cannot be seen during interphase. The chromosomal material (chromatin) has been stained but other structures are difficult to see. The nuclear membrane is visible.

Interphase is followed by **mitosis** or nuclear division. The chromatids are separated and distributed into the daughter nuclei. The events that take place during mitosis are continuous, but it is described in four main stages – prophase, metaphase, anaphase and telophase – for convenience.

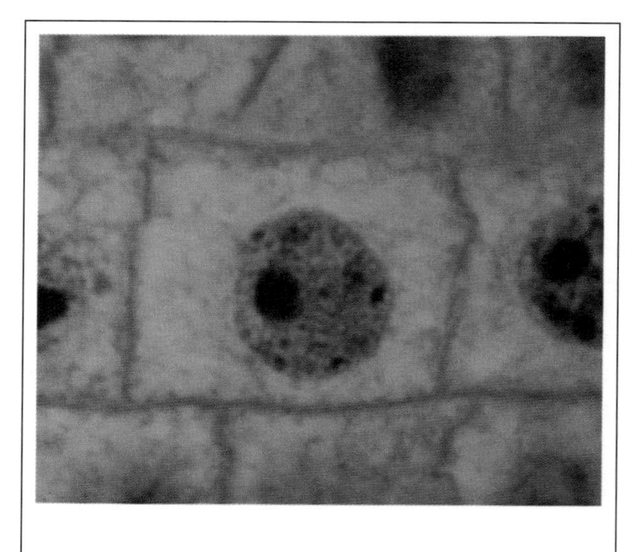

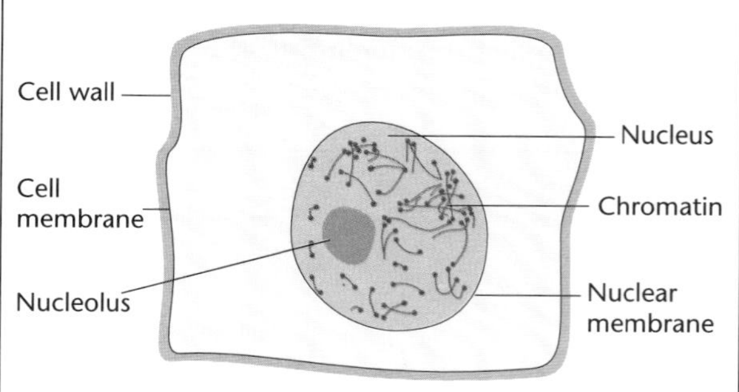

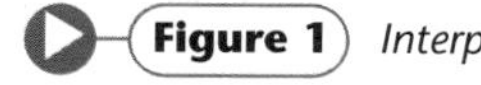
Figure 1 *Interphase in onion cells (×2500).*

Condensing – prophase

Look at figure 2. In **prophase**, the chromosomes first appear as long tangled threads which gradually become shorter and thicker. Eventually they are seen to consist of two **chromatids**, held together at the **centromere**. The **nuclear membrane** disintegrates. A **spindle** starts to be formed from fibres, which helps to move the chromosomes. In animal cells the **centrioles** separate to form the spindle. In figure 2 you can see that during prophase the chromosomes look like spaghetti on a plate.

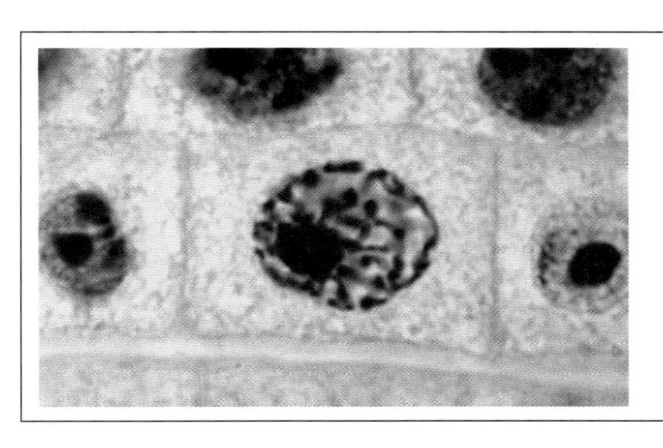

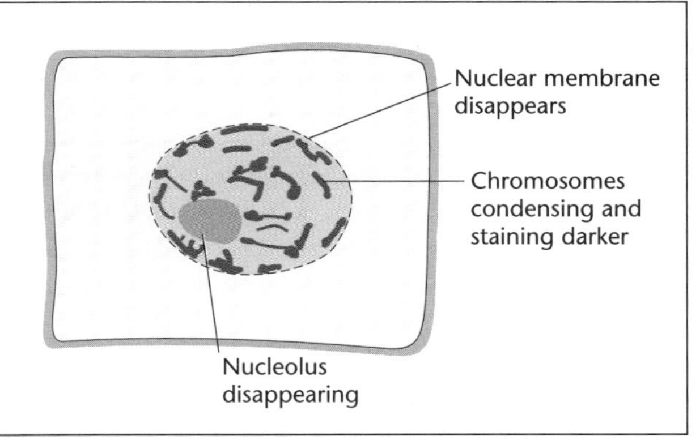

Figure 2 *Prophase.*

Organising – metaphase

The second stage of mitosis is **metaphase**, shown in figure 3.

You can see the barrel-shaped spindle across the central part of the cell. The chromosomes become attached to the spindle fibres by their centromeres. The chromosomes line up along the central part (**equator**) of the spindle in single file. The chromatids are now clearly visible.

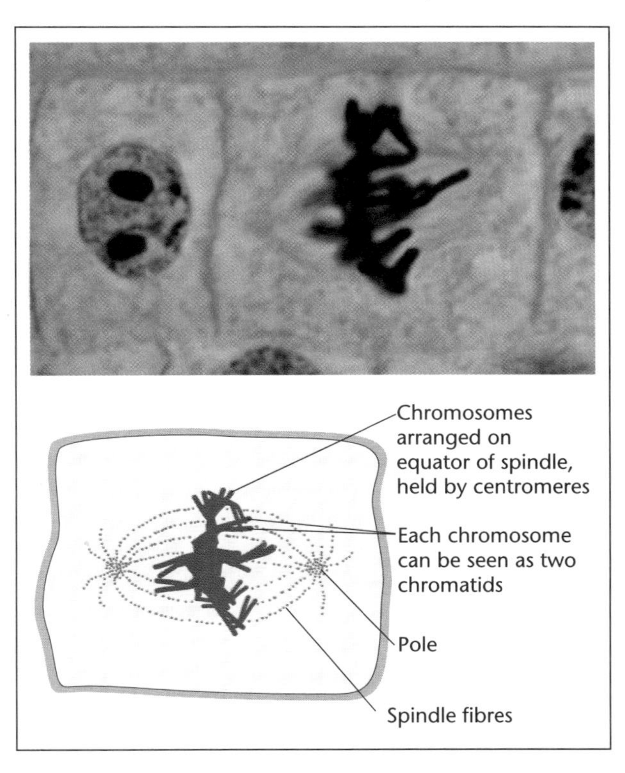

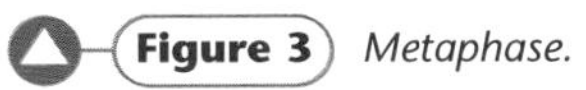
Figure 3 *Metaphase.*

Separating – anaphase

Anaphase is the third stage of mitosis. It is during anaphase that the chromatids separate.

Look at figure 4. The centromeres have divided into two. The spindle fibres shorten, and as they do so they pull the chromatids to opposite poles, centromeres first.

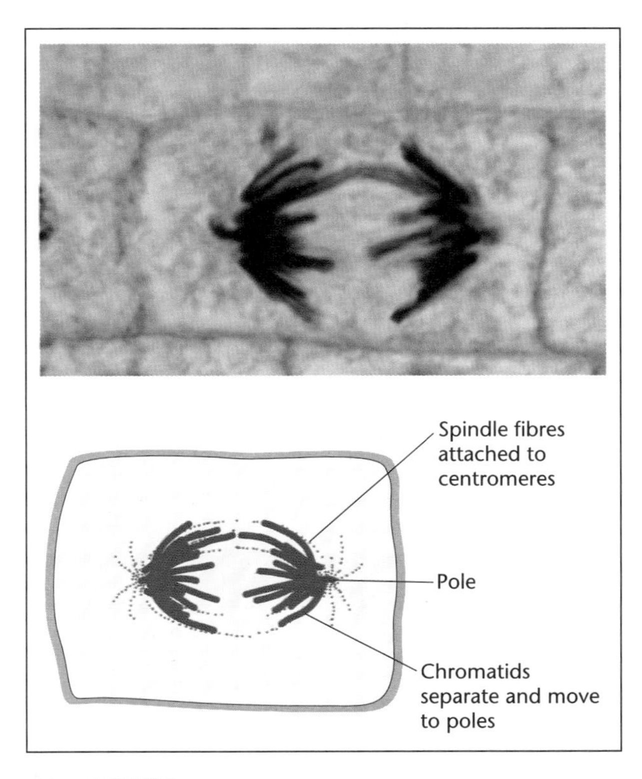

Figure 4 *Anaphase.*

3 Splitting up

In anaphase the chromatids have separated and they have been pulled to opposite poles. The cell now prepares for cell division – the spindle fibres disintegrate and the nuclear membrane reforms.

Restoring – telophase

Once the chromatids have separated they are called chromosomes. You need to remember that both the chromatids were formed by replication of the original chromosome, so are identical copies of it.

Look at figure 1 to see what happens in **telophase**. The spindle disintegrates and the nuclear membrane reforms. The separation is complete and the chromatids are now called chromosomes. The chromosomes become indistinct and the cell is ready to divide.

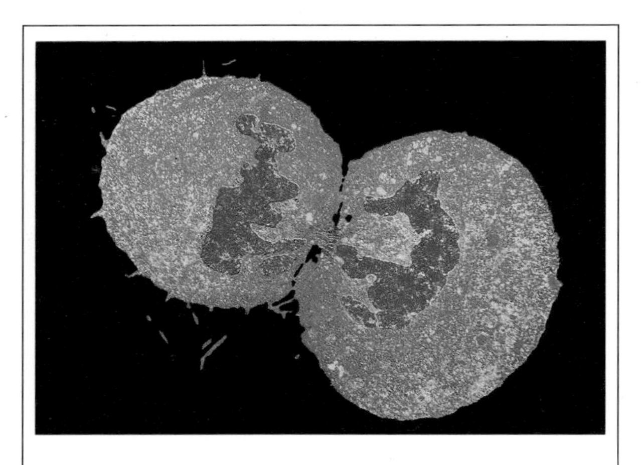

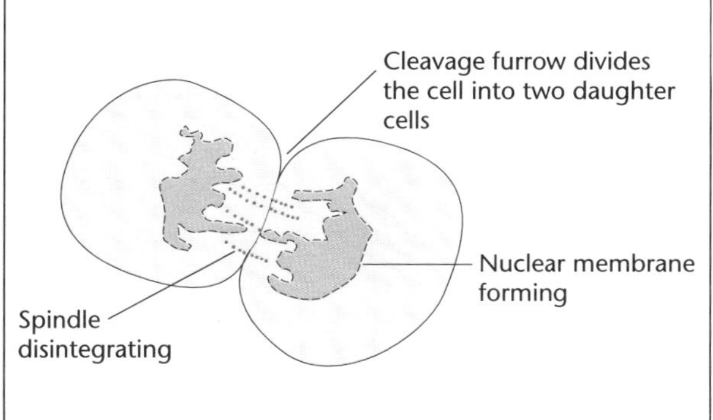

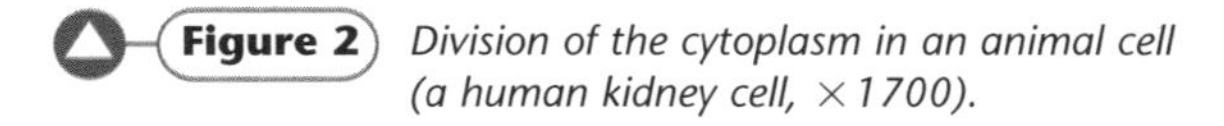

Figure 2 *Division of the cytoplasm in an animal cell (a human kidney cell, ×1700).*

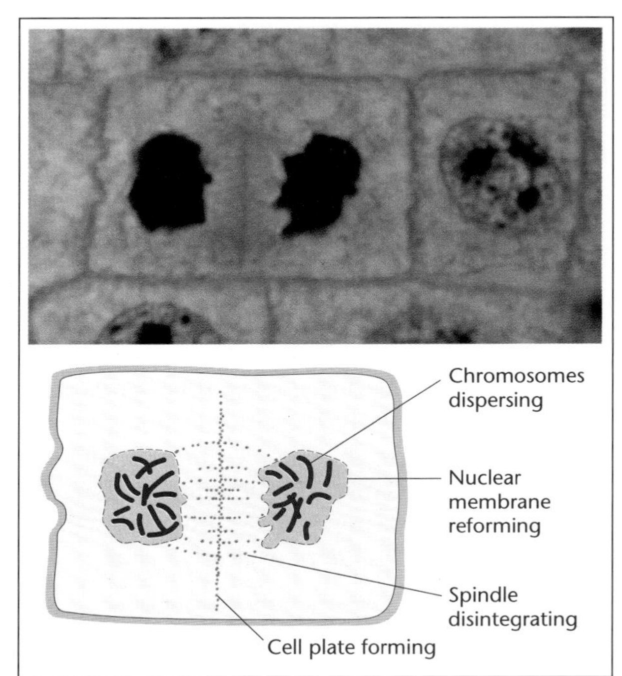

Figure 1 *Telophase.*

Pinching – division of the cytoplasm

After nuclear division, the cell itself can divide. The parent cell is 'pinched' into two daughter cells. Each daughter cell is identical, having the same homologous chromosome pairs as the other daughter cell and as the parent cell.

Look at figure 2. In animal cells the separation of the cytoplasm is caused by **contractile proteins** that can shorten (contract) and lengthen. The cell surface membrane in the middle of the dividing cell is drawn in to form a **cleavage furrow**. In plant cells a **cell plate** forms, which is covered with cellulose to form a separating cell wall. You can see this in figure 1.

1 **At the start of interphase, in a particular species there are four chromosomes in the nucleus, each made up of a double helix of two polynucleotide strands. How many polynucleotide strands of DNA will there be during each stage of the cell cycle in this species?**

The importance of mitosis

Mitosis produces daughter cells that are exact copies of the parent cell. This is important for four reasons:

- **Growth** – for tissue growth it is important that new cells are identical with existing cells, so that they carry out the same function.
- **Repair** – in a similar way, the tissue must replace damaged cells with exact copies of the original cells for the tissue to function properly.
- **Maintenance of the chromosome number** – new cells must have the same number of chromosomes as the cells they are replacing.
- **Asexual reproduction** – mitosis can be used to provide offspring that are genetically identical with the parent.

Out of control

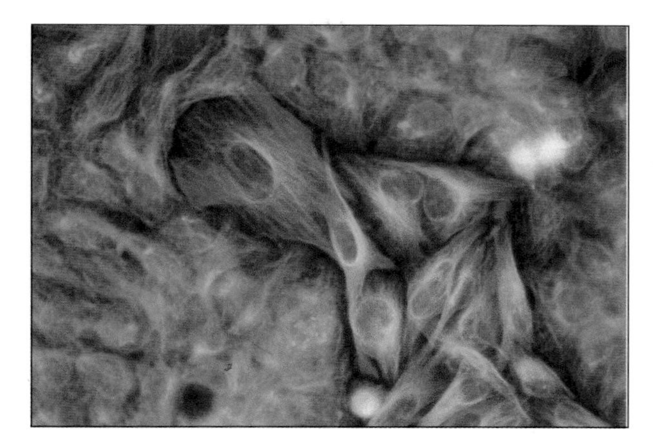

Figure 3 *Photomicrograph of human epithelial tumour cells (yellow) among healthy epithelial cells (×1200).*

Cells normally behave in a controlled way – they grow, divide and die, replacing cells to repair our tissues. Sometimes a cell receives faulty instructions from the genes that make it divide. If this happens the cell will divide too fast, making too many new cells. If a cell starts to divide endlessly like this, it will eventually form a **tumour**. Look at figure 3 which shows normal cells from skin tissue and a group of tumour cells in the same tissue.

Key ideas 138–41

During interphase DNA replicates in preparation for mitosis.

In mitosis, the parent cell divides to produce two new cells, each containing an exact copy of the DNA of the parent cell.

Mitosis increases the cell number so that growth, tissue repair and asexual reproduction can occur.

The four stages of mitosis are prophase (condensing), metaphase (organising), anaphase (separating) and telophase (restoring).

Nuclear division is followed by division of the cytoplasm.

4 Generation to generation

For the species to survive, organisms need to reproduce. Reproduction can be either **sexual** or **asexual** (without sex). In asexual reproduction, a single individual organism produces offspring using mitosis, without the help of another individual. Asexual reproduction is more common in plants, although it does occur in some animals. With asexual reproduction, each new individual is an exact copy of the parent, a **clone**.

Natural methods

Asexual reproduction can occur in a number of ways. Some examples are shown in figure 1. In its simplest form, asexual reproduction takes place by the organism splitting into two (**binary fission**). Another quick way of reproducing is by **budding**. Yeast, a single-celled fungus, sends out a small outgrowth which gets steadily larger and then breaks away to make a new cell. Many organisms produce spores, for example, mosses, ferns and fungi. When a plant reproduces asexually it is called **vegetative reproduction**.

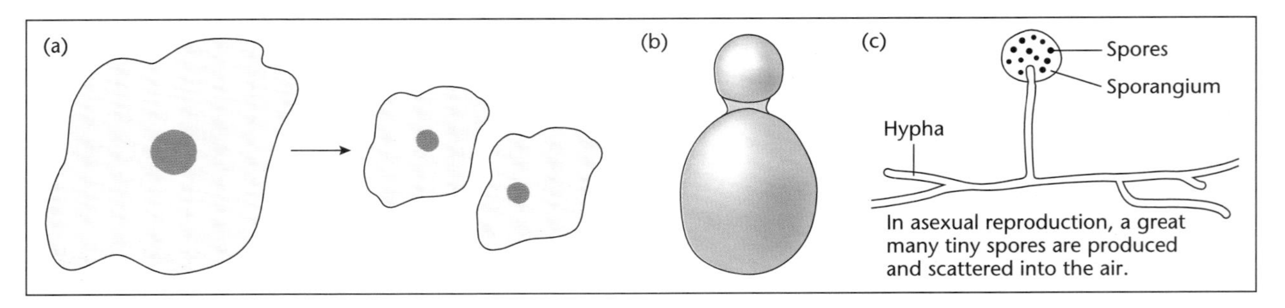

Figure 1 *Examples of asexual reproduction. (a) Binary fission in an amoeba. (b) Budding in a yeast cell. (c) Spore production in fungi.*

Asexual reproduction in plants

Many garden plants die down in autumn and reappear in the same place the following year. During the summer these plants form underground **storage organs** which fill up with food substances. One plant may produce many storage organs, each of which can develop into a new plant. Some plants reproduce by sending out side branches or **runners** which grow along the surface of the soil. Roots grow down from buds on the runner and new plants develop from the buds.

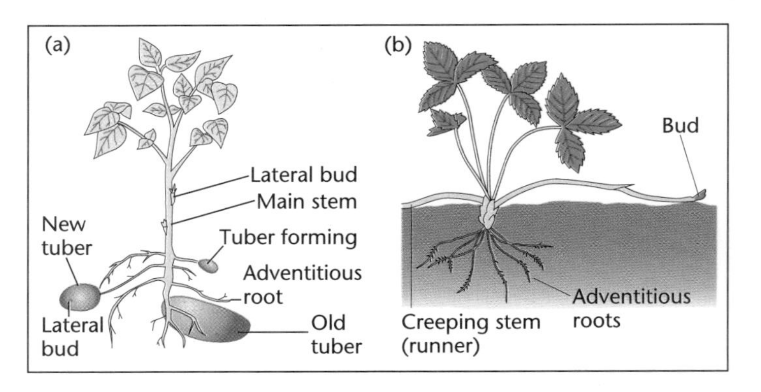

Figure 2 *(a) A single potato plant can produce many tubers. Each new tuber forms a new potato. (b) New strawberry plants grow from a runner.*

1 Explain how mitosis allows desirable characteristics to be preserved from one generation to the next.

Artificial methods

For many years plants have been propagated (multiplied) artificially by vegetative reproduction. Plant breeders make use of the plant's ability to reproduce asexually and in this way they can preserve desirable characteristics, such as hardiness. The various artificial methods used include **division**, **cuttings**, **layering** and **grafting**.

Division is the separation of one plant into several self-supporting ones. Look at figure 3. Many plants produce a mass of closely knit shoots or buds, forming a clump which can be divided. The clump can be split into sections, each with at least one shoot or bud and its own roots.

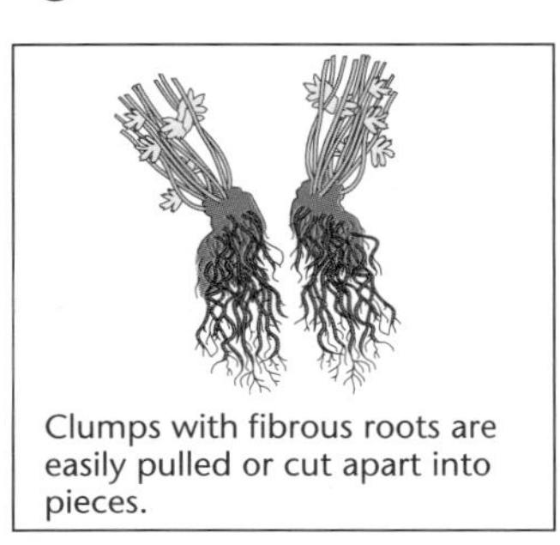

Clumps with fibrous roots are easily pulled or cut apart into pieces.

Figure 3 *Division.*

Propagation from **cuttings** uses the ability of a piece of plant tissue to reproduce into a fully developed plant, with roots and shoots. The tissue may be from the stem, leaf, root or bud. Roots that regenerate from stem, leaf or bud tissue are called **adventitious roots**.

Most cuttings are taken from a plant stem by making a cut between leaf joints or **nodes** (**internodal cutting**), or just below a node (**nodal cutting**) as shown in figure 4. The cells involved in growth are concentrated at the nodes, so most cuttings are trimmed just below a node to encourage root formation.

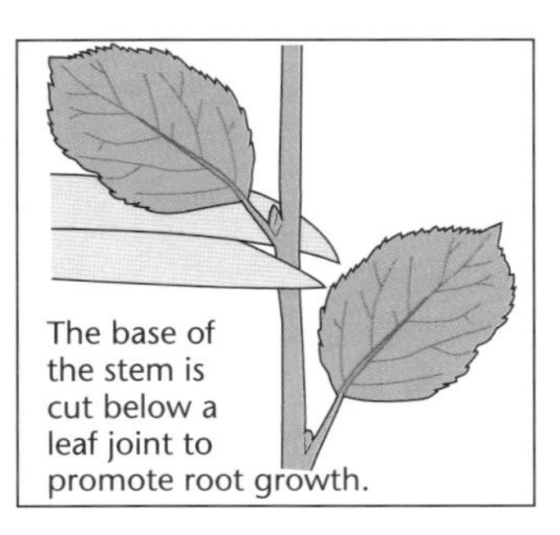

The base of the stem is cut below a leaf joint to promote root growth.

Figure 4 *Nodal cutting.*

Figure 5 shows **layering** which is used to propagate woody plants. Some plants can form new plants from buds on stems where they touch the ground. Actively growing stems are made to produce roots while they are still attached to the parent plant. The stem is buried in the soil behind its tip so that roots are encouraged in this area.

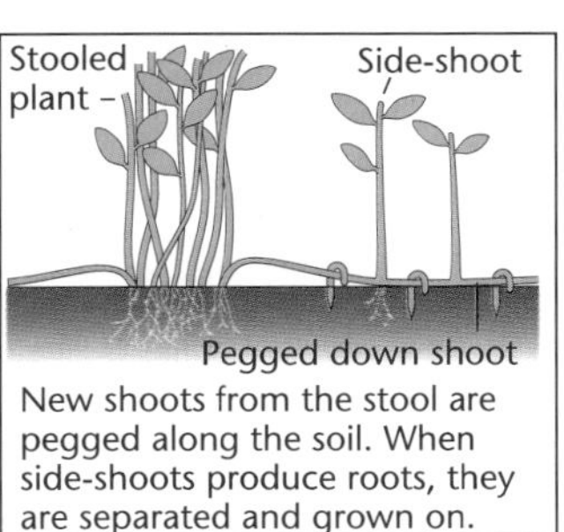

New shoots from the stool are pegged along the soil. When side-shoots produce roots, they are separated and grown on.

Figure 5 *Layering.*

Grafting, shown in figure 6, and **budding** both involve joining two separate plants so that they function as one. This creates a strong, healthy plant that has the best characteristics of its two parents. A prepared shoot (**scion**) is joined to the **rootstock**. The scion has the desired features of the shoot system, such as large fruit. The rootstock has vigorous root growth.

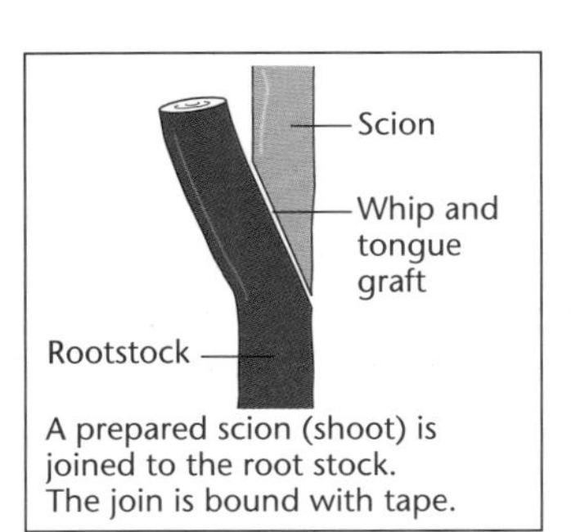

A prepared scion (shoot) is joined to the root stock. The join is bound with tape.

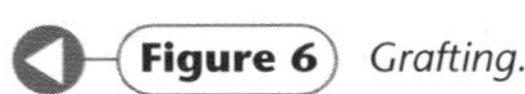

Figure 6 *Grafting.*

5 Cloning

Thanks to the scientists who brought us Dolly the sheep, cloning always seems to be in the news. In early 2000 the birth of the first cloned piglets was announced. It is being claimed that this breakthrough could mean an end to the world shortage of healthy organs for organ transplants. This leads us to the question: what is a clone? A **clone** is a group of cells or organisms that are genetically identical and have all been produced from the same original cell. Since every cell in an individual organism has the same genes it is, in theory, possible to produce a new organism from any cell or group of cells using **cloning**.

Making a clone

Even though adult cells are specialised, for example skin cells, they contain the genetic instructions from which a whole organism can be formed. Under normal circumstances only embryo cells have the ability to go through all the stages of development. A cell that has this capacity is **totipotent**. However, scientists have discovered how to make adult cells totipotent. Totipotent cells can be used to make clones.

Two major uses of cloning are the production of crops and the cloning of animals. Cloning of plants is now commonplace and relatively easy. However, the cloning of animals is less straightforward since most adult animal cells are not totipotent.

Producing better plants – propagation

Humans have been cultivating and propagating plants for many millennia. All asexual methods of plant reproduction produce clones. Since the 1950s, modern technology has led to the development of new propagation techniques. These new methods, together with modern equipment, make propagation much easier. One such method is called **plant tissue culture**, shown in figure 1.

Plant tissue culture or **micropropagation** is a form of **vegetative reproduction** used for the cloning of plants. This technique is used to propagate huge numbers of plants from a small amount of plant material. It enables us to produce plants that are difficult to propagate by traditional methods, and also new cultivars and disease-free stocks of crop plants. Tissue culture is widely used in the rapid multiplication of commercially important plant species.

Figure 1 *Plant 'seedlings' being grown in test tube cultures. Growing 'seedlings' from parts of plants, rather than from seeds, is useful for plants that are difficult to grow from seed.*

Plant tissue culture can produce many thousands of individuals of one clone. First some donor tissue is needed – this is called the **explant**. Tissue from the shoot tip (**meristem**) is most often used, but root tips, calluses (which grow on wounds), anthers, flower buds, leaves, seeds or fruits may also provide suitable tissue. Temperature, light intensity, nutrients and growth hormones are controlled. The procedure is basically the same regardless of what type of tissue is used. The photographs in figure 2 show a method of plant tissue culture that starts from seeds, and then produces clones from the seedlings.

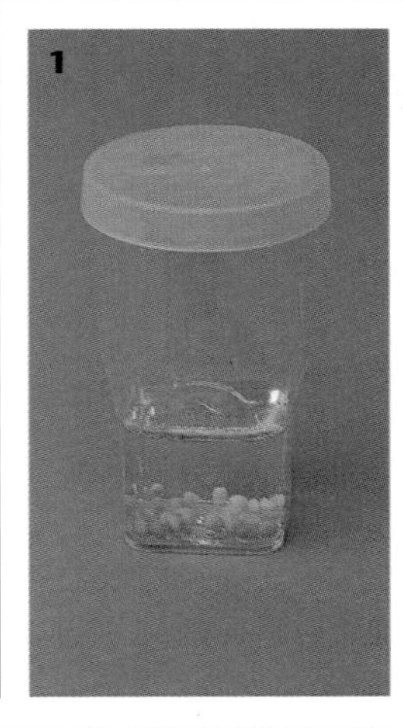

1. The seeds are surface sterilised by immersing them in a solution of sodium hypochlorite (bleach) and rinsing in sterile distilled water.
2. The seeds are transferred to a culture vessel, which contains the growth medium of nutrients set in agar.
3. Once the seedlings have grown to a height of 2 cm, explants are prepared. Here stem tissue is being used.
4. Using sterile conditions, the explant is transferred to a culture vessel, which contains a growth medium of nutrients and hormones set in agar. The explant is incubated at a constant temperature with constant light for a set period of time.

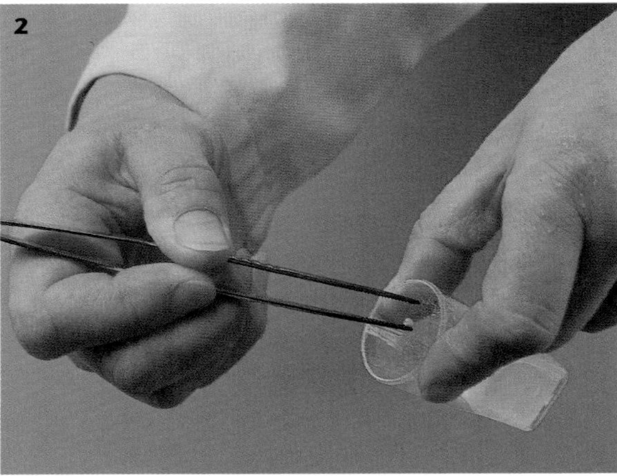

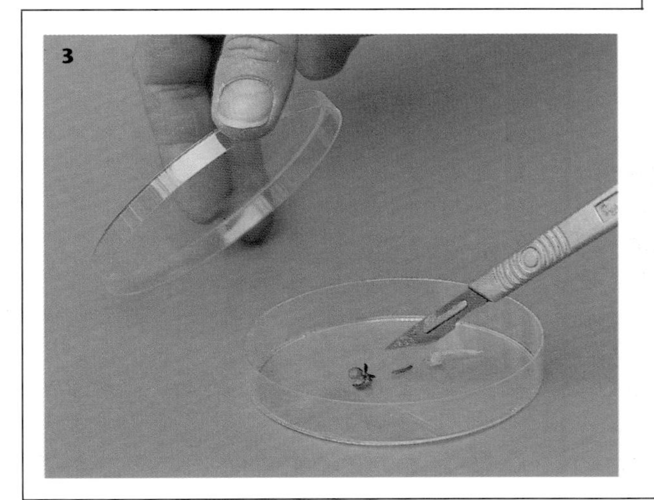

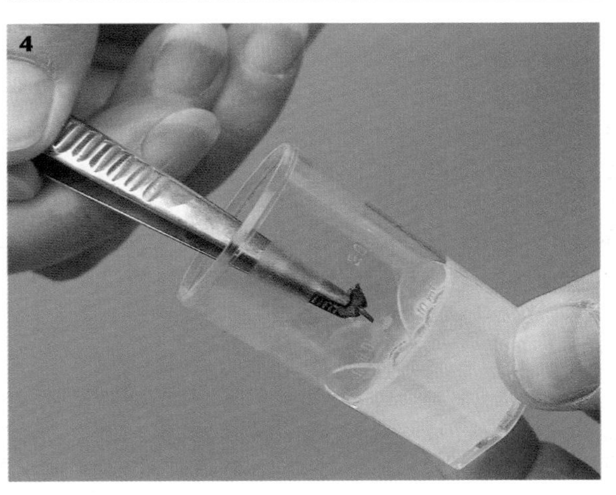

Figure 2 *Stages in plant tissue culture.*

The new shoots that develop are removed from the explant and are placed in a new culture medium. The plants are then acclimatised in special greenhouses before they can be planted outside. Each explant can initiate many pieces (calluses), and each callus can make a new plant, so large numbers of plants can be produced.

6 Cloning animal cells

Animals are more difficult to clone than plants because only embryo cells naturally have the ability to go through all the stages of development. In the 1980s a cloning method called **embryo splitting** was developed and adopted by livestock breeders. In 1997 Dolly the sheep was introduced to the world. Dolly was created using **nuclear transfer.** In January 2000, scientists announced that Tetra, a rhesus monkey, was the first primate to be produced by cloning using embryo splitting.

Embryo splitting

The division of embryos to produce identical young was first used more than 20 years ago. In this method of cloning, an early embryo is simply split into individual cells or groups of cells, as happens naturally with twins. Each cell or collection of cells develops into a new embryo. This is then placed into the uterus of a surrogate mother animal, which carries it to full term. In Tetra's case (figure 1), the embryo was split at the eight-cell stage into four two-cell embryos.

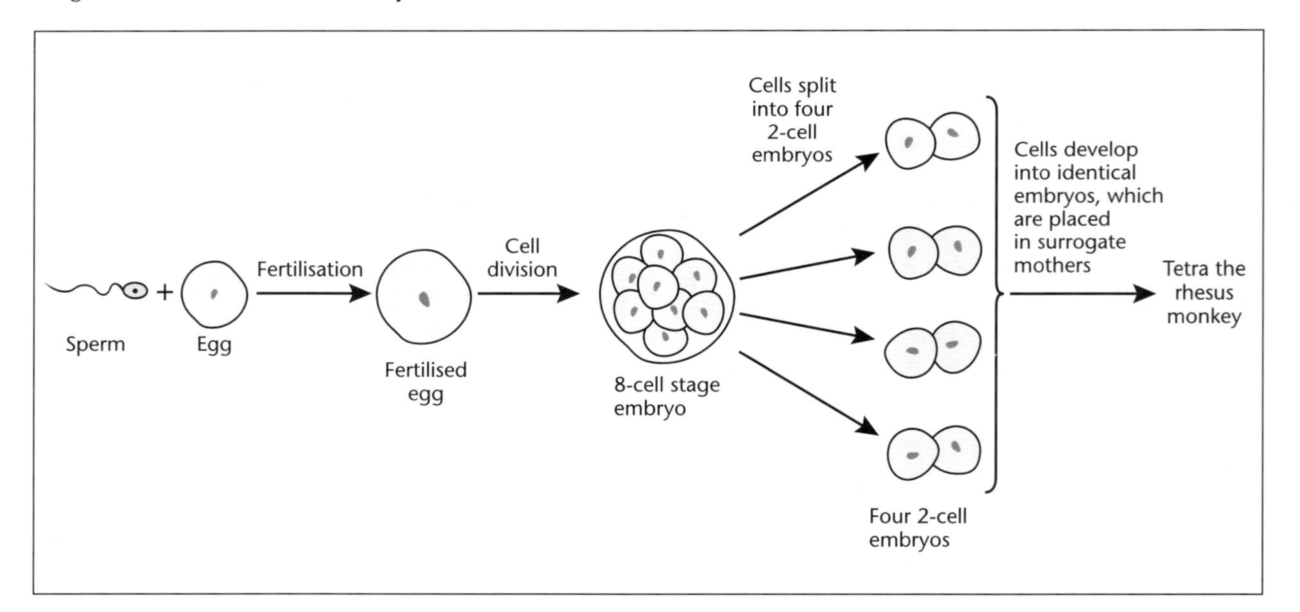

Figure 1 *Monkey embryos were created in the laboratory by combining sperm and egg cells. When the embryos grew to an eight-cell stage, they were split into four two-cell embryos. These were then nurtured into new embryos and were then implanted into the uteri of different mothers.*

Embryos divided this early in their development consist of cells each having the potential to develop into a complete animal – the cells are **totipotent**.

This method is not without its problems. The researchers made 368 embryos by splitting 107 embryos into 2- or 4-cell embryos. They obtained 4 pregnancies from 13 tries, with only one birth, Tetra.

Nuclear transfer

The disadvantage of using embryo splitting is that the clones are made from embryonic material, so it is not possible to clone an animal that has already proved its worth. The advantage of nuclear transfer is that the method allows cloning from adult cells. After many years of research most scientists believed that the cells of a mature animal are too specialised to be cloned. However, in 1997 Dolly the sheep was introduced to the world. Researchers led by Ian Wilmut had found a way.

Dolly was born in July 1996 using the method outlined in figure 2.

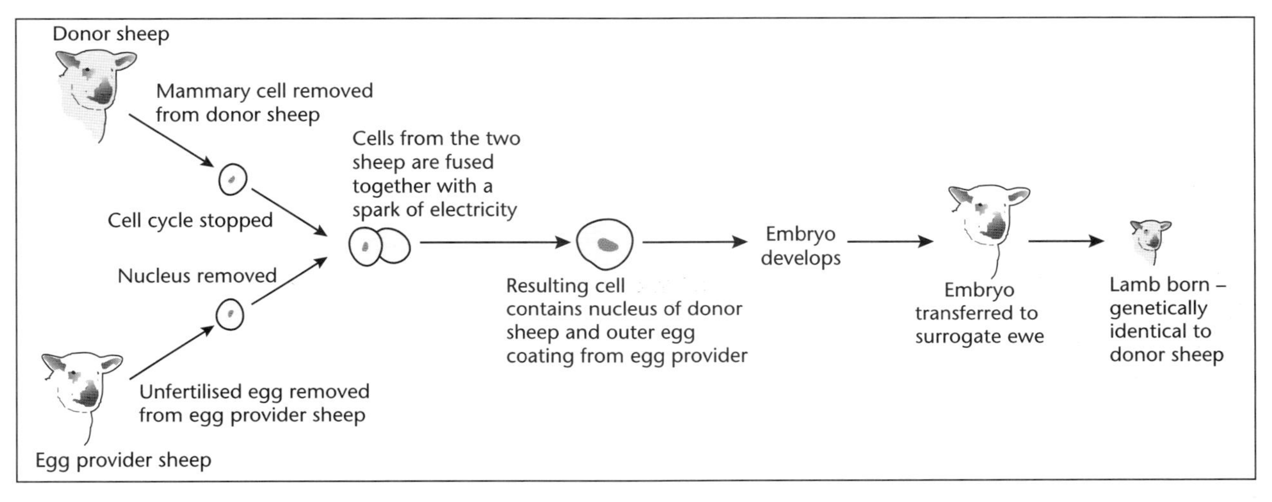

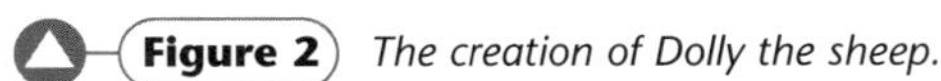
Figure 2 *The creation of Dolly the sheep.*

Wilmut and his colleagues used mammary gland cells from an adult sheep. The mammary gland cells were removed from the adult sheep and placed in a solution that starved them of nutrients and caused them to stop growing for a few days. Then, with a spark of electricity, they fused each mammary gland cell with an enucleated (without a nucleus) egg cell from a second sheep. The resulting cells were allowed to grow into embryos, which were then transplanted into surrogate ewes to complete their development.

To produce one clone, Dolly, 277 mature mammary gland cells were isolated. Although Dolly has been proved to be a clone, she is not a true clone. Clones produced by nuclear transfer have the nuclear DNA of one cell and the cytoplasmic DNA of another. However, the most important technical point of this research was that the nucleus of a specialised body cell from an adult animal could be reprogrammed to direct the development of a new animal – the cell could be restored to totipotency.

1 **By starving the mammary gland cells of nutrients, the cell cycle was stopped. Describe the events that take place during the cell cycle.**

Key ideas 142–7

Plants can be cloned using vegetative reproduction.

Animals can be cloned from embryo cells.

7 Sexual reproduction

Sexual reproduction is the production of a new individual from the fusing of two **gametes**. In animals the male gamete is the **sperm** and the female gamete is the **ovum**. This fusing is called **fertilisation**. The individual produced is unique – he or she is genetically different from either parent, but contains genetic information from both. In sexual reproduction, DNA is passed on from one generation to the next.

Battle of the sexes

In sexual reproduction the male and female gametes meet and fuse. In most species the male and female gametes are very different. Look at figure 1. You can see that the human female gamete, the **ovum**, is larger than the human male gamete, the **sperm**. The sperm swims to the ovum and fuses with it to form a fertilised egg. This will develop into the new person. The ovum's cytoplasm has many yolk droplets containing proteins and lipids, which will be used as food reserves by the developing embryo.

The sperm has a long tail and many mitochondria. Unlike the ovum, which cannot move (it is non-motile), the sperm can move itself using a swimming motion. These are not the only differences between the two. Only small numbers of ova are produced compared with the huge numbers of sperm.

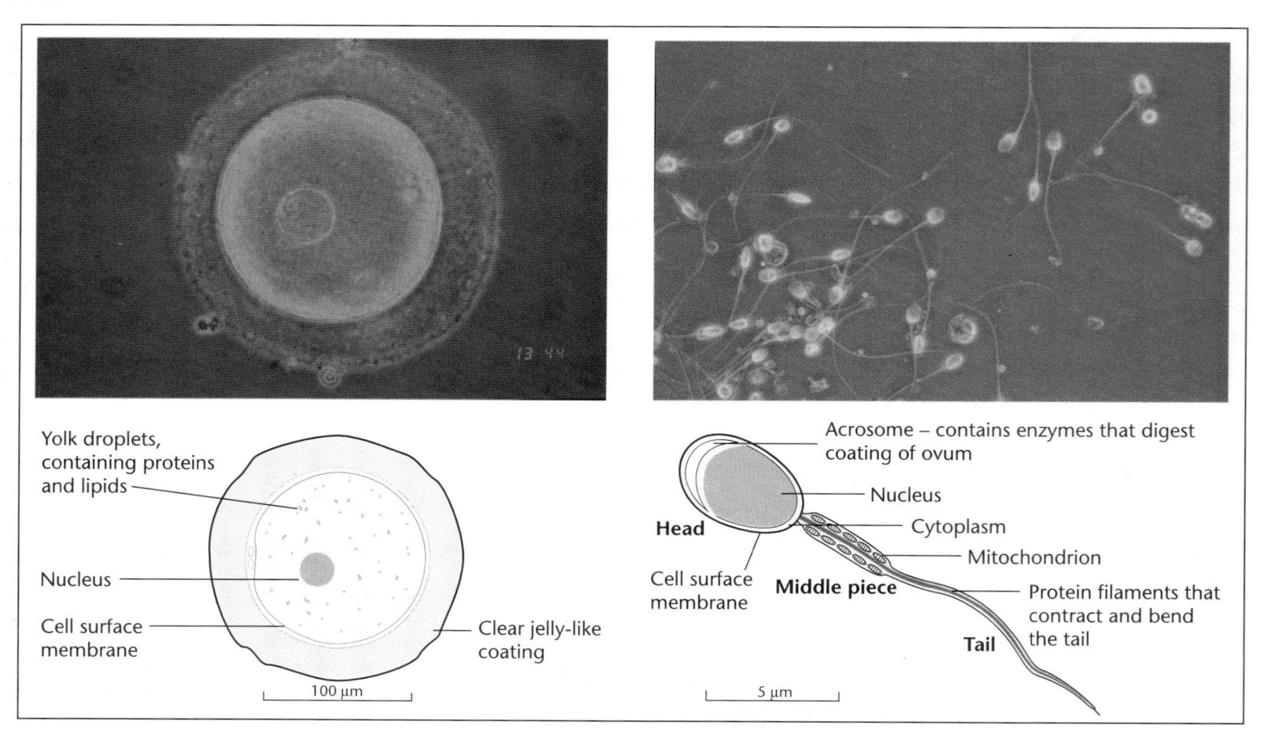

Figure 1 *Photomicrograph and diagram of (a) a human ovum (× 300) (b) a human sperm (photomicrograph × 450).*

1 Describe how:
a ova b sperm are adapted for their function.
2 Explain the advantages of having two individuals in sexual reproduction.

Getting the number right

Cells are **diploid** when the chromosomes are present in homologous pairs. In the majority of human cells there are 46 chromosomes occurring in 23 pairs.

The cell in figure 2 contains four homologous pairs of chromosomes. This cell is diploid and it has the **diploid number**, $2n$, of chromosomes. In a human cell the diploid number is 46, so $2n = 46$.

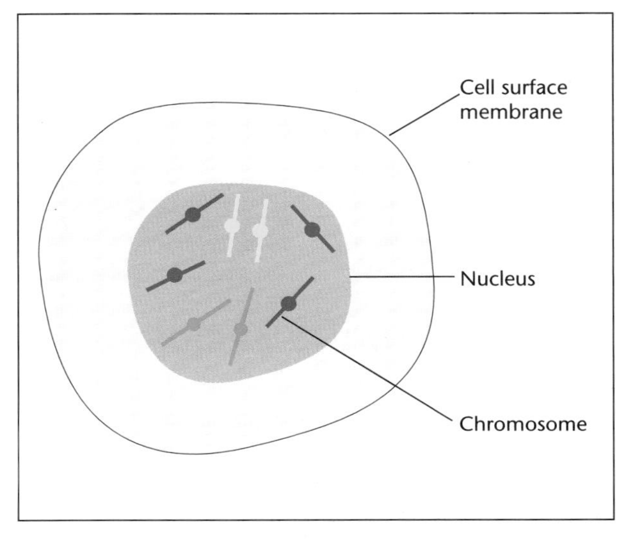

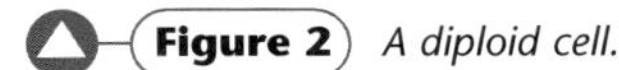
Figure 2 *A diploid cell.*

3 Look at figure 2.
a How many chromosomes are there in the nucleus?
b How many pairs of homologous chromosomes are there?
c What is the diploid number?

If two diploid human cells combined to form a new individual, the offspring would have 92 chromosomes, twice the normal number for the species. Each generation would have double the number of the previous generation and would no longer be the same species.

To avoid this, gametes contain only one chromosome from each homologous pair. We say that a gamete is a **haploid** cell. Haploid cells contain the **haploid number**, n, of chromosomes. The haploid number is half the diploid number. In a human cell the haploid number is 23, so n is 23.

As figure 3 shows, there is a change in chromosome number during sexual reproduction. These changes occur in all plants and animals. The production of gametes requires a special form of cell division called **meiosis**. In meiosis, the number of chromosomes is halved from the diploid number to the haploid number, thus producing gametes containing one chromosome from each homologous pair.

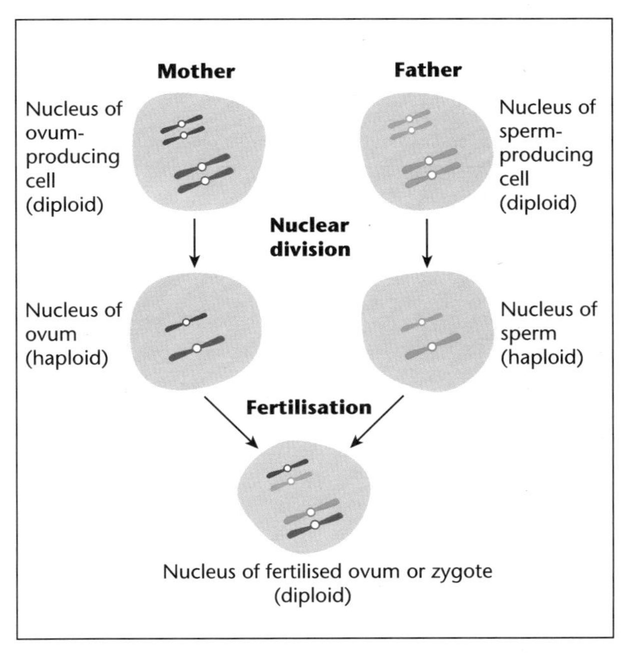

Figure 3 *How the number of chromosomes in the nucleus changes with gamete production and fertilisation. Only two pairs of chromosomes are shown for simplicity.*

8 Life cycles

Meiosis produces haploid gametes. When the gametes fuse at fertilisation to form a zygote, the diploid number is restored. This keeps the chromosome number constant from generation to generation.

You have seen that asexual reproduction involves mitosis. No gametes are produced and the offspring are identical with the parent. In sexual reproduction haploid gametes are produced by meiosis, and the offspring are not identical with the parents. Since every major group of organism carries out sexual reproduction, it would seem that sexual reproduction has advantages over asexual reproduction. Some species use both sexual and asexual reproduction at different stages of their life cycles.

A variety of life cycles

The life cycle of humans and of most other organisms follows the plan outlined in figure 1. In different species the zygote develops into the adult by different processes, but the basic division of the life cycle into diploid and haploid stages is the same.

The life cycle of many plants, especially mosses and ferns, shows an **alternation of generations**. A haploid gamete-producing adult plant called a **gametophyte** alternates with a diploid spore-producing stage called a **sporophyte**. Look at the life cycle of a moss in figure 2. You can see that meiosis and fertilisation divide the life cycle into haploid and diploid stages.

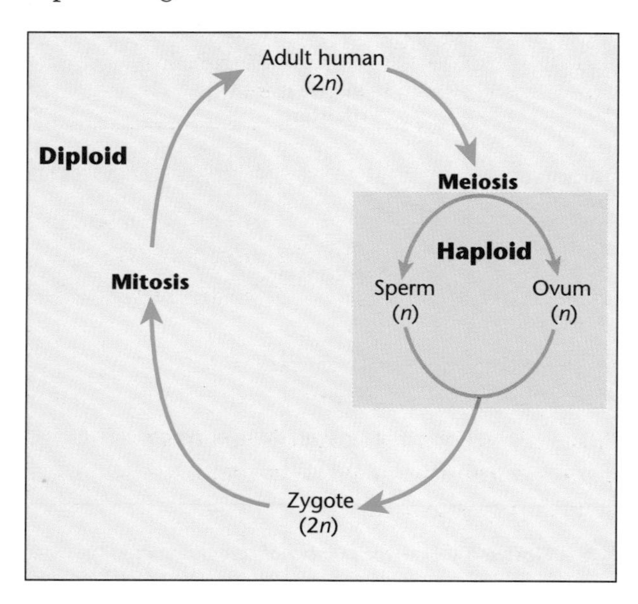

Figure 1 *The life cycle of a human. n = haploid, 2n = diploid.*

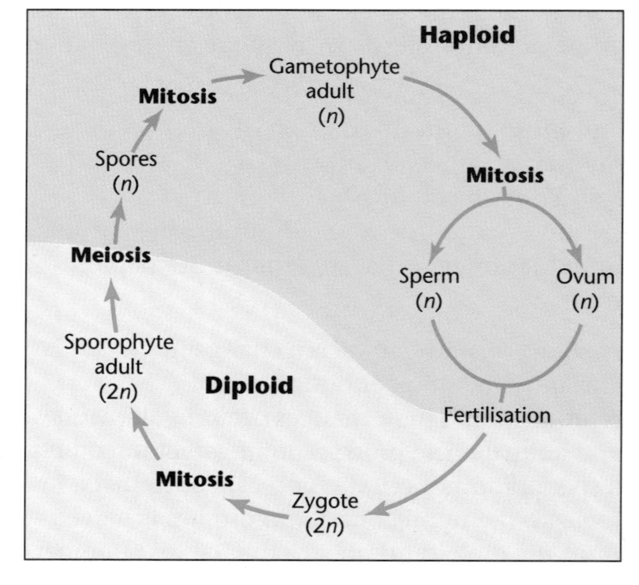

Figure 2 *The life cycle of a moss.*

More life cycles

Obelia geniculata, shown in figure 3, is also known as a sea-fir. It is a colony of tiny anemones attached in patterns to a communal stalk. *Obelia* is interesting because it has two body forms in its life cycle – the **polyp** and the **medusa**. The polyp is an immobile form. It reproduces by a process called budding, giving rise to the **medusa**, the active free-living swimming form of the animal.

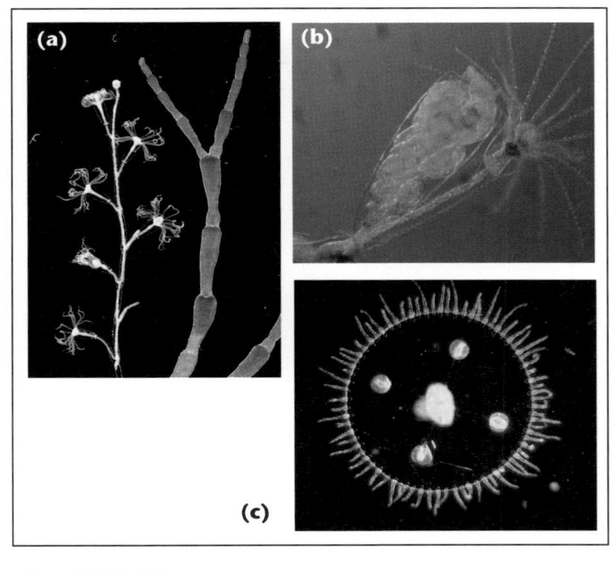

Figure 3 *(a)* Obelia geniculata *colony (next to a red alga). (b) A polyp budding, showing developing medusae. (c) A medusa.*

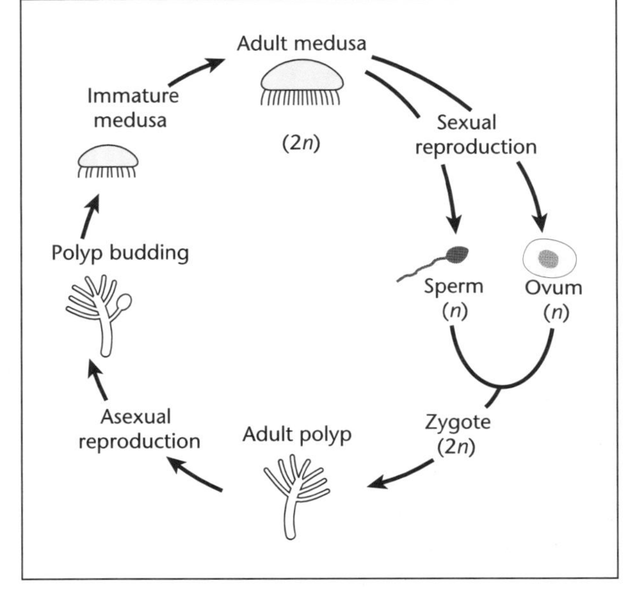

Figure 4 *The life cycle of* Obelia geniculata.

1 The life cycle of *Obelia* is shown in figure 4. Draw a simple sketch of the life cycle to show where mitosis, meiosis and fertilisation have occurred. On your diagram use $2n$ and n to show which stages in the life cycle are diploid and which are haploid.

Key ideas 148–51

Sexual reproduction involves gamete production and fertilisation.

In sexual reproduction, DNA from one generation is passed to the next by gametes.

Male and female gametes differ in terms of size, numbers produced and mobility.

During meiosis, cells containing pairs of homologous chromosomes divide to produce gametes containing one chromosome from each homologous pair.

In meiosis, the number of chromosomes is reduced from the diploid number ($2n$) to the haploid number (n).

The diploid number is restored when gametes fuse at fertilisation.

Meiosis is important because it ensures a constant chromosome number from generation to generation.

Unit 8 – Questions

9

(1) The photomicrographs in figure 1 show stages of mitosis in bean cells (×500).

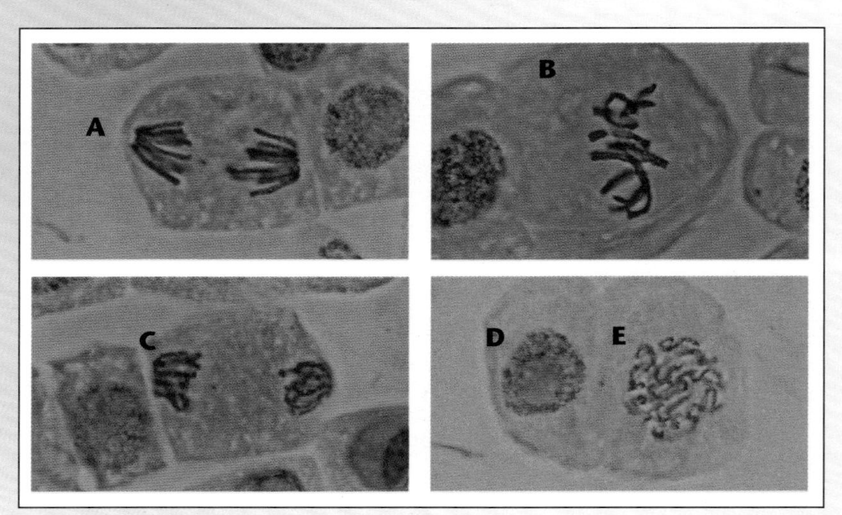

Figure 1

a) Using the letters **A** to **E**, list the stages according to the order in which they occur. (2 marks)

b) Describe the events that are taking place in each of the lettered cells. (10 marks)

(Total 12 marks)

(2) Microscope slides were prepared using the growing root tip of an onion root. The number of cells at each stage of mitosis was counted and the results are shown in table 1.

Stage of mitosis	Interphase	Prophase	Metaphase	Anaphase	Telophase
Number of cells	449	11	6	24	13

a) Calculate the percentage time spent in interphase. (1 mark)

b) Describe the events that occur during interphase. (3 marks)

c) What conclusions can be made about the time spent in each stage of mitosis? (3 marks)

(Total 7 marks)

③ Figure 2 shows the life cycle of a common fern.

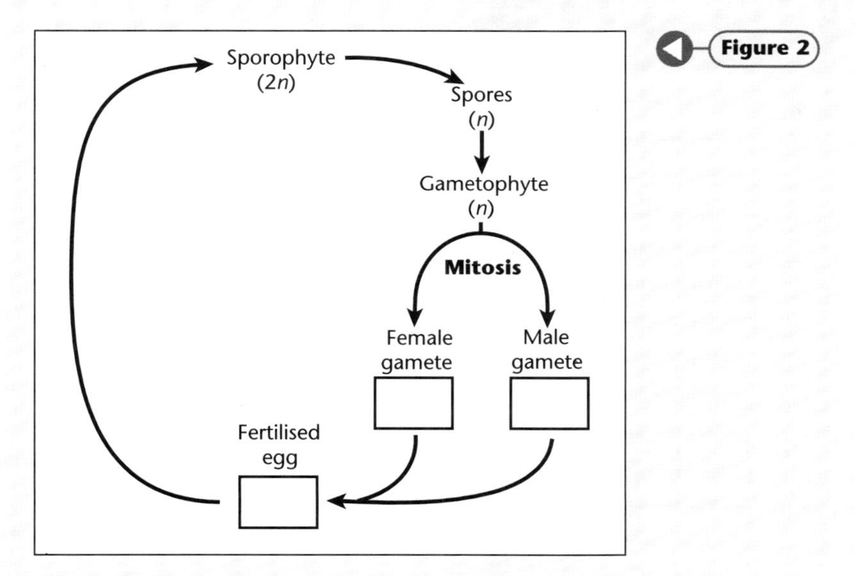

Figure 2

a) Sketch the diagram. Complete the boxes on your sketch to show which stages are haploid (*n*) and which are diploid (2*n*). (3 marks)

b) Mark with the letter M on your sketch the point at which meiosis occurs. (1 mark)

(Total 4 marks)

④ The diploid number of a cat is 38. How many chromosomes would you expect to find in:

a) a female gamete

b) a male gamete

c) a kidney cell?

(Total 3 marks)

⑤ Gamete production involves meiosis.

a) i) What are gametes? (1 mark)

ii) How do gametes differ from normal cells? (1 mark)

b) i) State what happens during meiosis. (2 marks)

ii) Explain why meiosis is important. (2 marks)

c) Suggest a reason why it may be an advantage to some organisms to have both a haploid and a diploid body stage in their life cycle. (1 mark)

(Total 7 marks)

⑥ Animal and plant cells can be cloned.

a) Describe how plants are produced using vegetative propagation. (4 marks)

b) Animals are more difficult to clone than plants. Give a reason why this is the case. (1 mark)

c) Describe how animals are cloned from embryo cells. (4 marks)

(Total 9 marks)

1 Engineering genes

Genetic engineering is a term used to describe all the different techniques used to extract, separate and transfer genes from one organism (the **donor**) to another organism (the **recipient**). Genetic engineering is also called **recombinant gene technology**. First a useful gene is identified and is extracted from the donor. The gene is cloned to produce many copies. These cloned genes may be used in different ways, such as:

1. for studying gene action
2. inserted into another organism to improve some feature of the organism
3. inserted into another organism so that it will synthesise **gene products** – proteins or hormones that are useful in medicine or agriculture.

Cloning genes

Figure 1 shows how the required gene is cut out of the donor DNA and cloned either in a bacterium or in a test tube.

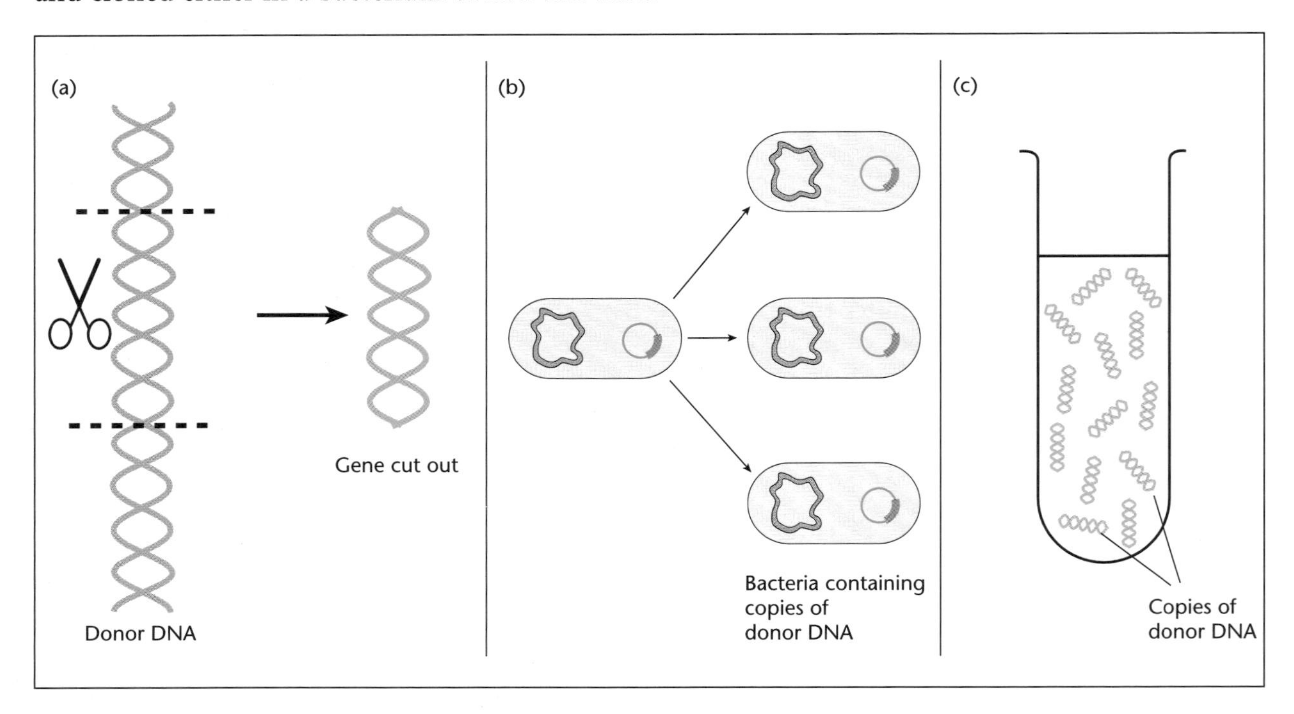

Figure 1 *(a) The required gene is cut out of the DNA of the donor organism using enzymes.*
(b) This gene may be inserted into the DNA of a bacterium using enzymes. The gene is cloned by growing the bacteria in large numbers.
(c) Alternatively, the gene may be replicated in a test tube using enzymes.

Transferring into a recipient

Once cloned, the required gene is transferred into a recipient organism where it will have its useful effect. The gene is often attached to a **vector** to carry it into its new cell. To allow the gene to function in its new cell, it then has to be attached to the DNA of the cell. If the recipient is a plant or animal cell, the gene is attached to the chromosomes. If the recipient is a bacterial cell, the gene may be inserted into a ring of DNA called a **plasmid**. Plasmids are found in the cytoplasm of some bacteria.

The recipient may use the information in the transferred DNA to synthesise gene products. Gene products are the proteins synthesised by transcription and translation of DNA.

1 Describe how the processes of transcription and translation could produce a gene product in a genetically engineered organism.

Figure 2 shows how animals, plants and bacteria can all be genetically engineered to make gene products. This is one use of genetic engineering. Another is producing organisms that have some useful feature, such as plants that have resistance to pests.

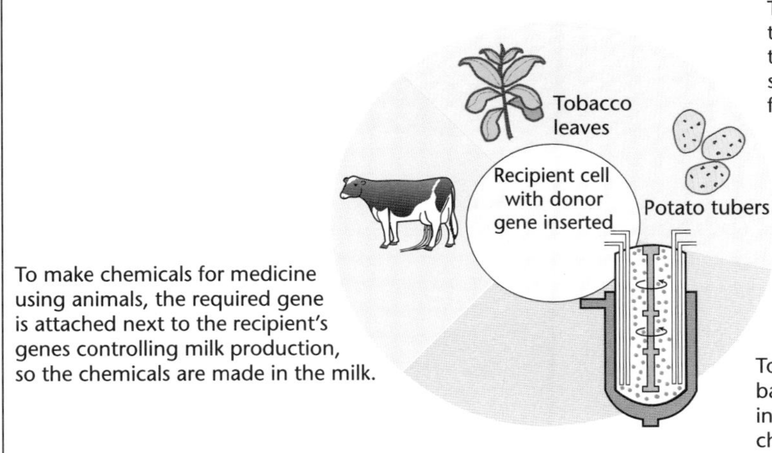

Figure 2 *Transferred genes are used in a variety of ways to make gene products, as shown here.*

Key ideas 154–5

Genes are transferred from a donor organism to a recipient organism using recombinant DNA technology.

Genes are cut from the chromosomes of the donor and joined to the genes of the recipient using enzymes.

Recipient organisms may use the donated genes to synthesise gene products.

2 Transferring genes

Genes can be removed from one organism (the donor) and inserted into another organism (the recipient) using genetic engineering. One use of this technology is to change the genes of a recipient organism. To be useful, the transferred genes must be taken up by the genetic material already present in the recipient organism.

Using scissors – cutting DNA

The first stage in genetic engineering involves finding and removing the gene of interest. You will remember that genes are found at specific loci on chromosomes. Before a gene is transferred it must first be separated from the chromosome using enzymes which cut DNA. These enzymes are called **restriction endonucleases**. Each of these enzymes recognises a specific sequence of bases within DNA called a **restriction site**.

Figure 1 shows the action of one such enzyme. It catalyses the hydrolysis of bonds between the nucleotides. When the enzyme cuts, it leaves a single-stranded section of DNA called a **sticky end** on the DNA.

The DNA of the recipient organism is cut using the same restriction endonuclease. This produces sticky ends complementary to those on the donor DNA.

1. **What is hydrolysis?**
2. **Using your knowledge of enzyme action, explain why a restriction endonuclease is used to cut the required section of DNA from the donor.**
3. **Explain why the DNA of the recipient organism is cut using the same restriction enzyme as that used to cut out the donor DNA.**

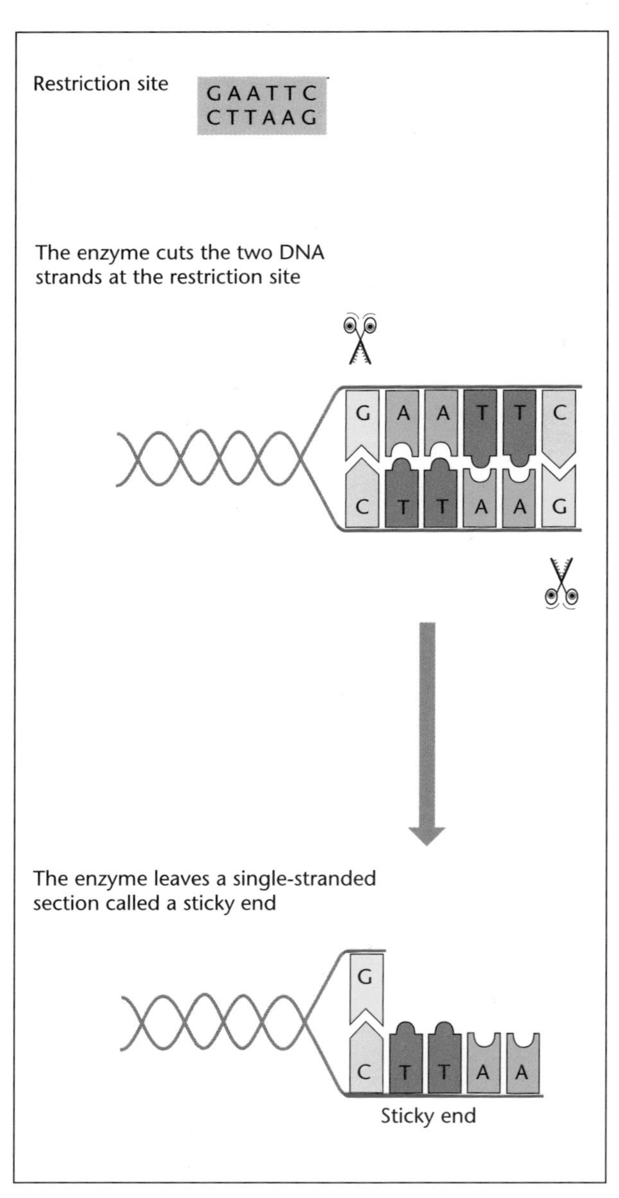

Figure 1 *The action of a restriction endonuclease.*

Using glue – joining DNA

The DNA from each organism has been cut using a restriction endonuclease. The next step is to join these pieces of DNA to produce a molecule of **recombinant DNA** (DNA from two organisms). The enzyme **ligase** is used to join the DNA together. The sticky ends help the DNA to join more easily.

4 What sort of reaction does ligase catalyse?

One way of making recombinant DNA is shown in figure 2. Notice how the sticky ends of the two different DNA molecules base pair and ligase closes the gap in the strands.

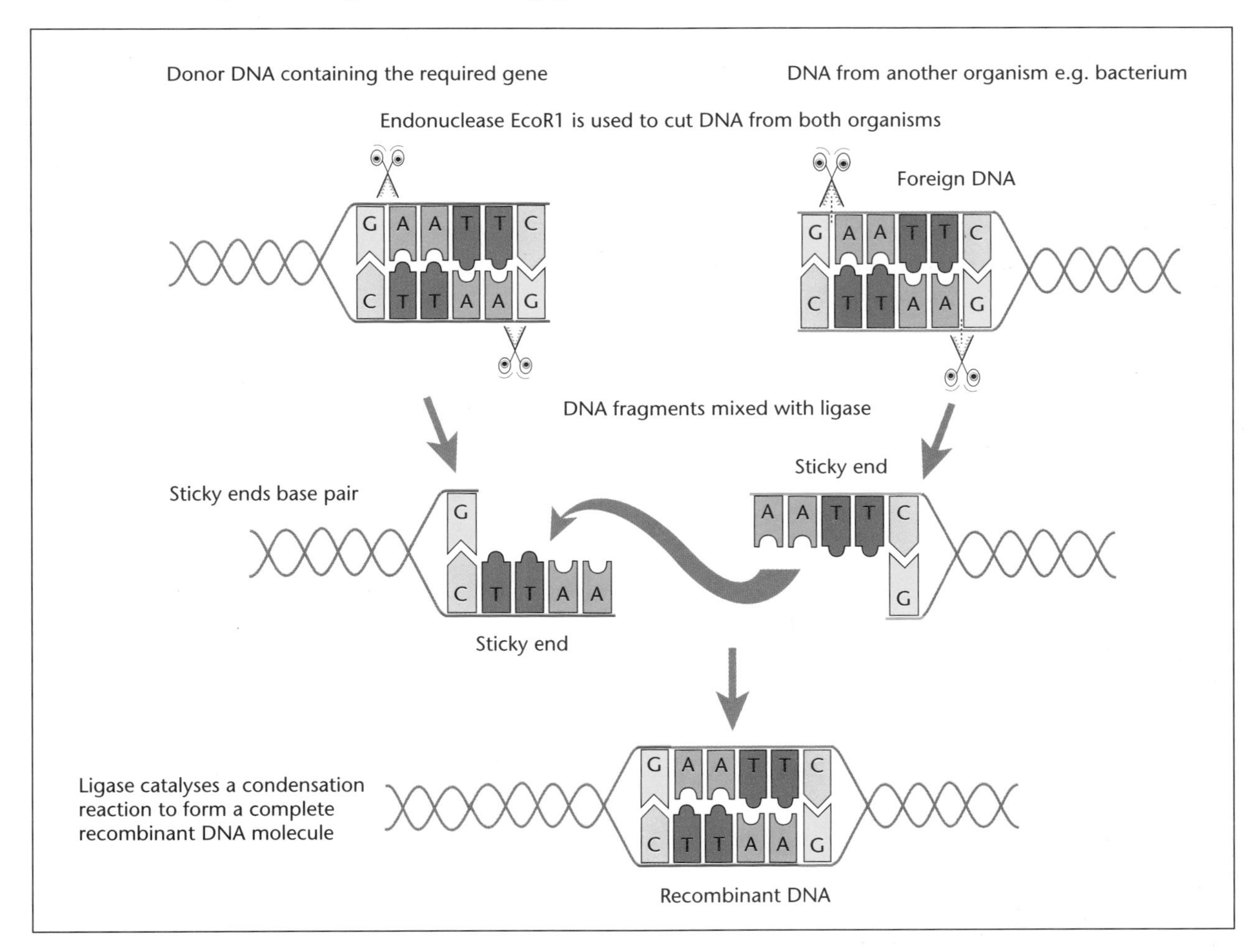

Figure 2 *Making recombinant DNA.*

Key ideas 156–7

In genetic engineering, genes are taken from a donor organism and inserted into a recipient organism.

Restriction endonuclease enzymes are used to cut the required sections of DNA.

Ligase enzyme is used to join DNA from two different organisms.

3 Putting genes into bacteria

Microorganisms are widely used as recipient cells to receive transferred genes from another organism. If bacteria are mixed with fragments of DNA, some of the DNA can enter the cell. **Plasmids** are used to speed this up. Plasmids are small circular pieces of DNA found in bacteria, separate from the main bacterial DNA. Bacteria take up plasmids from their surroundings very easily, so using a plasmid increases the chances of transferring a gene into a bacterium.

Cutting and joining plasmids

Plasmids are used as **vectors** (carriers) to transfer donor genes into recipient bacteria cells. The steps in the procedure are described in figure 1.

Once the donor gene has been joined to the plasmid using ligase enzyme, the recombinant plasmid is put into a bacterial cell. When the bacterial cell divides, it produces new cells which also contain the recombinant plasmid. Bacterial cells reproduce rapidly, allowing the transferred gene to be cloned and so producing many copies of the gene.

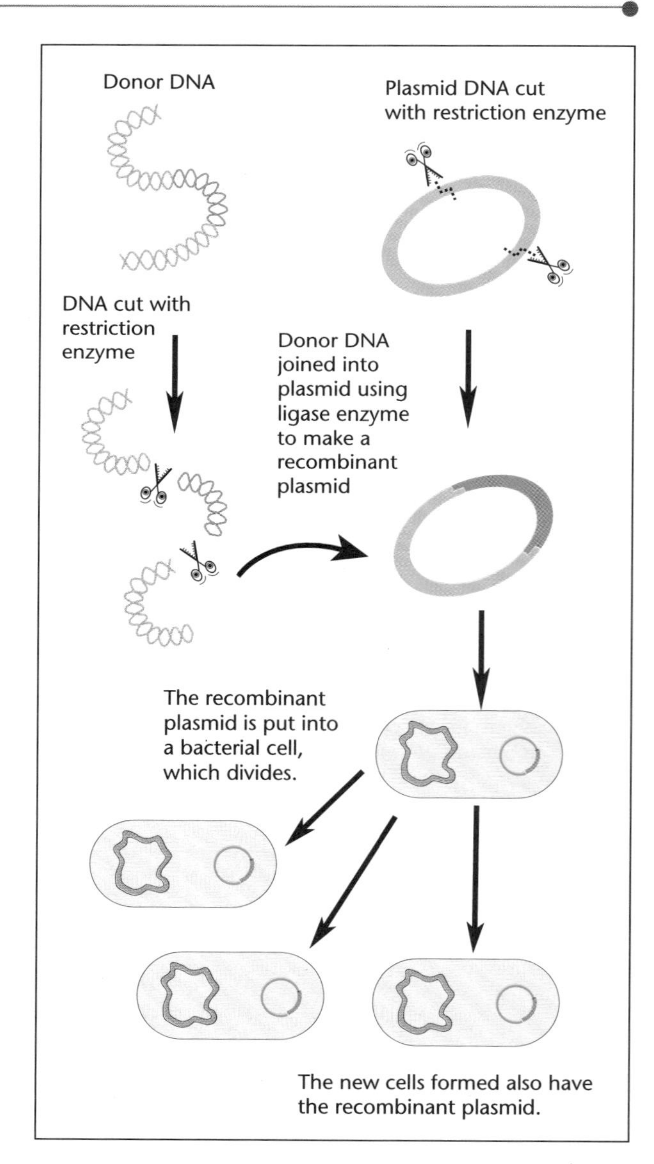

Figure 1 *How a gene is inserted into a plasmid.*

Genetic markers

Plasmids contain genes that give bacteria antibiotic resistance. These genes are used as **genetic markers** in genetic engineering. Plasmids containing genes for resistance to two antibiotics, ampicillin and tetracycline, are commonly used as vectors. This makes it possible to detect the bacterial cells that contain the genetically engineered plasmids later in the process.

Look at figure 2 showing a plasmid containing genes for resistance to the two antibiotics. The gene to be transferred will be joined at a site within the tetracycline resistance gene. This disrupts the sequence of bases in the tetracycline resistance gene, so the tetracycline resistance is destroyed. When the recombinant plasmid is put into a bacterial cell, the bacterium will only be resistant to ampicillin.

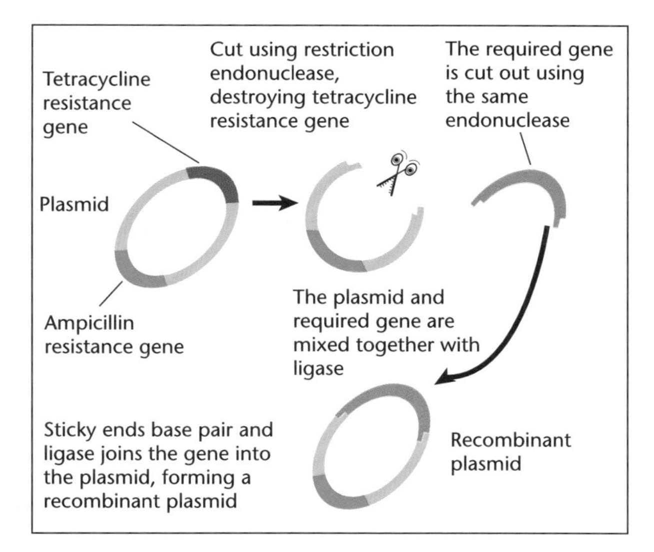

Figure 2 *A plasmid with two antibiotic resistance genes. These genes are used as genetic markers.*

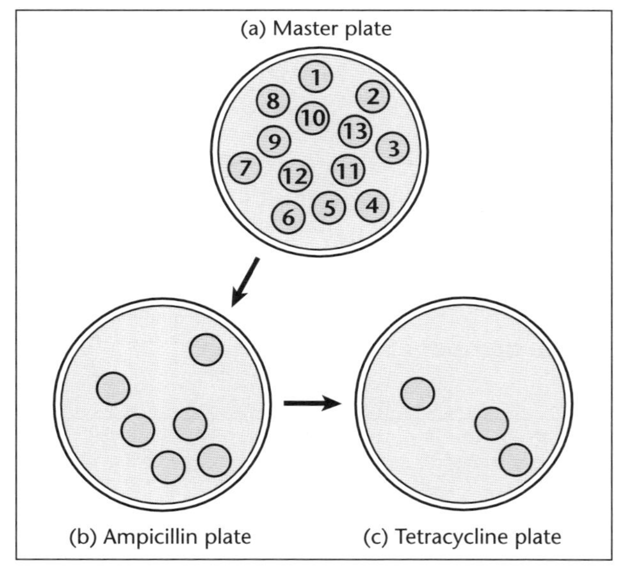

Figure 3 *Replica plating.*

After the plasmids and bacteria have been mixed, the bacterial cells that have taken up the recombinant plasmids need to be separated out. Look at figure 3(a). You can see that the bacteria are grown on culture plates where they form visible clusters called **colonies**. Each colony is formed from one cell, so all the bacterial cells in a colony are identical.

The colonies are then transferred to the same position on a new plate. This has a culture medium containing ampicillin, as shown in figure 3(b). Only those bacteria containing the ampicillin resistance gene will grow. Any bacteria that did not take up the plasmid do not have this gene, so they will not grow.

Figure 3(c) shows that the colonies that have grown on the plate containing ampicillin are now transferred onto plates containing tetracycline. This is called **replica plating**. Bacteria that contain the recombinant plasmid cannot grow in the presence of tetracycline, since the tetracycline resistance gene has been inactivated. By comparing the two plates, any colonies that are resistant to ampicillin but not to tetracycline can be identified.

Q

1 Which of the bacteria colonies on the master plate in figure 3 contain recombinant plasmids?

Once detected, the bacteria containing the transferred gene can be grown (cultured) on a large scale in industrial fermenters. Useful substances such as antibiotics, hormones and enzymes have been produced in this way.

Key ideas 158–9

Plasmids are used as vectors to transfer genes into bacteria.

Rapid reproduction of bacteria allows a transferred gene to be cloned, producing many copies of the gene.

Genetic markers in plasmids and replica plating can be used to detect bacterial cells that contain genetically engineered plasmids.

Bacteria containing a transferred gene can be grown on a large scale in industrial fermenters.

Antibiotics, hormones and enzymes have been produced using genetically engineered bacteria.

4 Improving nature

Some people inherit genetic disorders caused by faults in their genes. Many of these disorders are due to mutations of DNA. Changes in DNA can lead to changes in enzyme activity which results in faulty metabolism. Some human genes can be cloned in bacteria using methods like those described on the previous pages, and then transferred into humans to treat a genetically inherited disorder. This is **gene therapy**.

The cystic fibrosis story

You will remember that membranes contain proteins that are used in active transport of ions across the membrane. One carrier protein is used to transport chloride ions (Cl^-) across the membrane. This carrier protein is called **CFTR**. Cystic fibrosis is caused by the mutation of a gene that codes for CFTR. Look at the gene for normal CFTR in figure 1.

Base 1627

GGACCGTGGTAATTTCTTTTATAGTAGAAACCACCAAGGATACTACTTATATCT

Code for 449th amino acid

Figure 1 *Part of the gene coding for normal CFTR protein.*

You may need to refer back to pages 124–5 to answer questions on this page.

1. **How many amino acids are coded for by this part of the gene?**
2. **The cystic fibrosis mutation has nucleotides missing at positions 1654–1656.**
   a. **What is the sequence of the mutant DNA?**
   b. **What effect does this mutation have on the number of amino acids in the protein?**

Figure 2 shows the effect of the faulty protein. You can see that there are too many chloride ions inside the cell. This causes water to enter the cells from the intercellular fluid.

The effects of this imbalance are most noticeable in cells covered by a layer of mucus. The mucus has too little water, making it very thick. In the breathing system the mucus lining the air passages is difficult to move, so mucus builds up. People with cystic fibrosis have persistent coughs, suffer from chest infections most of the time and their gas exchange is reduced.

In the intestines the thick mucus blocks ducts, interfering with the secretion of digestive juices and with absorption of digested food.

In the reproductive system, ducts carrying gametes may be blocked.

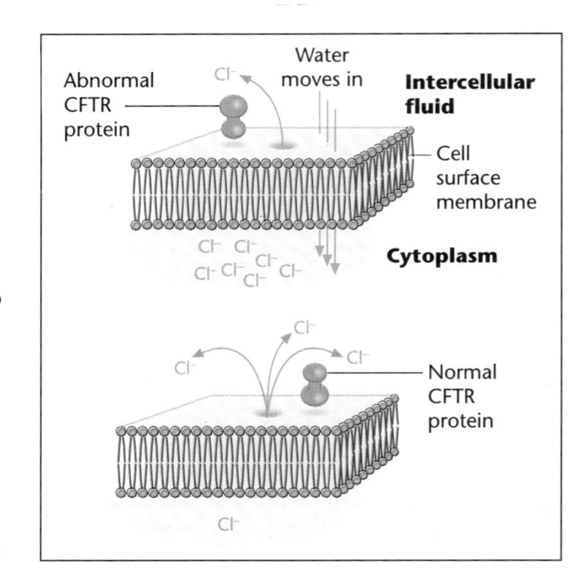

Figure 2 *The effect of abnormal CFTR protein.*

3 **Explain why too many chloride ions in cells cause water to enter from the intercellular fluid.**

4 **Explain why gas exchange is reduced by thick mucus in the lungs.**

5 **Name the ducts in the digestive system likely to be blocked by mucus.**

By-passing the fault

To treat cystic fibrosis, a cloned gene of normal CFTR is introduced into the body. To work properly, the cloned gene has to enter cells and attach to a chromosome. Human cells do not have plasmids, so another vector is used to carry the gene into cells. The vectors are mixed in a liquid and squirted into the nasal cavities using a spray similar to those used by people with asthma.

Look at figure 3 which shows one type of vector used for human cells. A virus is used instead of a plasmid. This virus is able to enter epithelial cells in the breathing system. The CFTR gene is inserted into the virus DNA using the same methods as for plasmids. Parts of the virus DNA are removed to prevent it replicating inside the cells and causing infections. The virus DNA attaches to a human chromosome and the CFTR gene codes for a normal membrane protein. In trials of this method the transferred gene has been unstable, so treatment has to be repeated regularly. There is also the risk of a response to virus antigens.

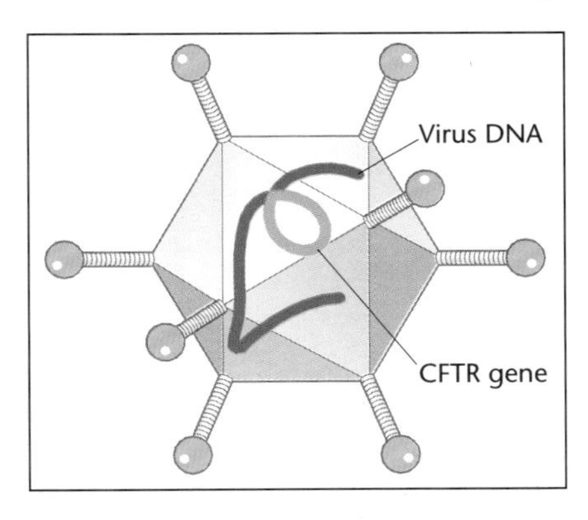

Figure 3 *Viruses are used as vectors in the treatment of cystic fibrosis.*

6 **Explain how a response to virus antigens would make the treatment unsuccessful.**

7 **Explain why most CFTR genes carried in a liposome do not reach the nucleus.**

The second vector that has been used is a **liposome**. Liposomes are microscopic fluid-filled pouches made by mixing lipids with water or water solutions. Liposomes containing the cloned CFTR gene are sprayed into the lungs. The membranes of liposomes contain sugars that are recognised by cell membrane receptors. The liposomes then enter the cell by endocytosis as described on page 79. In trials of this method very little of the CFTR reaches the nucleus, so it has limited success.

Problems with gene therapy

Like all new treatments for disease, gene therapy is expensive. It takes a long time to produce a usable product and to find a way of getting the cloned gene to the cells where it is needed.

Key ideas 160–61

Gene therapy is transferring genes with a normal function into cells with faulty genes.

Vectors used for gene therapy in humans are viruses and liposomes.

Cystic fibrosis treatments have been trialled with limited success.

5 Altered animals

Bacteria may be used to clone human genes. However, it is more efficient to use animal cells rather than bacterial cells to synthesise human gene products. This is because protein synthesis in bacteria is different, and so an artificial human gene has to be made and inserted into the bacterium rather than isolating the gene from human DNA. In addition many human gene products are changed in the cell after they are synthesised by adding carbohydrates. Bacteria cannot carry out these modifications.

Synthesis in sheep

Humans secrete an enzyme called **alpha-1-antitrypsin**. This enzyme helps to protect the lungs from damage during an infection. It is used in the treatment of cystic fibrosis and emphysema. The gene is obtained from human cells and is cloned using bacteria. Figure 1 shows the stages in transferring this cloned gene into a sheep. An animal that contains a gene from another organism is called a **transgenic** animal.

The transgenic zygotes are put back into the uterus of the female sheep using another, larger syringe. These sheep are surrogate mothers as the zygote is different from the original. The new lambs will contain the human gene. When they reach reproductive age and breed, the females produce milk containing the enzyme alpha-1-antitrypsin. The enzyme can be extracted from the milk and used in medicine.

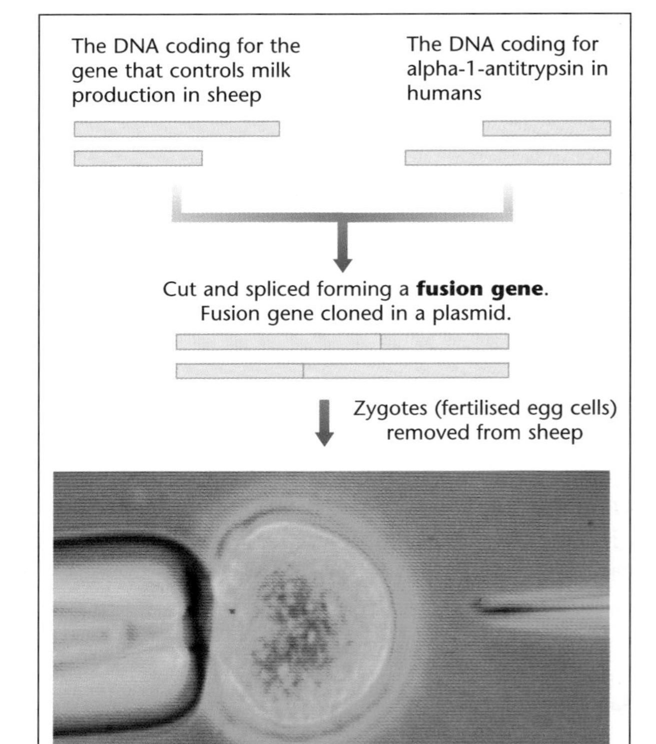

Figure 1 *The stages in transferring a cloned human gene into a sheep.*

Animal exploitation

Animals have been genetically modified for many purposes. Look at the following two summaries of some potential effects of genetically modified animals.

Sheep used for producing alpha-1-antitrypsin make 30 g of enzyme per litre of milk. Each litre of this milk is worth over £700. It is estimated that world demand for this enzyme could be met by about 2000 genetically engineered female sheep. The donor animals are not stressed by the process. The same enzyme obtained by the more traditional methods of extraction from blood is more variable in quality. It may also contain more impurities that cause allergic reactions in patients using the enzyme. Other human proteins could also be produced by this method, such as clotting proteins for haemophiliacs and CFTR for cystic fibrosis sufferers.

Figure 2 *Using genetically engineered animals to make human gene products is a controversial subject. What do you think about it?*

The quality of food has been improved by transferring genes into farm animals. Genes that improve the growth rate and increase resistance to disease have been used. This produces animals that are able to survive on poorer quality grassland, or can resist drought. Such developments may have great potential benefits as land becomes scarcer and the human population grows. There is however concern about the ethics of developing such animals. It can be argued that the techniques used by genetic engineers copy those used by nature, and are similar to traditional methods of selective breeding that farmers have used for centuries. However, many people believe that human interference in life processes is not acceptable.

Human rights

If sheep can be genetically changed, then so can humans. Genetic engineering techniques exist that make it possible to transfer genes into human zygotes. Currently this is not an accepted practice. Why not? Few people would disagree with the use of gene therapy to cure defects such as sickle-cell anaemia or cystic fibrosis. However, if it becomes possible to alter complex features such as intelligence and athletic ability, there is concern about whether it would be felt desirable to carry out such changes, and about who would decide what changes should be made to the human race.

Figure 3 *If humans were genetically altered, who would have the say as to what characteristics are desirable?*

1 List the issues raised by the potential genetic modifications described on these two pages. You should think about the ethical concerns over rearing genetically modified farm animals, and also the transferring of genes into human zygotes.

Key ideas 162–3

Genes from other organisms can be transferred into animals to make transgenic animals.

Transgenic animals may be used to produce human gene products.

The quality and quantity of food may be improved by transferring genes from other organisms.

6 Altered plants

Plants have been genetically modified to improve the quality of food and to help farmers control pests. It is also possible to use transgenic plants to produce human gene products and vaccines. The development of **genetically modified** or **GM crops** is one of the fastest-growing industries, used in both food and medicine production.

Genetic weeding

One way of genetically modifying crops gives them resistance to the herbicide (weedkiller) glyphosate. This herbicide works at low concentrations, is not toxic to humans and is rapidly broken down by soil microorganisms. It works by inhibiting an enzyme used by chloroplasts in amino acid synthesis.

Look at figure 1, which shows how a glyphosate-resistant plant is produced. You can see that a plasmid is used in the same way as described on page 158. The plasmid used is called a **Ti plasmid** because it causes plants to produce tumours (Ti = tumour-inducing). This plasmid is found in a bacterium called *Agrobacterium* which can infect plants, causing swelling on shoots. A gene coding for the production of an enzyme used to synthesise amino acids is spliced into the Ti plasmid, making a recombinant plasmid. *Agrobacterium* containing the recombinant plasmid are added to plant leaf cells growing in a culture.

The plasmid attaches the new gene into the plant chromosome. These plasmid genes cause the plant cells to divide rapidly and form a mass of non-specialised cells called a **callus**. The plant cells that contain the plasmid are found by growing the calluses on a growth medium containing glyphosate. Plants can be regenerated (made again) easily from a few callus cells. So once the glyphosate-resistant calluses have been found they are used to produce whole plants.

1 Why does glyphosate kill plants?

2 The regenerated plants are clones. Explain why.

Instead of using *Agrobacterium*, a more common method now used to introduce DNA into plants is **ballistics**. A special gun is used to fire minute gold or tungsten pellets coated with DNA into the plant tissue. This technique is used to produce insecticide-resistant plants. The plants synthesise a toxin that kills insect pests which feed on the plants.

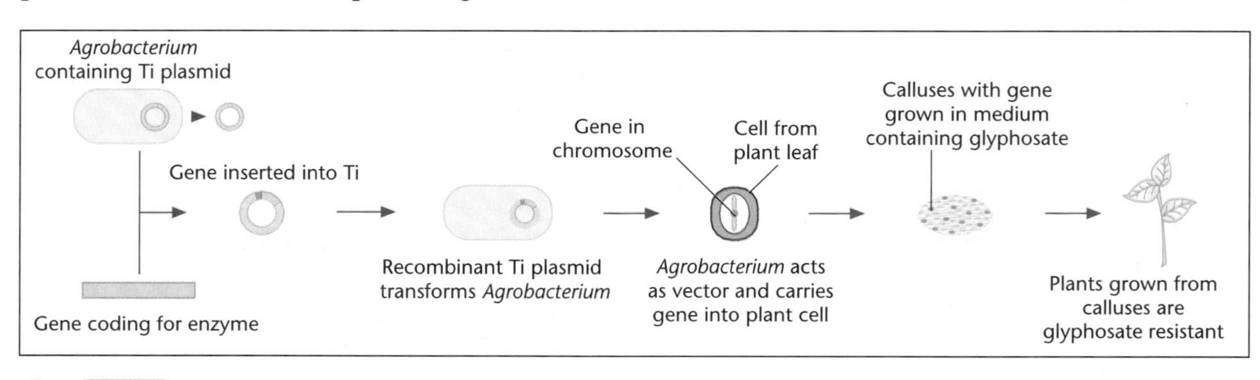

Figure 1 *Producing glyphosate-resistant plants. If the crop plants are resistant to glyphosate, then the herbicide can be sprayed on the field to kill weeds, leaving the crop plant unaffected.*

Plant potential

Many other types of GM cloned plants are being developed. Table 1 shows the range of GM plants commercially available and being developed.

Table 1 *The range of GM crops.*

In commercial use in the late 1990s	Developed but not commercially used in the late 1990s	Being researched
Herbicide resistance	Virus disease resistance in plants	Crops with increased vitamins
Insecticide resistance	Nematode resistance in cereals	Vaccine crops, e.g. hepatitis B antigen in tobacco
Slow-ripening tomatoes	Frost resistance in tomatoes and potatoes	Plants producing oils and plastics
Pre-coloured flowers and cotton	'Pharmed' plants to produce human proteins, e.g. insulin	Stress-tolerant crops, e.g. with drought resistance

3 Look at table 1.

a Make a list of the GM crops likely to bring benefit to many people.

b Make another list of the GM crops likely to benefit commercial companies.

Divided opinions

There are two main viewpoints about GM crops, summarised in figure 2. The main worries about GM crops are about the effects on the environment or on human health. The list below shows the main concerns for the environment:

- Herbicide-resistance genes could be transferred into weeds.
- Disease-causing organisms with altered genes could escape to the environment.
- Toxins produced by GM crops to combat pests could build up in herbivores, and be transferred along food chains.
- Breakdown of GM crop tissues could release toxins, causing changes in soil ecology.
- Pollinating insects could be damaged.

The concerns about health are less easy to separate. The two main concerns are:

- possible allergic reactions to new components in food
- transfer of antibiotic resistance genes from GM food to bacteria.

Figure 2 *GM foods – pros and cons.*

Key ideas 164–5

Genes transferred into plants can be used to improve crop quality and produce medicines.

There is concern about the commercial exploitation and the environmental and health risks of GM crops.

7 Chain reactions

Many of the procedures used in gene technology need large amounts of DNA. Scientists are able to produce millions of copies of specific DNA sequences easily and quickly in the laboratory without using bacteria. They use the process of DNA replication.

Repeat cycling

DNA replication can be made to occur artificially and repeatedly in a laboratory process called the **polymerase chain reaction** (**PCR**). PCR is a very accurate method and in theory it can make many copies from a single DNA molecule. To start the process short pieces of RNA known as **primers** are needed. These provide the starting sequence for DNA replication. The following are also needed: the double-stranded DNA that is being replicated, nucleotides and the enzyme DNA polymerase.

Figure 1 shows an outline of the procedure.

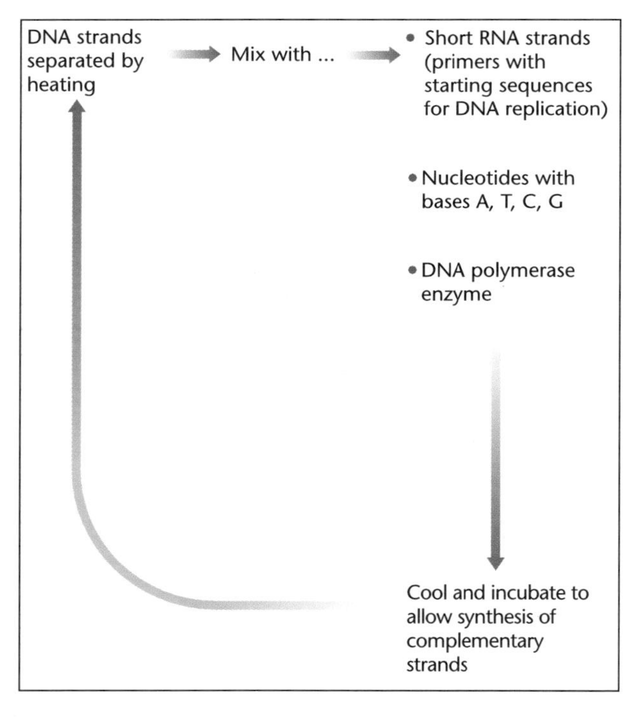

Figure 1 *Flow diagram outlining the process of PCR.*

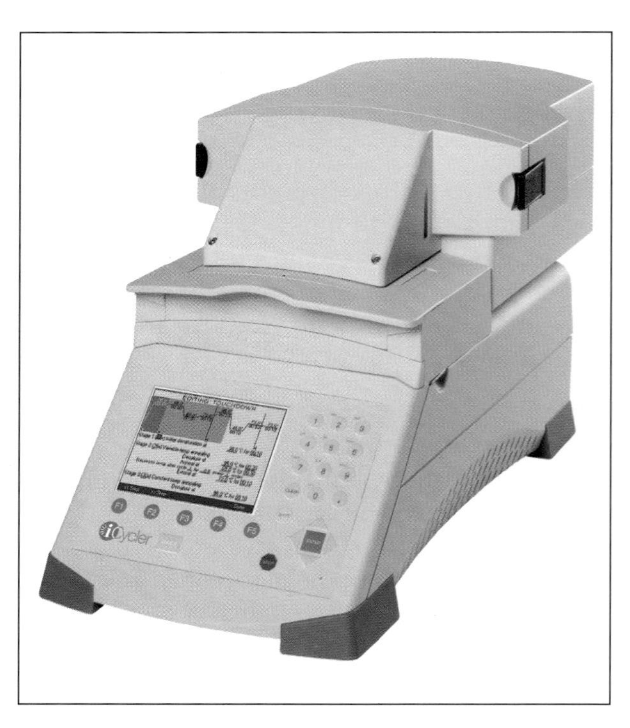

Figure 2 *A PCR machine.*

This process is carried out in an automated system controlled by a computer. You can see the equipment in figure 2.

Making the chains

Look at figure 3 which shows the events that occur during PCR. You can see that many copies of the required DNA are made by many cycles of replication.

1 **Strand separation**: the double-stranded DNA is split into two single-stranded templates by heating it to 95 °C for 30 seconds.

2 **Binding of primers**: the mixture is suddenly cooled to 37 °C for 30 seconds. You can see that this causes the primers to bind to the complementary strands of DNA.

3 **DNA synthesis**: the mixture is heated to 72 °C and kept at this temperature for 60–120 seconds. This is the optimum temperature for the DNA polymerase enzyme used. New strands of DNA are made alongside the old ones from the nucleotides present in the mixture.

4 **Repeat cycling**: the mixture is heated again to separate the newly formed DNA strands. The cycle of cooling and heating is repeated. The number of copies of DNA doubles with each cycle. After 25 cycles more than a million copies of the DNA will have been made.

1 In PCR, DNA replication is semi-conservative. With the aid of diagrams, describe the process of semi-conservative replication.

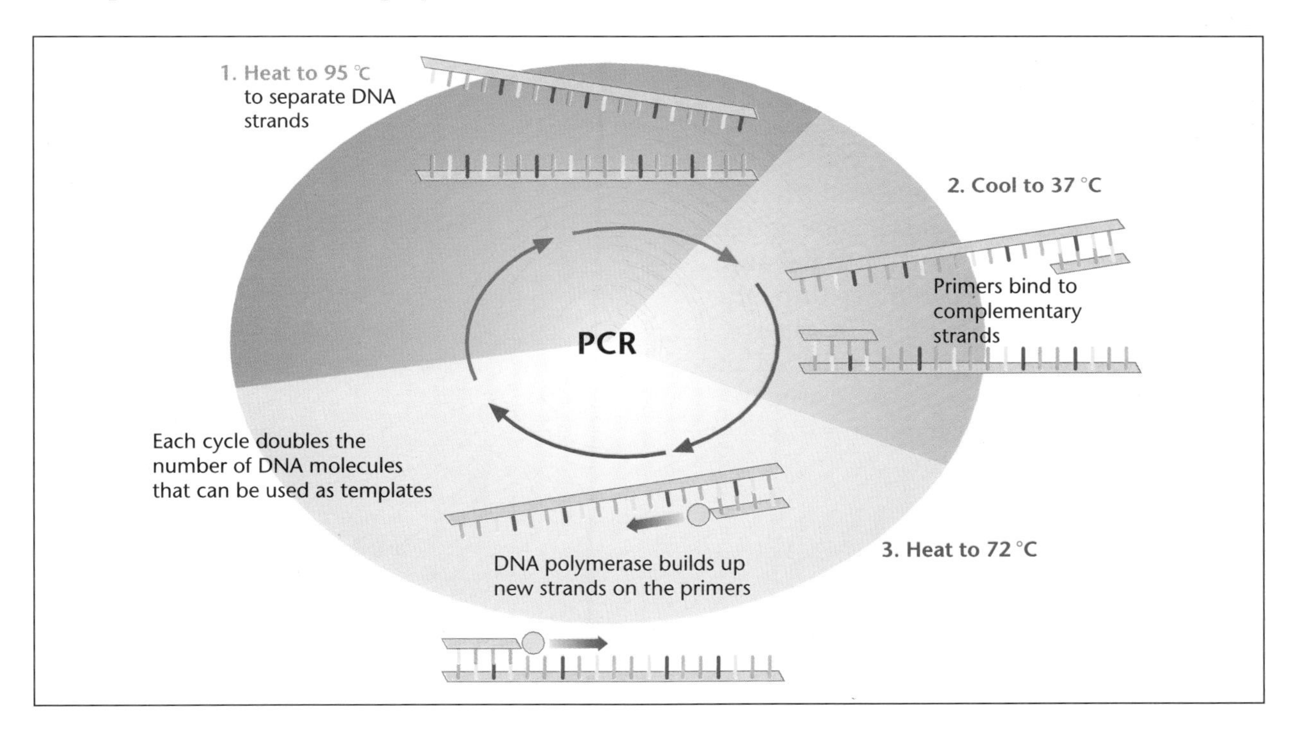

Figure 3 *The process of PCR.*

Key ideas 166–7

Millions of copies of specific DNA sequences can be replicated from very small quantities quickly by PCR.

Heat-stable DNA polymerase is used.

PCR involves repeated cycles of heating and cooling.

8 Finding genes

Before a gene can be transferred, it has to be separated from the other genes of the donor organism. A lot of information about the gene to be transferred can be worked out from its gene product. Its size can be estimated from the amino acid sequence of the product by using the genetic code. Knowing the size of the gene helps genetic engineers isolate the gene from all the other genes of the organism.

Separating DNA by size

To find a gene by its size, some cells from an organism containing the required gene are crushed and DNA extracted. This DNA is cut into sections using restriction endonucleases. DNA fragments of different sizes are formed.

1 Suggest why cutting with endonucleases forms fragments of different sizes.

These DNA fragments are separated from each other by **gel electrophoresis**. Look at figure 1 showing the gel that is used. It is flat and forms a mesh that DNA can move through. This is similar to the paper used in paper chromatography. Wells are cut in the gel and DNA samples from the organism placed in them. A mixture of DNA fragments of known sizes is placed in wells at the edge of the gel. These are **size markers**.

The gel is placed in an electrophoresis tank with a buffer solution to keep a constant pH. Look at figure 2 of an electrophoresis tank. Electrodes generate an electric field across the gel. The phosphates in DNA give it a negative charge, so it tends to move towards the positive electrode. As the DNA fragments travel through the gel, smaller fragments move further as they pass through the gel more quickly.

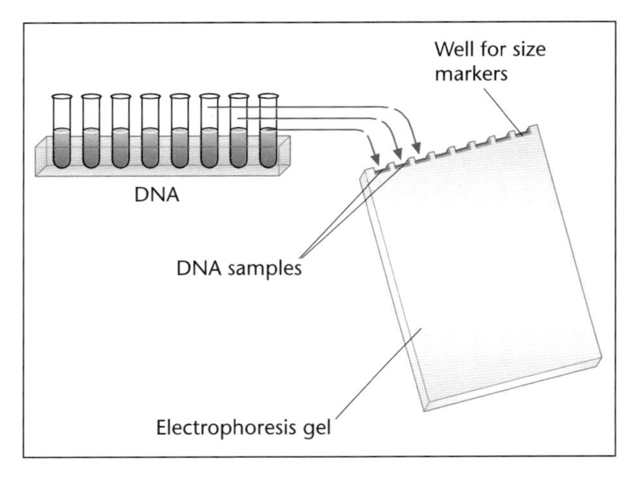

Figure 1 *Electrophoresis gel is used to separate DNA fragments of different sizes.*

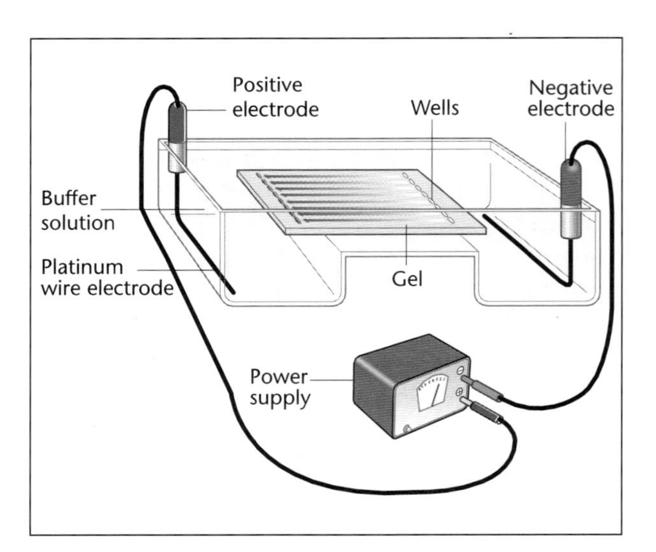

Figure 2 *An electrophoresis tank.*

Finding fragments of DNA

The gel is removed from the tank and the DNA is made visible by adding a stain and putting the gel in ultraviolet light. The stained DNA shows up as fluorescent bands, which are photographed for further study. An example is shown in figure 3. The size marker DNA is in wells 1 and 14. The sizes of these fragments are already known, measured in **kilobases** (1 kilobase = 1000 nucleotide bases). The size of the DNA fragment in each band in wells 2–13 can be worked out by comparing them with the size markers. If you know the approximate DNA sequence of the desired gene, you can work out the size of fragment to look for on the gel.

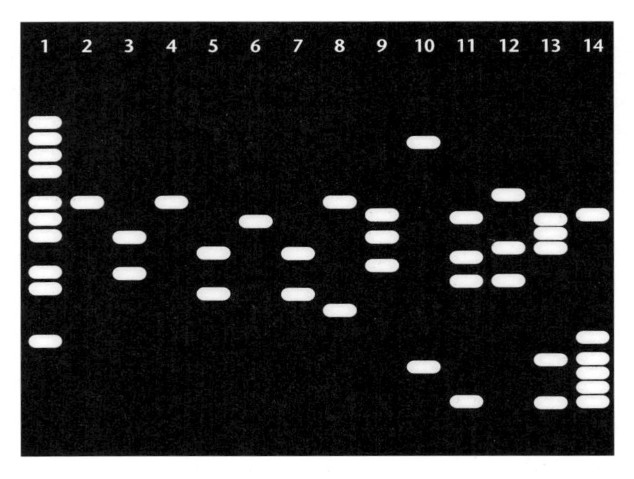

Figure 3 *Bands of DNA on a gel after electrophoresis.*

2 Look at figure 3. Which DNA samples contain:
  a the largest DNA fragment?
  b the smallest DNA fragment?

3 How can the approximate sequence of the DNA of a gene be worked out from the amino acid order of the protein it codes for?

Finding out about fragments

To study genes, the fragments of DNA obtained from an organism are used to make a **genomic library** (a gene or DNA store). Each different sized fragment is put into a different bacterium and kept for further study. A genomic library contains at least one copy of every DNA sequence of an organism. Once the genes are in a bacterium they will be copied every time the bacterium reproduces.

The **Human Genome Project** (HUGO) works on genomic libraries of human chromosomes. This project was started in 1990 and involved the co-operation of researchers in several countries. Its aim is to work out the sequence of the 3.2 billion base pairs in human DNA and to find their location in specific genes on the 23 human chromosome pairs. This project is expected to be finished in 2001. Already information from the work has been used to improve diagnosis and treatment of human genetic disorders.

Key ideas 168–9

DNA fragments from endonuclease digestion contain sequences of specific nucleotides.

Phosphate groups give DNA fragments a negative charge so they move in an electric field.

Gel electrophoresis separates DNA fragments by size in an electric field.

Gene sequences from DNA fragments can be used to make recombinant DNA, or for detailed study.

9 Finding the order

Genetic researchers need to know the order of the DNA nucleotides of the genes they study. Working out the order of the nucleotides in DNA is called **sequencing**. The analysis involves a number of techniques including PCR, radioactive labelling and electrophoresis. One method used is the Sanger method named after Fred Sanger who won a Nobel Prize in 1979 for developing the technique.

Sanger sequencing

This method is based on the premature ending of DNA synthesis. DNA synthesis can be ended by using modified nucleotides called **terminators**. These nucleotides lack an oxygen atom. To detect the DNA, radioactive primers or more commonly nucleotides labelled with fluorescent dyes are used.

PCR is used to make large quantities of the DNA that is going to be sequenced. DNA synthesis is started using a radioactive primer. The radioactivity can be detected using photographic film. Four separate reactions are run, each containing:

- the DNA to be sequenced
- the four normal nucleotides, and mixed with these a modified version of one of the nucleotides (modified adenine nucleotide in one tube, modified cytosine nucleotide in another, and so on)
- the primer
- DNA polymerase enzyme.

DNA polymerase attaches to the labelled primer and uses the free nucleotides to synthesise a new strand by using the unknown strand as a template. You can see in figure 1(b) that if a modified nucleotide is added to the growing DNA, synthesis stops. As the enzyme uses nucleotides at random, the new strands will terminate at different places depending on where the modified nucleotide is added. At the end of the reaction, each tube contains fragments of DNA of differing lengths. These fragments can be separated according to their size using electrophoresis.

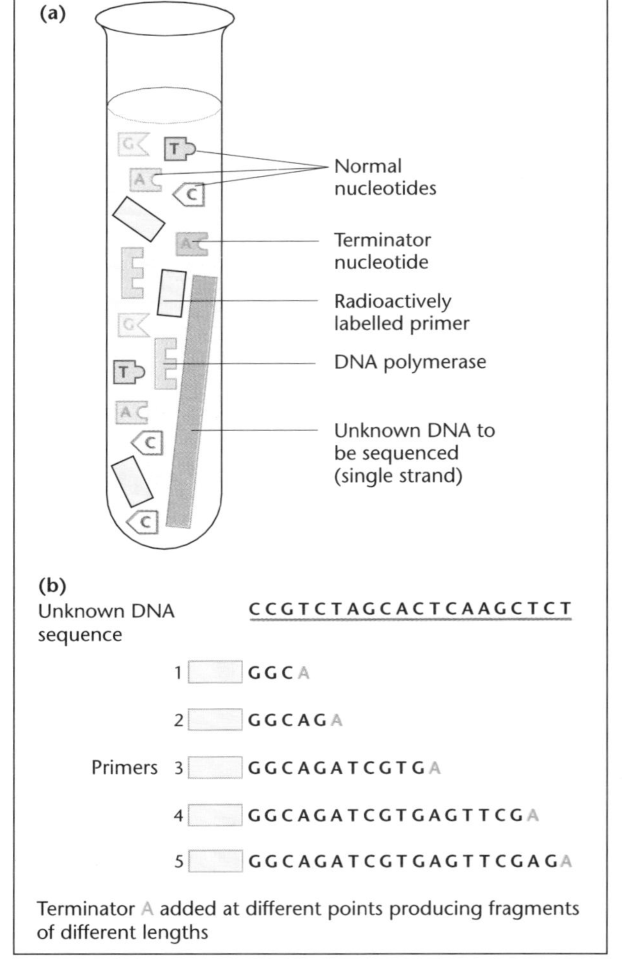

Figure 1 *(a) The substances needed for Sanger sequencing. This tube contains modified A terminator nucleotides.*
(b) Different fragments obtained using terminator A nucleotides in the mixture.

1 Figure 1 shows the result of using terminator A. List the fragments that would be produced using terminator T.

All sequenced out

The fragments are separated using gel electrophoresis, the smaller fragments moving the furthest. Once the electrophoresis gel has run, unexposed photographic film is laid on the gel to produce an **autoradiograph**. The radioactive DNA fragments create dark shadows on the film, each shadow made by millions of fragments of the same length at the same point on the gel. The autoradiograph in figure 2 shows the positions of the radioactive primers attached to each fragment.

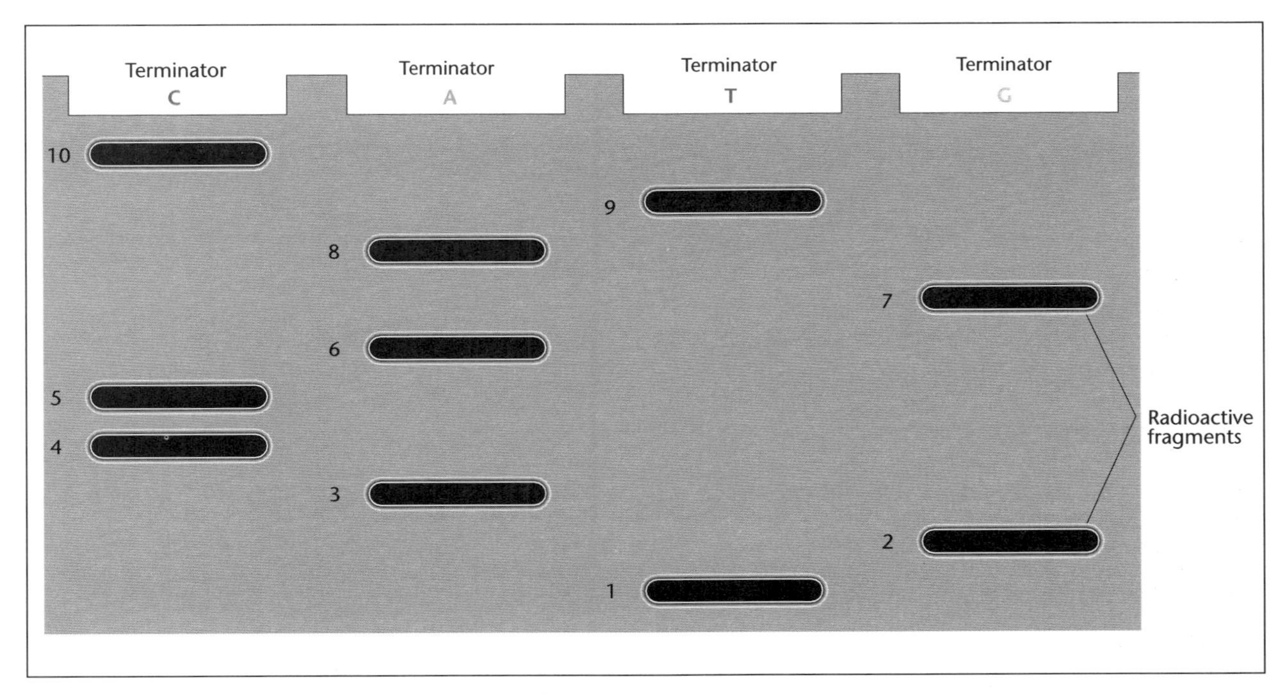

Figure 2 *Autoradiograph resulting from DNA sequencing.*

DNA sequencing can be automated using computers. These automated computer-controlled systems use nucleotides with fluorescent dyes attached instead of radioactive primers. A different coloured dye is used for each type of nucleotide. A PCR machine is used to create the fragments and only one lane on the electrophoresis gel is used rather than four. The gel is left to run for up to 10 hours. During this time an argon laser scans across the bottom of the gel detecting the passing fluorescent nucleotides. Computer software automatically interprets the data and produces the DNA sequence.

2 Using the gel in figure 2, write down the DNA sequence of fragment 10.

Key ideas 170–71

The sequence of nucleotides in DNA can be determined using PCR, radioactive labelling and electrophoresis.

Unit 9 – Questions

10

(1) a) What is a plasmid? (2 marks)

b) Figure 1 shows a plasmid being used in genetic engineering.

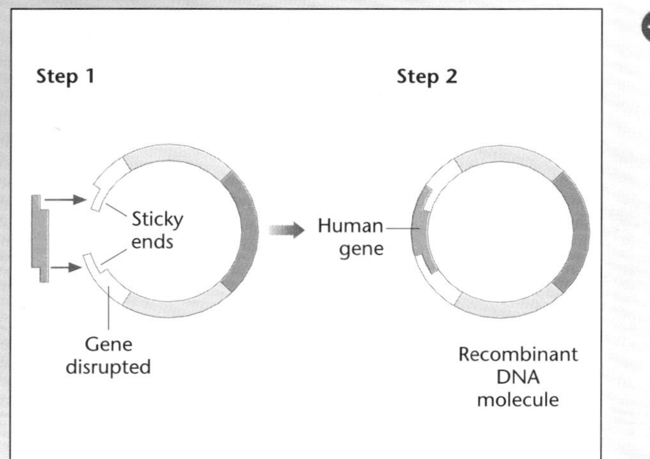

Figure 1

i) What type of enzyme is used for step 1?

ii) What type of enzyme is used for step 2? (2 marks)

c) Figure 2 shows the base sequence of the sticky ends of the gene inserted into the plasmid.

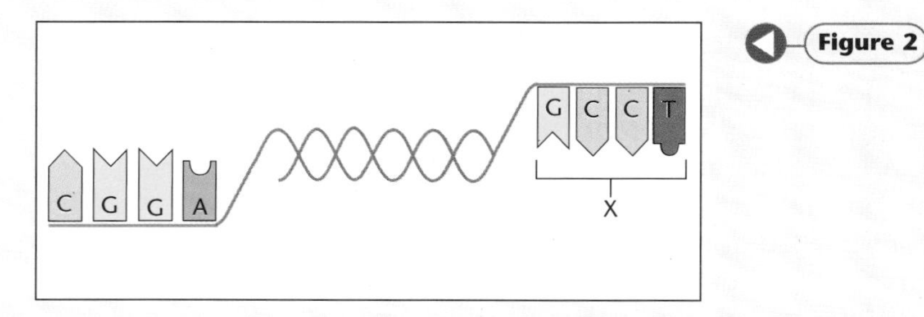

Figure 2

Give the base sequence of the sticky end of the plasmid that joins with the part labelled X on the gene. (1 mark)

(Total 5 marks)

(2) a) What is meant by the following terms?

i) recombinant DNA

ii) replica plating (2 marks)

b) Describe how bacterial resistance to antibiotics is used in genetic engineering. (5 marks)

(Total 7 marks)

3 Figure 3 shows the position on a plasmid of four restriction sites. The distance between them is shown in kilobases (1 kilobase = 1000 bases).

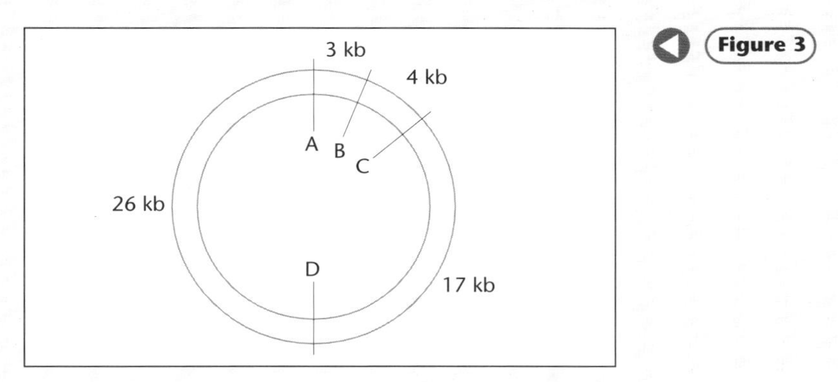

Figure 3

The plasmids were cut using restriction endonucleases, two at a time. The fragments were separated by gel electrophoresis. Figure 4 shows the relative positions of the fragments on the gel.

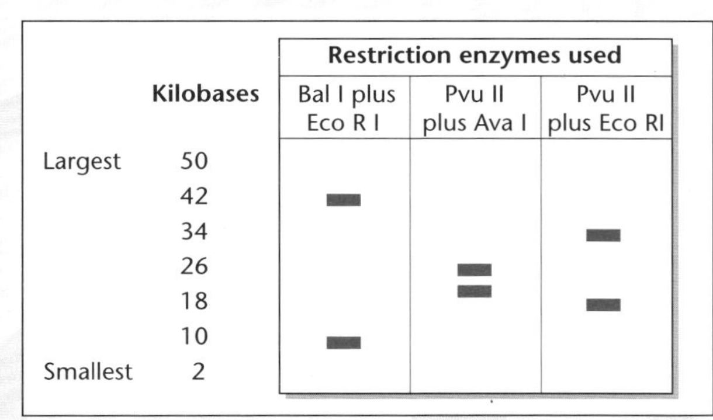

Match each enzyme to its restriction site on the plasmid. (3 marks)

(Total 3 marks)

4 A sample of DNA was obtained from blood found at a crime scene. DNA sequencing was used to determine the DNA sequence of the sample. The results are shown in figure 5.

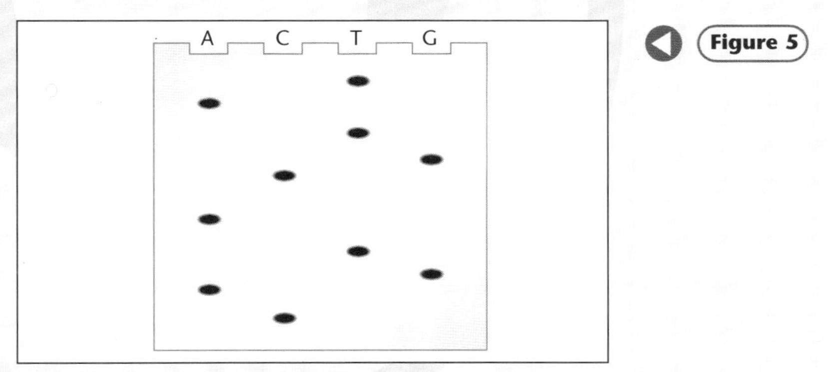

Figure 5

Using the autoradiograph, answer the following questions.

a) Name the nucleotide at the end of the shortest fragment. (1 mark)

b) Name the nucleotide at the start of the longest fragment. (1 mark)

c) Write down the sequence of the longest fragment. (1 mark)

d) Write down the DNA sequence of the DNA found at the crime scene. (2 marks)

(Total 5 marks)

Module 2 – Test yourself

1. a) What is the purpose of the process called polymerase chain reaction (PCR)? (1 mark)
   b) What is the role of a primer in PCR? (1 mark)
   c) Why is it necessary to separate the strands at the start of each cycle of the PCR process? (1 mark)
   d) Name the enzyme used to make new DNA. (1 mark)
   e) Starting from one molecule of DNA, how many molecules would you have after 25 cycles of PCR? (2 marks)

   (Total 6 marks)

2. a) Explain why prepared microscope slides designed to show meiosis are usually made from male tissue rather than female tissue. (1 mark)
   b) The graph in figure 1 shows the movement of chromosomes during mitosis. Curve **X** shows the mean distance between the centromeres of the chromosomes and the corresponding pole of the spindle.

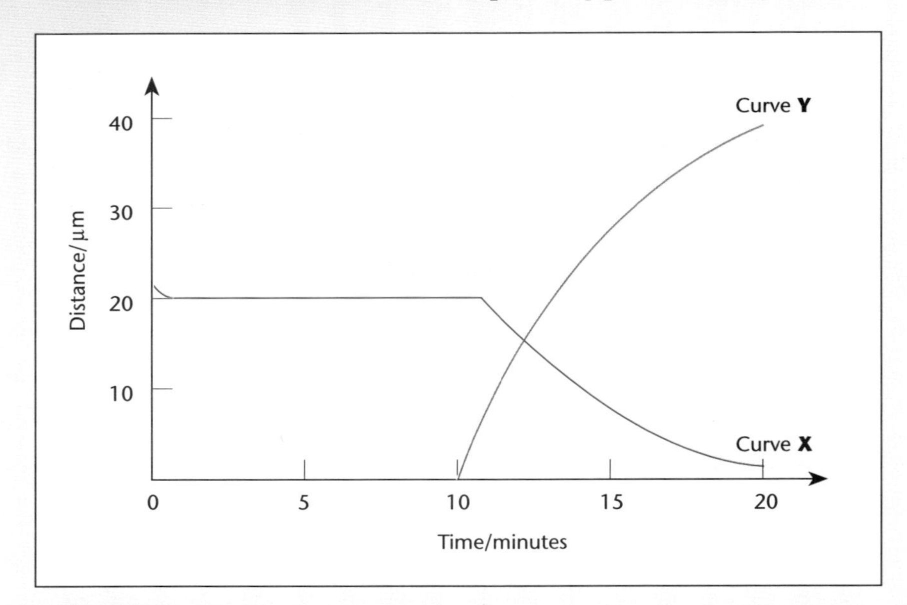

Figure 1

   What does curve **Y** represent? (1 mark)
   c) i) At what time did anaphase start? (1 mark)
      ii) Explain one piece of evidence from the graph to support your answer. (2 marks)

   (Total 5 marks)

3) a) Explain why the synthesis of human gene products is more efficient using the cells of plants and animals than using bacteria. (2 marks)
b) Give two examples of human gene products that can be synthesised using animal and plant cells. (2 marks)
c) i) Give two arguments for developing genetically modified food plants.
ii) Give two arguments against developing genetically modified food plants. (4 marks)

(Total 8 marks)

4) Figure 2 shows part of a DNA molecule.

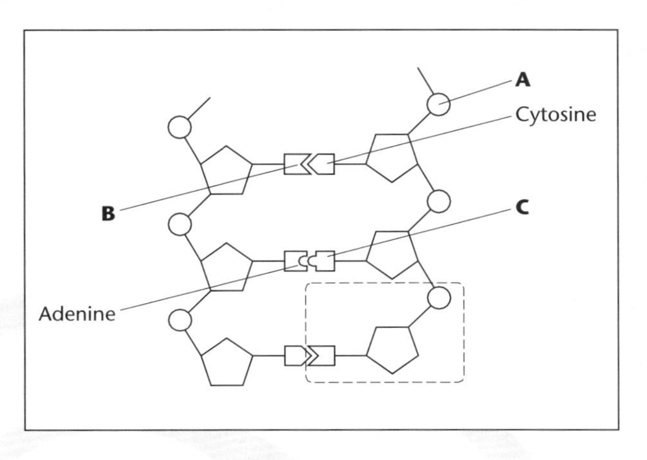

a) i) Name parts **A**, **B** and **C**. (3 marks)
ii) What name is given to the part of the molecule in the box? (1 mark)
b) i) Why is the replication of DNA described as semi-conservative? (2 marks)
ii) What features of DNA make it an ideal molecule for storing genetic information? (4 marks)

(Total 10 marks)

5) Figure 3 shows a molecule of transfer RNA.

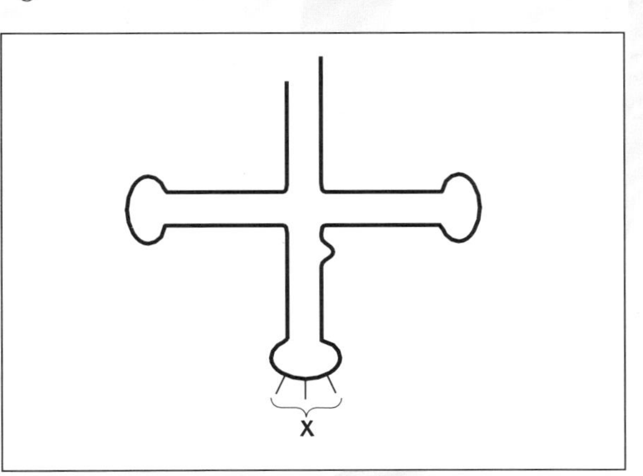

a) i) Name the part of the molecule labelled **X**. (1 mark)
ii) Explain the significance of part **X** in protein synthesis. (4 marks)
b) Give two structural differences between DNA and RNA. (2 marks)

(Total 7 marks)

Module 2 – Test yourself

6) A sequence of messenger RNA is shown below:

UAGGCGCCAGGUAAU

a) What is the maximum number of amino acids for which this piece of mRNA can code? (1 mark)

b) i) Write down the DNA base sequence from which this mRNA was transcribed. (2 marks)

ii) Describe the role of tRNA molecules in the process of protein synthesis. (3 marks)

c) Describe the possible consequences if the third base in the sequence changed to C. (3 marks)

(Total 9 marks)

7) Restriction enzymes are widely used in genetic engineering. There are many different restriction enzymes, each one cutting DNA at a specific base sequence. The restriction enzyme **EcoR1** acts on DNA by cutting it at the sequence shown in figure 4.

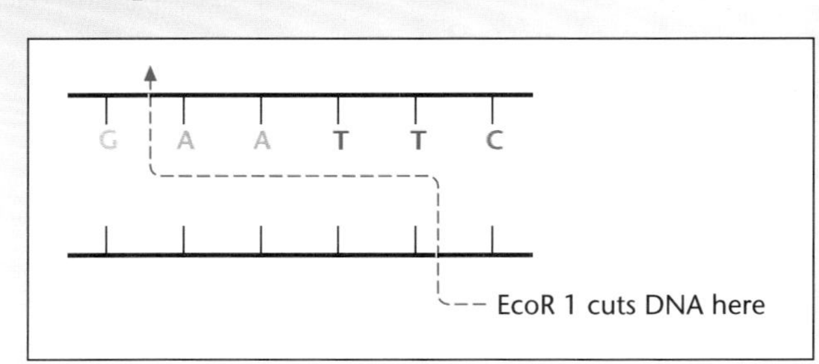

Figure 4

a) Copy the diagram and complete it by adding the base sequence to the complementary strand of the DNA molecule. (1 mark)

b) Explain why an enzyme like EcoR1 can only cut DNA at a specific base sequence. (2 marks)

c) Explain why EcoR1 cannot be used for cutting out all genes. (2 marks)

(Total 5 marks)

8) The numbers of cells in different stages of mitosis in an onion root tip were counted. The results are shown in table 1.

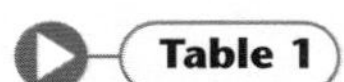
Table 1

Stage of mitosis	Number of cells
Interphase	450
Prophase	210
Metaphase	30
Anaphase	12
Telophase	48

a) Calculate the percentage time spent in prophase. (2 marks)

b) Explain one reason why these data might differ if another onion root tip was used. (2 marks)

(Total 4 marks)

9 Figure 5 shows a metabolic pathway that occurs in a certain type of plant to make a dark yellow pigment, which colours its flowers.

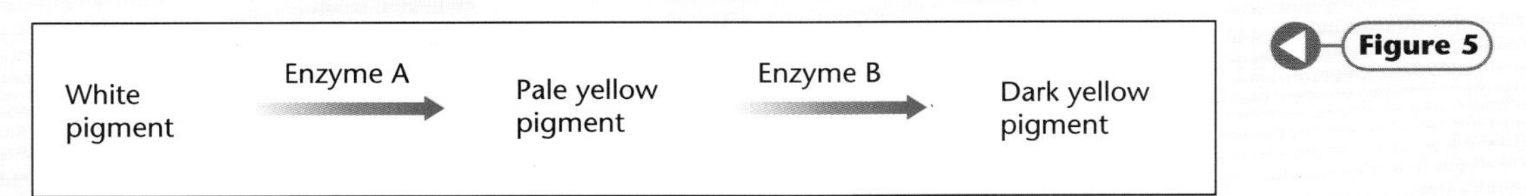

Figure 5

Explain how:

a) a mutation in the gene coding for enzyme **B** might give rise to a plant with pale yellow flowers (2 marks)

b) a mutation could result in a plant with white flowers. (2 marks)

(Total 4 marks)

10 DNA contains all the information that a cell needs to synthesise proteins. One of the stages of protein synthesis is shown in figure 6.

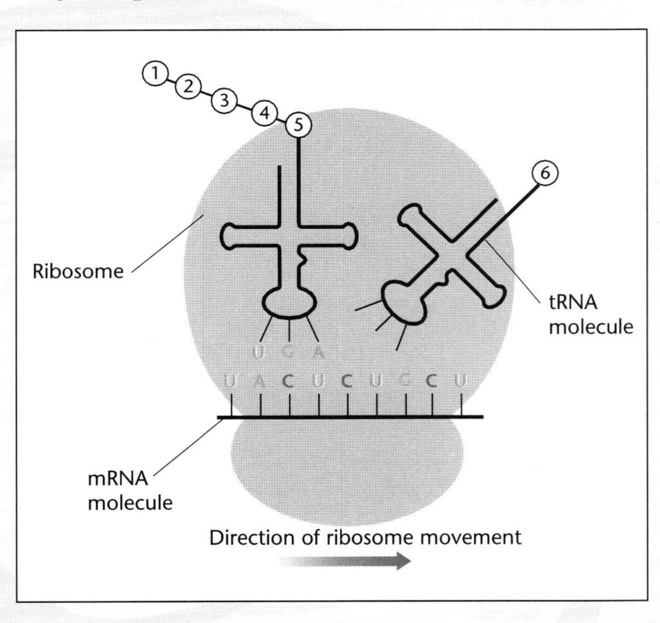

a) Name the stage being shown in the diagram. (1 mark)

b) Describe how the mRNA shown in the diagram was made. (3 marks)

c) Give the sequence of the anticodon bases on the tRNA molecule that is carrying amino acid number 6. (1 mark)

d) Name the bonds that join amino acid molecules 1 to 5. (1 mark)

(Total 6 marks)

Module 3

Physiology and Transport

This module explores transport systems in plants and animals. It is related to module 1, which was concerned with obtaining food and gases from the environment, as transport systems move these from one part of the body to another.

Unit 10 looks at how the blood system supplies cells with oxygen from the lungs, with small food molecules from the intestines and removes wastes produced by the chemical reactions of the body. The unit also considers how the circulation of blood and the ventilation of the lungs can be changed to meet the needs of the body during exercise.

Unit 11 focuses on how plants transport water and mineral ions in one set of vessels in the xylem, and small food molecules in another set of vessels in the phloem. The unit also looks at some of the ways plants cope with living in extreme environments.

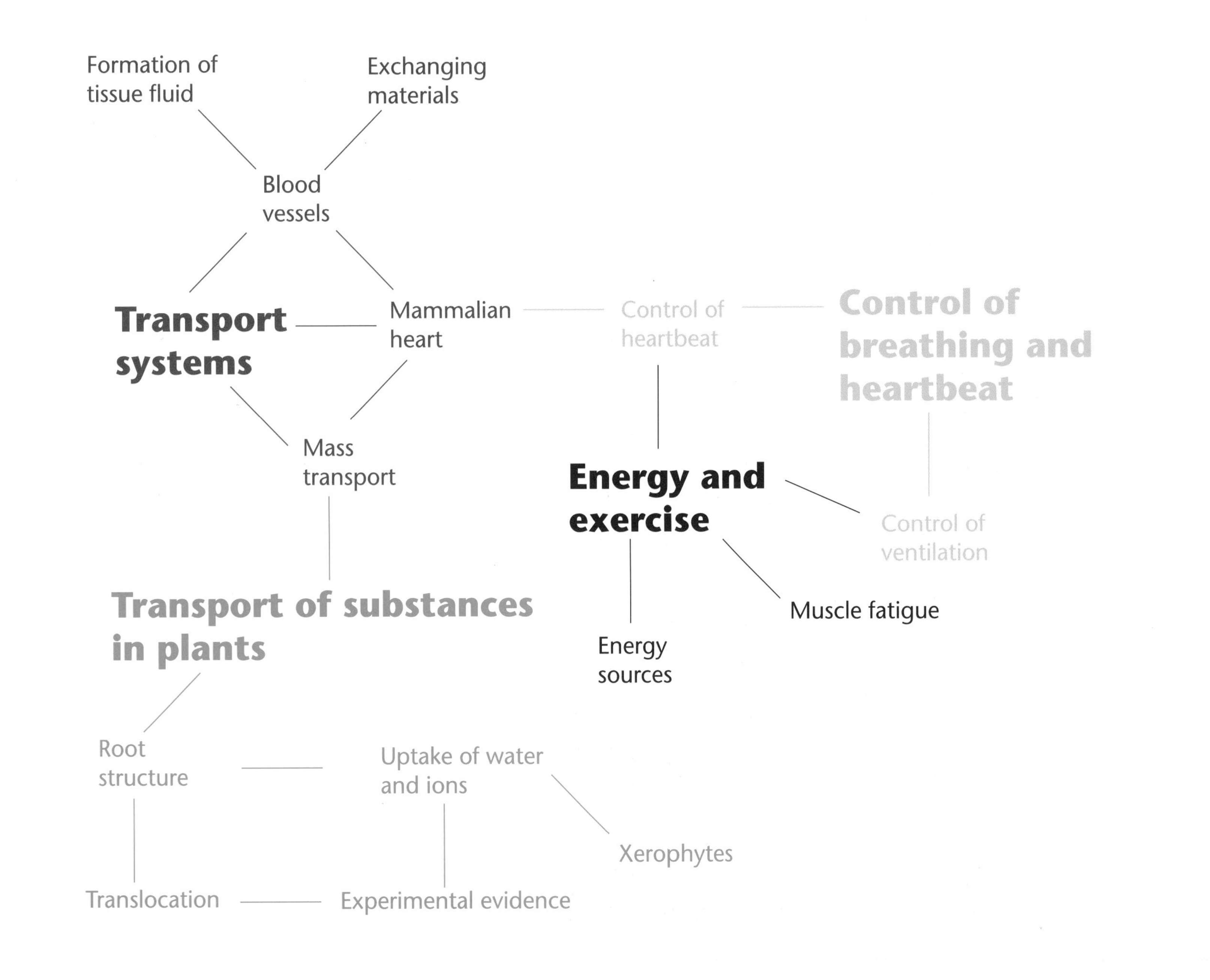
Formation of tissue fluid
Exchanging materials
Blood vessels
Transport systems
Mammalian heart
Mass transport
Control of heartbeat
Control of breathing and heartbeat
Energy and exercise
Control of ventilation
Muscle fatigue
Energy sources
Transport of substances in plants
Root structure
Uptake of water and ions
Xerophytes
Translocation
Experimental evidence

1 Supplying cells

You will remember that if an organism has a lot of active cells, there is a problem of supply. To move enough molecules to and from cells in large organisms, a **mass transport** system is used. These systems carry large quantities very quickly from place to place.

Mammals use a blood circulatory system for mass transport. Molecules are exchanged with the outside environment at exchange surfaces, and here the transport system is very close to the exchange surface to help rapid diffusion. For example, on page 93 you can see that the gas exchange surface and blood supply are very close, and on page 25 the food absorption surface is next to a blood supply. The flow of the transport system keeps a steep diffusion gradient.

Going for gold

When you increase metabolic activity in cells, it puts extra demand on the supply of raw materials and removal of waste products. Look at figure 1 showing the first person to run a mile in less than four minutes. You can see that at the end of the race he is hot, exhausted and needs help to stand.

To run in a race, an athlete's muscles have to use a lot of extra energy. To provide this energy a number of changes take place. Some of these changes start before the race begins, due to hormones in the blood. Working muscles need energy in the form of ATP, which is made by respiration. To produce this ATP, oxygen and glucose have to be supplied in greater quantities than normal. Working muscle produces a lot of carbon dioxide and heat. These have to be removed as quickly as possible.

Figure 1 *Roger Bannister at the end of the historic first 'four-minute mile' in 1954.*

1 Why does excess heat have to be removed from muscles?

2 How do hormones in the blood cause cells to change their activity?

Meeting the needs

Look at figure 2 showing the blood supply to a muscle. You can see that the blood arriving at the muscle is releasing oxygen and glucose, and that the blood leaving the muscle is collecting carbon dioxide and heat.

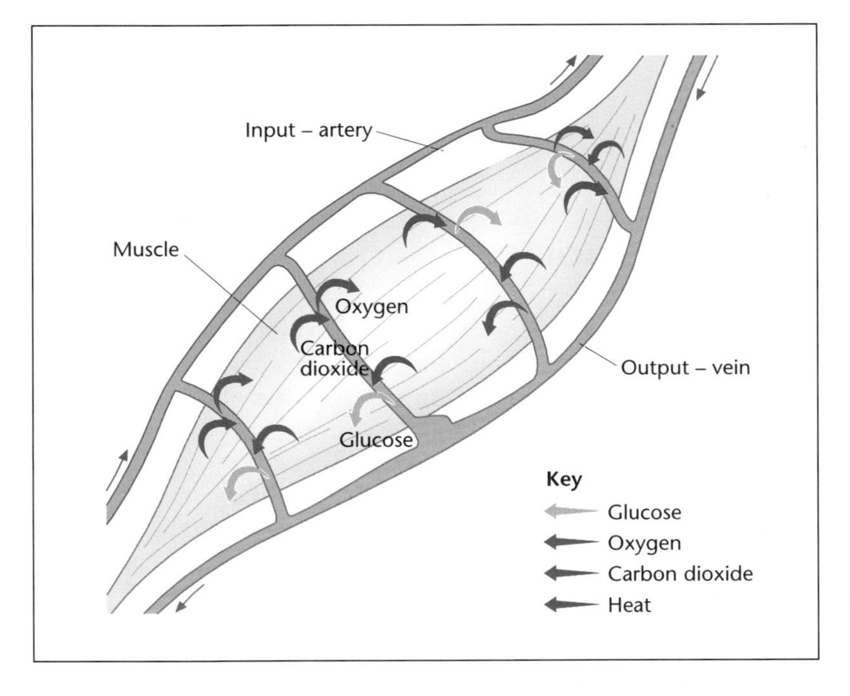

Figure 2 *The blood supply to a muscle.*

The body makes a number of changes during exercise to keep the supply of raw materials at a high level and remove the waste:

- The rate of respiration in the muscles increases.
- Blood flow through the muscles increases.
- The heart rate increases.
- The blood pressure rises.
- The ventilation rate increases.
- Glycogen stores in the muscles are converted to glucose.
- Oxygen stores in the muscles are released.

3 For each of the changes in the list, explain why it helps muscles to contract efficiently.

When muscles stop contracting, the body has to recover and gradually return to normal. The change back to normal does not take place straight away because stores of oxygen and glycogen have to be replaced, and the excess heat generated in respiration must be lost from the body.

Key ideas 180–81

Body systems co-operate to supply the needs and remove the wastes from cells.

The systems can adjust the supply lines to meet changing demands in body cells.

2 The supply network

The blood circulatory system has three main parts – **blood, blood vessels** and the **heart**. These work together to collect and deliver materials from all organs of the body.

The transporter – blood

Blood carries many different substances. These are picked up in some organs and left in other organs. As a result, blood leaving an organ has a different composition from blood entering it. Blood reaches all cells, but not every cell needs all of the substances carried by blood. Remember that cell surface membranes are used to control which substances enter and leave cells.

Look at the diagram of blood in figure 1. Notice there are four main components. The major transporters are plasma and red blood cells. The two other components, white blood cells and platelets, are part of the body's defence system.

Figure 1 *The structure and functions of blood.*

Red blood cells contain haemoglobin which:

- carries oxygen
- buffers blood (prevents pH changes)
- carries 10–15% carbon dioxide.

Plasma contains water which:

- acts as a solvent for chemicals
- flows when the heart exerts pressure
- carries dissolved minerals, glucose (blood sugar), amino acids, vitamins, 85% carbon dioxide as hydrogencarbonate ions, and metabolic wastes
- carries lipids in complexes called **chylomicrons**
- spreads heat from warm organs to cooler organs.

Plasma also contains proteins called **albumins** which:

- help blood flow
- maintain blood water potential.

The pump – the heart

The heart is made mainly of muscle, which moves the blood. When this muscle contracts, it puts pressure on the liquid blood inside the heart. As liquid cannot be compressed (squashed into a smaller volume), this makes blood move through the vessels. The beating of the heart causes the blood to flow in a circuit around the body.

Pipes – the blood vessels

Arteries carry blood *from* the heart *to* organs. This is distribution. **Veins** carry blood *from* organs back *to* the heart. This is collection. Capillaries lie between all the cells in the organs to allow exchange of molecules between the blood and the cells.

Look at figure 2 showing the blood circulatory system. You can see that there are two circuits. One goes from the heart to the lungs and back to the heart. This is the **pulmonary** (lung) circulation. The other circuit is from the heart to the rest of the body organs and back to the heart. This is the **systemic** (body systems) circulation. This interlocking arrangement is called a **double circulation**.

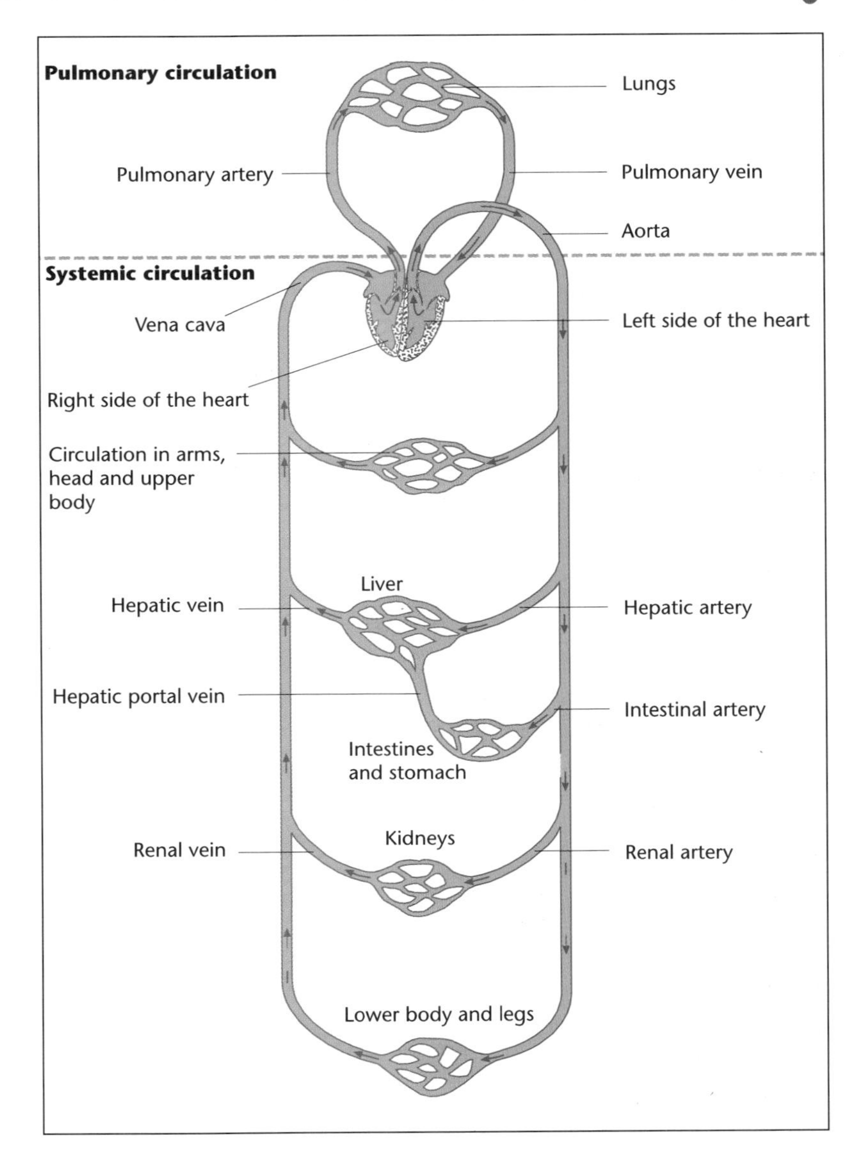

Figure 2 *Plan diagram of the human blood circulation.*

1 a Look at figure 2. How many times would blood from a body organ pass through the heart before reaching another body organ?

b What is the advantage of a double circulation?

Key ideas 182–3

Blood transports a variety of substances.

The heart pumps blood under pressure.

Vessels carry blood in two interconnecting circuits.

Arteries distribute blood from the heart, veins return blood to the heart, and capillaries allow exchange between the blood and the cells.

3 Pushing blood around

The heart pumps blood by contracting and relaxing its muscle. When the heart muscle contracts, it pushes the blood out of the heart. When it relaxes, the pressure inside the heart falls and allows blood to enter the heart. The blood can only flow in one direction because of heart valves that only open in one direction.

Working parts

The heart is made of a special sort of muscle called **cardiac muscle**. This contracts and relaxes continuously without becoming tired. This muscle started working before you were born, and will not stop until the day you die.

Look at figure 1 of the heart and the main blood vessels attached to it. You can see that there are two sides to the heart separated by a muscle **septum** (wall). Each side has two chambers. The top one on each side has thin muscle walls. These chambers are the **atria**. The bottom chamber on each side has thick muscle walls. These are the **ventricles**. You can also see valves separating the atria and ventricles, marked **A**. These are the **atrioventricular valves** which stop blood flowing back from the ventricles to the atria. In the arteries leaving the heart, you can see another set of valves, marked **B**. These are the **semilunar valves** and they stop blood flowing back into the heart.

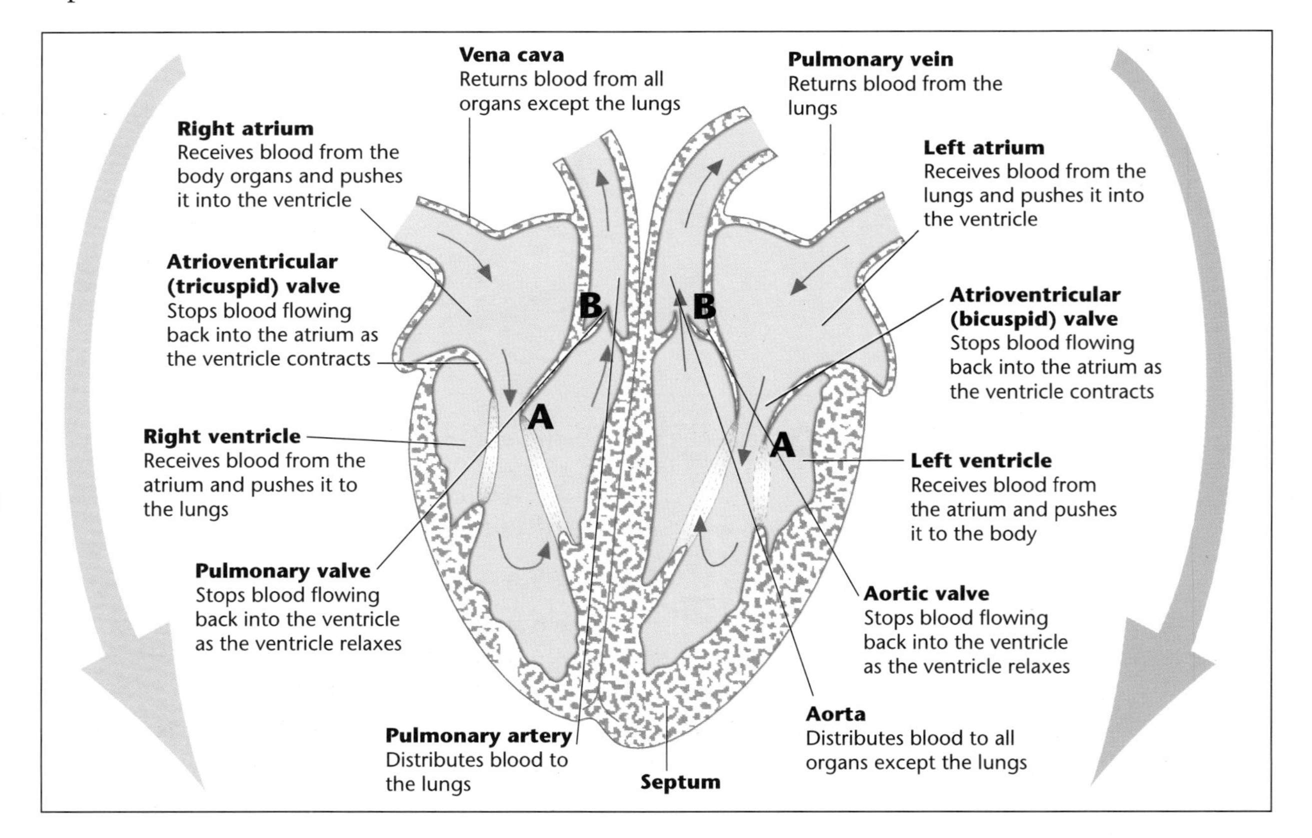

Figure 1 *The structure and function of the parts of the heart.*

Hearts with holes

Some people are born with a hole between the left and right sides of the heart. The blood circulation in a developing baby is different from the circulation after birth. During pregnancy, the mother supplies all the oxygen a fetus needs from the placenta. A fetus does not use its lungs for gas exchange until after birth, so the pulmonary circulation does not function. Look at figure 2 of the heart and blood vessels of a fetus and compare it with the heart in figure 1. You can see that there is a gap in the septum between the right and left atria, so blood can short-circuit across from the right atrium to the left atrium. You can also see an extra blood vessel, which is another short-circuit.

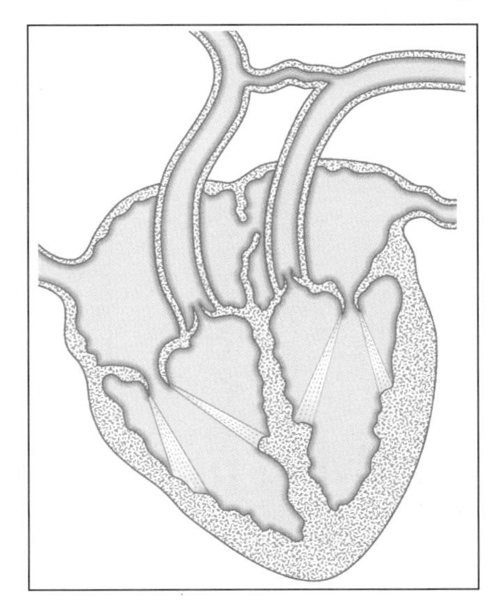

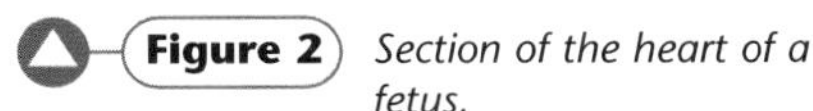
Figure 2 *Section of the heart of a fetus.*

1 a Copy and label the diagram in figure 2.
b Name the blood vessels that are connected by the extra vessel.

At birth, the first breath closes these gaps, so blood starts to flow in the pulmonary circulation. In some babies, the gap between the atria does not seal properly. These newborn babies have a bluish tinge to the skin because the blood in the systemic circulation does not have enough oxygen. Their blood pressure is also lower as some blood is pushed from one side of the heart to the other when the heart contracts. In other babies, there may be holes in the septum between the two sides of the heart due to faulty growth of the heart.

2 Explain why people with a hole in the heart do not have enough oxygen in the blood.

Leaky valves

In some people, the heart valves do not fit properly so blood leaks back. Disease or faulty heart development before birth can cause this. If valves leak, some of the blood goes backwards. This reduces the pressure of the heart, so the blood circulation is less efficient. The heart may then enlarge to try and produce extra pressure.

3 Explain why people with leaky valves are short of breath and always tired and lacking energy.

Key ideas 184–5

The heart is a two-sided pump circulating blood to the lungs and to the body organs at the same time.

The blood flow through the two sides of the heart is kept separate by the septum.

The separation of blood flow keeps a very high oxygen level in the blood distributed through the aorta.

4 Cycling through

The heart contracts and relaxes rhythmically to pump blood out around the double circulation. The flow of blood through the heart during one contraction and relaxation is called the **cardiac cycle**. Both sides of the heart work together.

Each cycle consists of two phases:

1. relaxation, when the heart is filling with blood. This is **diastole**.
2. contraction, when the heart is pushing blood out. This is **systole**.

Applying pressure

When the atria and ventricles contract, their walls press inwards. This reduces the volume inside the heart and the pressure increases. The build-up of pressure on the blood forces it to move. When the atria and ventricles relax, the volume inside the heart increases and the pressure falls. This allows more blood to enter the heart.

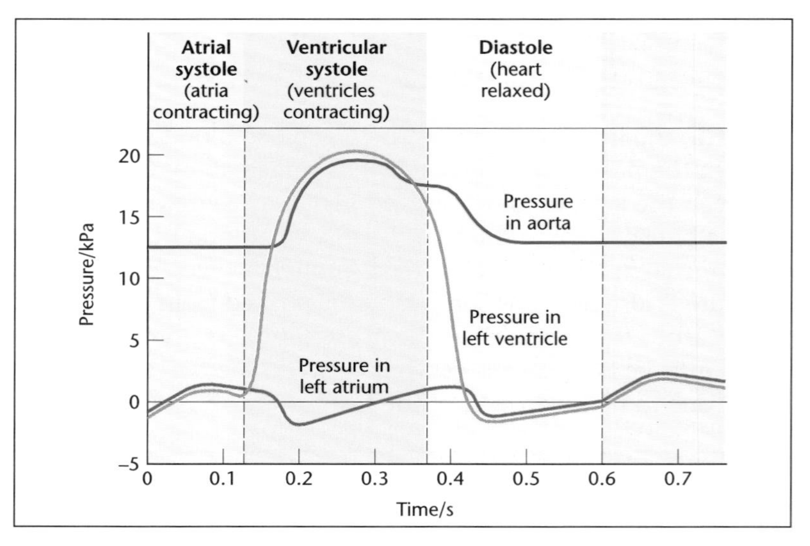

Figure 1 *Pressure changes in the left side of the heart during one cardiac cycle.*

Figure 1 shows the pressure changes in the left-hand side of the heart during one cardiac cycle. As the atrium contracts, the pressure inside it rises. Follow the curve of the pressure inside the left atrium (blue), and you can see that it is higher than the pressure inside the left ventricle (purple) until just after 0.1 s. This means blood is flowing from the atrium to the ventricle.

Now follow the curve of the pressure inside the left ventricle (purple). The ventricle starts to contract and the pressure rises above the pressure in the atrium. This means no more blood can enter the ventricle from the atrium. At 0.14 s, the pressure inside the left ventricle rises above the pressure in the aorta (red). At this point blood is flowing from the left ventricle into the aorta.

As the ventricle relaxes, the pressure inside falls below the pressure in the atrium again, so blood starts to flow from the atrium to the ventricle.

1 What pressure change causes blood to flow into the right atrium?

2 Make a sketch of figure 1 showing the pressure changes in the left-hand side of the heart. Draw in a rough curve showing the changes in pressure happening in the right-hand side of the heart.

One-way system

The pressure changes you can see in figure 1 also control the opening and closing of valves. The valves are important for **unidirectional** (one-way) flow. When the pressure behind the valve is higher than in front of it, the valve opens. When the pressure in front of the valve is higher, the valve closes. While it is closed the pressure behind it can build up to push it open again.

Look at figure 2. You can see that during diastole, when the heart is relaxed, the atrioventricular valves are open so blood can flow from the atria into the ventricles. The semilunar valves are closed to stop blood in the arteries flowing back into the ventricles. As the atria contract, the valves stay in the same positions until the ventricles start to contract.

Look at figure 3 of systole, and compare it with figure 2 of diastole. Now the ventricles are contracting, and the atrioventricular valves are closed to stop blood in the ventricles flowing back into the atria. You can also see tendons underneath these valves holding them against the ventricle walls. These tendons stop the valves opening backwards. The semilunar valves are open so blood can flow into the arteries. As the atria relax, the valves stay in the same positions until the ventricles start to relax.

Now look back at figure 1. When the pressure in the left ventricle rises above the pressure in the left atrium, the atrioventricular valve closes. You can see this happens at about 0.16 s. The semilunar valve closes when the pressure in the aorta rises above the pressure in the left ventricle.

3 At what time in the cardiac cycle does the left semilunar valve close?

4 When the pressure in the atrium rises above the pressure in the ventricle, the atrioventricular valve opens. At what time in the cardiac cycle does:

a the left atrioventricular valve open?

b the left semilunar valve open?

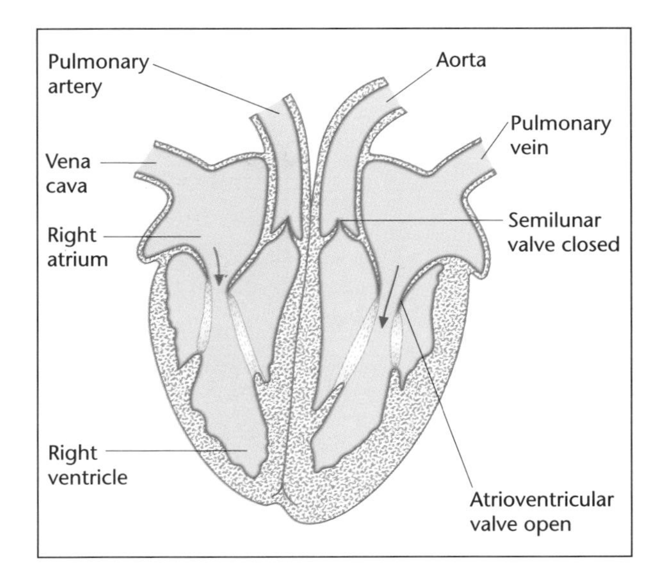

Figure 2 *Heart valves during diastole.*

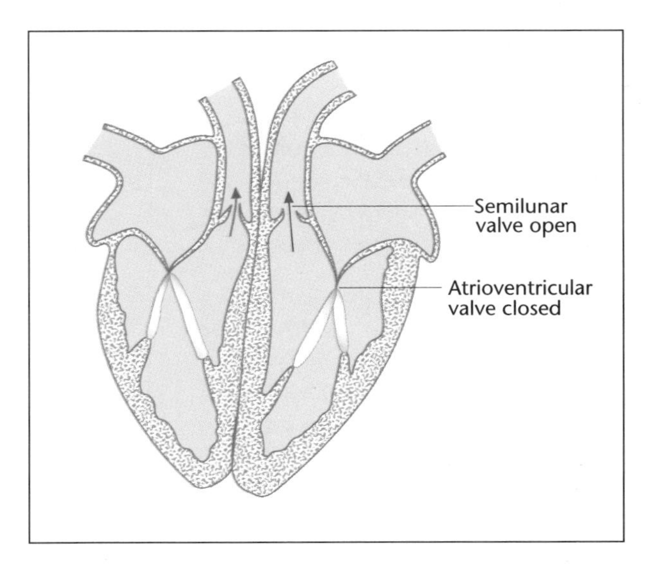

Figure 3 *Heart valves during systole.*

Key ideas 186–7

The heart muscle contracts and exerts pressure on the blood, causing it to flow.

The left side of the heart exerts more pressure than the right side.

Alternate contraction and relaxation of muscle causes pressure changes that fill and empty the heart.

The valves in the heart keep blood flowing in one direction.

5 Controlling the heart rate

Most muscles contract when they are stimulated by nerves. However, the heartbeat starts from within the heart muscle itself, not stimulated by nerve impulses from elsewhere. Since the heart muscle initiates the heartbeat, the heart is said to be **myogenic**.

The heart contains two areas of specialised cardiac cells, the **sinoatrial node (SA node)** and the **atrioventricular node (AV node)**. These control the heartbeat.

The beating heart

In figure 1 you can see the SA node in the wall of the right atrium, near where the vena cava enters it, and the AV node lying between the two atria. The SA node determines the basic rate of the heartbeat. Look at figure 1 to follow the sequence of events that occurs during one beat of the heart, listed below.

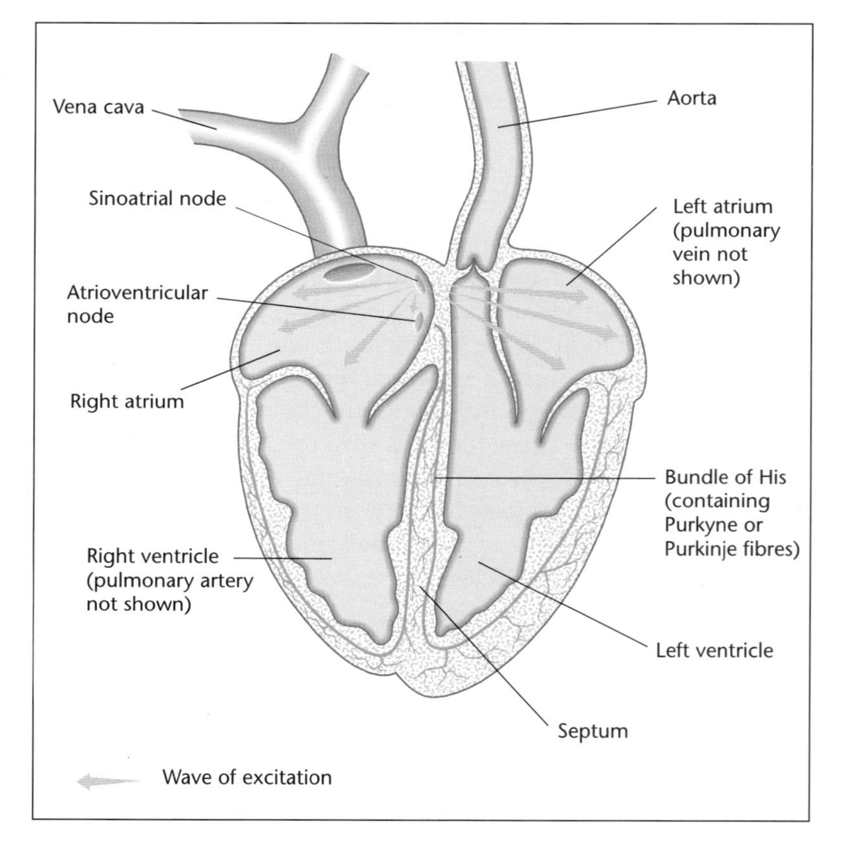

Figure 1 *The heart rate is controlled by a wave of excitation starting at the SA node.*

1. The initial stimulus for the heartbeat starts at the **SA node**, which sets up a wave of excitation. The wave of excitation spreads out from the SA node across both atria, causing the atria to contract, and this pushes the blood into the ventricles.
2. The wave of excitation reaches the **AV node**, which directs it along the **Purkyne fibres** that form the **bundle of His**.
3. The atria relax.
4. The bundle of His passes along the septum to the bottom of the ventricles, and from here the fibres pass up the sides of the ventricles. Once the wave of excitation reaches the bottom of the ventricles, the ventricles contract from the bottom upwards, which forces blood from the ventricles into the aorta and pulmonary artery.
5. There is a short delay before the next wave of excitation occurs. During this time the atria and ventricles are relaxed and the atria are filling with blood from the pulmonary vein and vena cava, and the process starts again.

1 Draw a flow diagram to show the events that take place during one heartbeat.

Abnormal rhythm

The heart usually beats regularly between 60 and 90 times per minute. Occasionally the SA node becomes defective, causing the heartbeat to be too fast, too slow or irregular. If the abnormality is bad enough the heart will pump less blood per beat, which can lead to chest pain, faintness or shortness of breath. More often the person with the problem just becomes very aware of the heartbeat, feeling it skip, or being fast, slow or irregular, or suddenly changing rhythm.

If the SA node stops working properly or the electrical pathways in the heart become blocked, doctors can implant a small battery-operated device called an **artificial pacemaker** to help the heart beat in a regular rhythm.

Figure 2 shows a modern pacemaker. The pacemaker has two parts – a battery-powered generator and the wires that connect it to the heart. The generator is implanted just beneath the skin, below the collarbone. The leads are threaded into position through veins leading back to the heart. It takes about one hour to fit a pacemaker and it needs only a local anaesthetic.

Most patients fitted with pacemakers suffer from a condition in which the heart beats too slowly. A **demand pacemaker** is used to treat this condition. The pacemaker monitors the heart's activity and takes control only when the heart rate falls below a programmed minimum, normally 60 beats per minute.

Pacemakers are also used to treat other conditions, such as heart block (when the heart stops beating altogether) and a heartbeat that is too rapid.

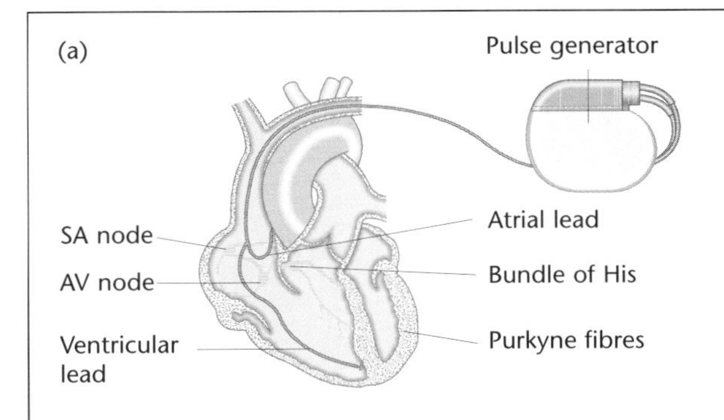

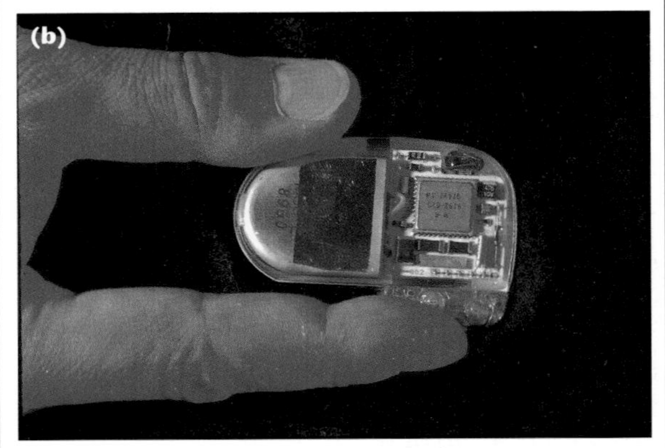

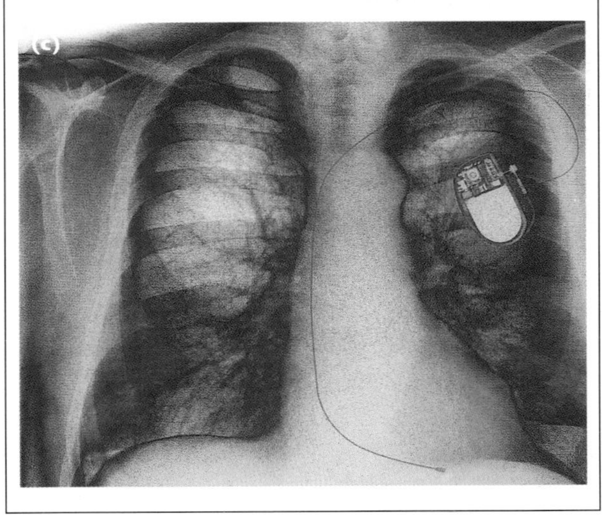

Figure 2 *(a) An artificial pacemaker and its connections to the heart.*
(b) The generator that is inserted below the collarbone.
(c) The pacemaker fitted in the chest. The red lead connects it to the heart.

Key ideas 188–9

The SA node initiates the heartbeat by sending a wave of excitation across the atria, causing the atria to contract.

The AV node directs a wave of excitation along the bundle of His, causing the ventricles to contract.

6 Beating faster

The SA node initiates each heartbeat. However, the rate at which the heart beats is not set at a fixed pace – it can be altered. At rest the heart rate is 60–80 beats per minute. The heart pumps out 4–5 litres of blood every minute, which is sufficient to meet the body's oxygen need.

During vigorous exercise, the muscles have to work harder. They require more oxygen and they produce more carbon dioxide, which has to be removed from the body. The heart must respond to meet these demands, and must return the body to its normal state as quickly as possible by increasing the heart rate. The **cardiac centre** in the **medulla** of the brain controls the heart rate.

Control systems

The cardiac centre is one of many **control systems** in the body. A control system receives information about the changes that are occurring in the body, and sends out instructions to respond to them. Look at figure 1.

A change in the body that can be detected is called a **stimulus**. A **receptor** detects the stimulus and converts it to a form that is understood by the body, such as a nerve impulse or a chemical message. A **co-ordinator** receives the information from the receptor and responds by sending signals to **effectors**. An effector, such as a muscle or other organ, responds to the signals by performing an action, a **response**.

There are many control systems in the body. Control systems allow the body to respond to stimuli both outside the body (external stimuli) and inside the body (internal stimuli). The body's internal environment is maintained in the same state by the action of control systems. The heart is an effector that responds to signals from the cardiac centre.

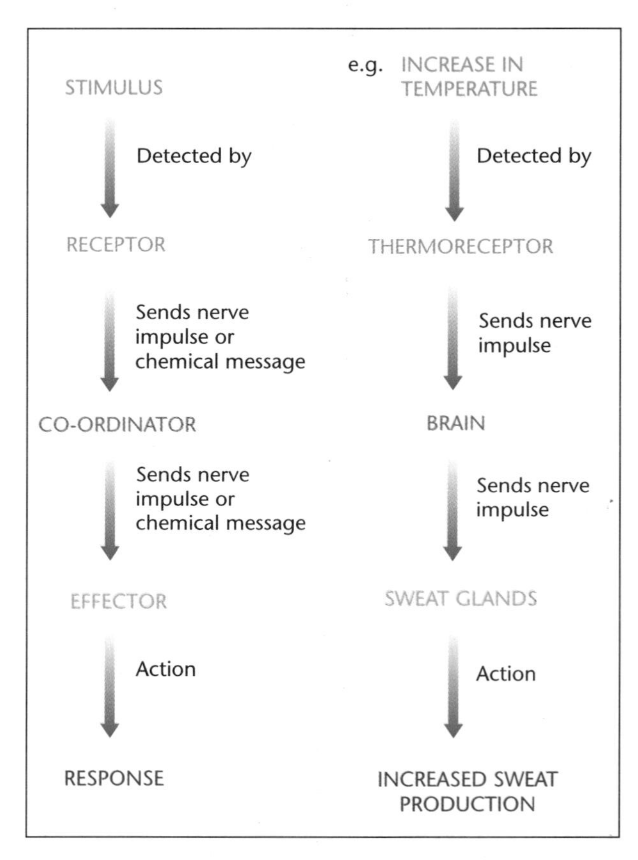

Figure 1 *The components of a control system.*

Responding to exercise

The cardiac centre is located in the medulla of the brain. It receives impulses from **chemoreceptors** (receptors that detect chemicals) and **pressure receptors**. These receptors are located in the walls of the aorta, and in a pocket in the carotid arteries called the **carotid sinus**.

During muscular activity, increased respiration leads to a rise in blood carbon dioxide levels. The medulla increases the rate of the heartbeat in response to this stimulus. Follow the sequence of events listed below using figure 2.

1 Increased respiration produces more carbon dioxide, which leads to a decrease in pH. The receptors in the aorta and carotid sinuses detect this fall in blood pH that occurs during increased muscular activity.

2 These chemoreceptors send a greater number of nerve impulses to the cardiac centre than normal.

3 The cardiac centre responds by sending nerve impulses along the sympathetic nerves to the SA node, the AV node and the ventricle walls, causing the heart rate to increase.

4 The blood supply to the lungs is increased, so carbon dioxide is taken to the lungs for removal more quickly.

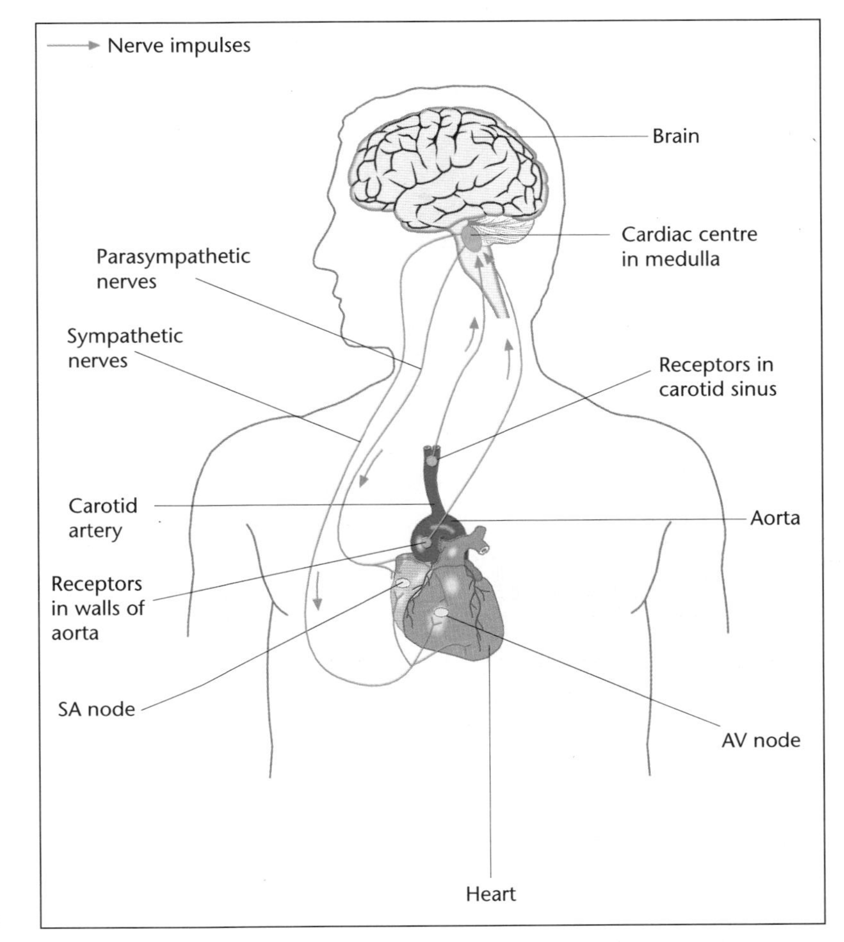

Figure 2 *The control of the heartbeat during increased muscular activity.*

To supply blood to reach all the tissues needing oxygen, not just the heart rate but also the blood pressure must be controlled. Pressure receptors in the walls of the aorta and carotid sinuses send nerve impulses to the medulla when the blood pressure needs to be increased. The medulla responds by sending nerve impulses along sympathetic nerves to the arterioles (small arteries). The muscles in the arterioles contract, causing the blood pressure to rise. This contraction is called **vasoconstriction.**

1 Look at the control system described above. Name:
- **a the stimulus**
- **b the receptors**
- **c the controller**
- **d the effector**
- **e the response.**

2 Describe what will happen if there is a decrease in:
- **a the carbon dioxide level in the blood**
- **b blood pressure.**

Key ideas 190–91

Chemoreceptors send signals to the medulla when the heart rate needs to be increased.

Pressure receptors send signals to the medulla when the blood pressure needs to be increased.

7 Controlling the breathing rate

The heart rate and blood pressure are controlled to respond to changes in the body's needs. The same is true of the breathing rate. You may have noticed the following points about the control of breathing:

1. Normal breathing is **involuntary** – it occurs without conscious thought.
2. You can vary the rate and depth of breathing consciously.
3. You breathe faster after exercise.

The control apparatus

Breathing is controlled by nerves which are under the control of the **respiratory centre** in the medulla of the brain. Figure 1 shows the nerves going from the medulla to the intercostal muscles and to the diaphragm.

The control of breathing depends on information from several receptors, as outlined below.

- As you breathe in, the lungs become stretched. Stretch receptors in the lung tissues send nerve impulses to the respiratory centre along the vagus nerve.
- Chemoreceptors in the medulla are sensitive to carbon dioxide levels in the blood.
- Chemoreceptors called the **aortic body** in the aorta and the **carotid body** in the carotid arteries are also sensitive to levels of carbon dioxide in the blood.

All these receptors send nerve impulses to the respiratory centre in the medulla. The respiratory centre combines information from them all and controls the breathing rate via nerve impulses to the intercostal muscles and the diaphragm.

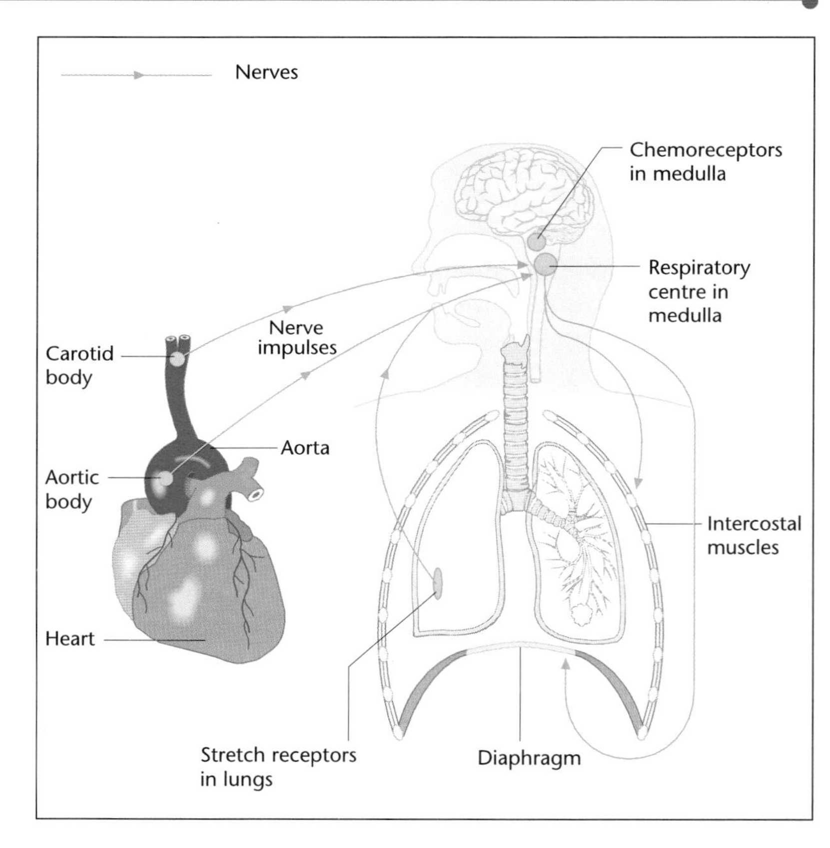

Figure 1 *The nerves involved in the control of breathing.*

1 Draw a simple diagram to show the nerve pathways involved in the control of breathing.

Breathing in and out

The respiratory centre in the medulla is responsible for maintaining ventilation 24 hours a day. In figure 2 you can see that ventilation starts with inspiration.

1. The respiratory centre sends nerve impulses along nerves to the diaphragm and intercostal muscles. These muscles contract and the lungs expand (inspiration).
2. Stretch receptors in the walls of the bronchi and bronchioles are sensitive to the expansion of the lungs. When the lungs are inflated, these stretch receptors send impulses to the respiratory centre, which stops sending impulses to the diaphragm and intercostal muscles. This stops inspiration.
3. The diaphragm and intercostal muscles relax and expiration occurs.
4. When the stretch receptors are no longer stimulated, expiration stops and the respiratory centre causes inspiration to take place again.

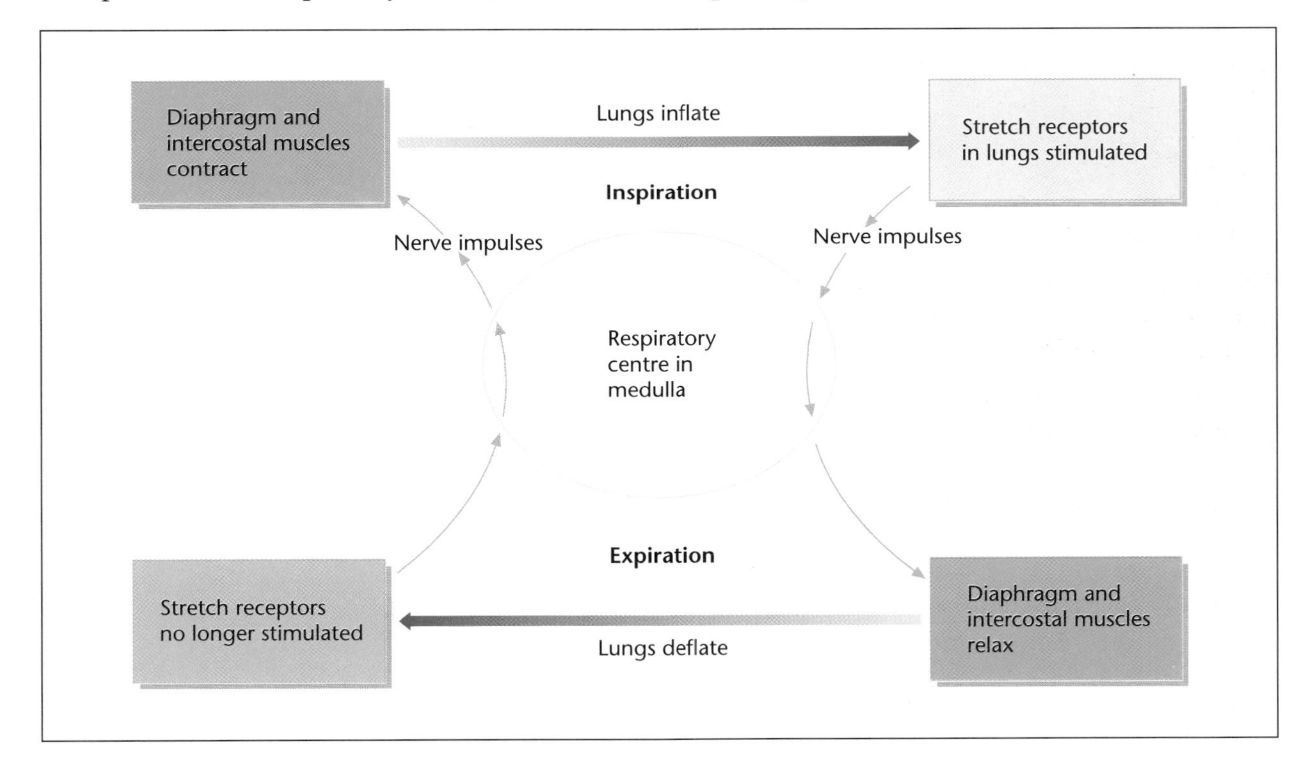

Figure 2 *The control of normal breathing.*

2 Look at the control system for normal breathing. Name:
- a the stimulus
- b the receptor
- c the controller
- d the effector
- e the response.

Key ideas 192–3

The respiratory centre in the medulla of the brain controls normal breathing in response to information from the stretch receptors in the lungs.

There are chemoreceptors in the medulla, the aortic body and the carotid body that detect increased carbon dioxide levels in the blood.

8 Breathing quicker and deeper

You will remember from page 180 that during vigorous exercise the muscles require more oxygen and produce more carbon dioxide. The circulatory system responds by pumping more blood to the lungs to meet these demands. The lungs also respond by increasing the rate and depth of breathing.

Responding to exercise

It is the rise in carbon dioxide levels in the blood during exercise that triggers changes to the rate and depth of breathing. Study the sequence of events in figure 1.

- The aortic and carotid bodies and the chemoreceptors in the medulla detect higher levels of carbon dioxide during increased muscular activity.
- The chemoreceptors send a greater number of nerve impulses to the respiratory centre.
- The respiratory centre responds by sending nerve impulses to the diaphragm and intercostal muscles more quickly, causing the rate and depth of breathing to increase.
- The excess carbon dioxide is removed from the blood and the level returns to normal.

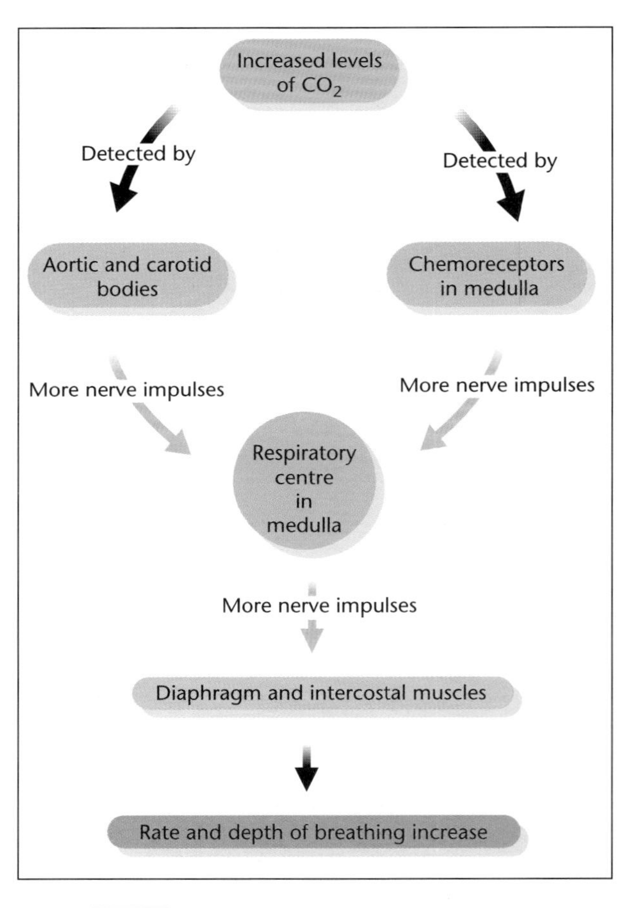

Figure 1 *The control of breathing during increased muscular activity.*

1 Describe what will happen if there is a decrease in carbon dioxide levels.

2 Look at the control system above. Name:

a the stimulus

b the receptors

c the controller

d the effector

e the response.

A bad night's sleep

Lots of people snore while they are asleep, but there are some people who actually stop breathing. These people have a medical disorder called **central sleep apnoea**. It is a rare disorder in which the sufferer may not take a breath for an unusually long time, then suddenly inhale rapidly (snore). Also the person may inhale at regular intervals but exhale with difficulty.

Central sleep apnoea is a disorder of the nervous system. It is caused by a delay in the nerve impulses from the brain. If the medulla switches off, even for only short periods, breathing will stop. In most cases the sufferer is aroused from sleep by an automatic breathing reflex and ends up getting very little sleep. Usually the sufferer has no memory of these brief awakenings.

Central sleep apnoea is difficult to diagnose because the symptoms are similar to those of other sleep disorders. The symptoms include snoring, holding your breath while sleeping, waking up gasping for air, headaches in the morning, excessive grogginess and a desire to sleep during the day. Left untreated these symptoms can be dangerous. It is common for people with sleep apnoea to fall asleep at work or while driving.

Figure 2 *A good night's sleep?*

3 Using your knowledge of the control of breathing, explain how breathing stops during central sleep apnoea.

The mask

There are many treatments for sleep apnoea. The most common treatment is the CPAP (continuous positive airway pressure) mask shown in figure 3. This mask is worn over the nose while sleeping. It is connected via a hose to a unit that supplies a constant push of air. CPAP is designed to pressurise the nasal passages and the trachea, so that they do not collapse. The latest devices reduce the pressure of the incoming air during expiration, so that the sufferer can expire with less effort. The mask comes in different sizes to fit a wide range of people.

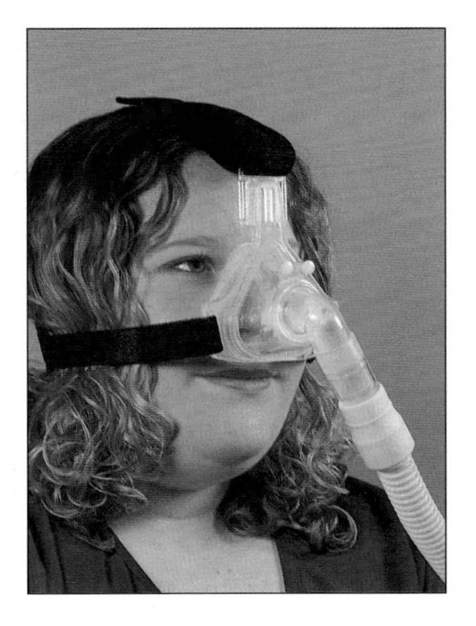

Figure 3 *The CPAP mask used to treat sleep apnoea.*

Key ideas 194–5

Chemoreceptors in the aortic body, carotid body and the medulla detect increased levels of carbon dioxide during increased muscular activity.

The respiratory centre receives signals from these chemoreceptors and responds by increasing the rate and depth of breathing.

9 Pipework

Blood moves through the body in tubes called **blood vessels. Arteries** carry blood away from the heart. **Veins** return blood to the heart. **Capillaries** are very small vessels connecting the arteries and the veins.

Structure

Arteries and veins share the same basic structure. There is a wall surrounding a central space or **lumen**. The lining of the wall is an **endothelium** (an internal epithelium), with a smooth surface that helps blood to flow smoothly. The structure of the wall is related to the function of the vessel. Arteries and veins have all three layers; capillaries have only the endothelium.

Tubing – arteries and veins

Figure 1(a) shows an artery. The layer of muscle and elastic tissue is very thick. Arteries carry blood away from the heart, so the blood inside them is under high pressure. Every time the heart beats, a surge of blood passes through which causes the artery wall to bulge slightly. The thick elastic layer then causes the wall to spring back. This is called **elastic recoil** and it helps to keep blood pressure high. You can feel these surges of blood if you press on an artery. This is a **pulse**.

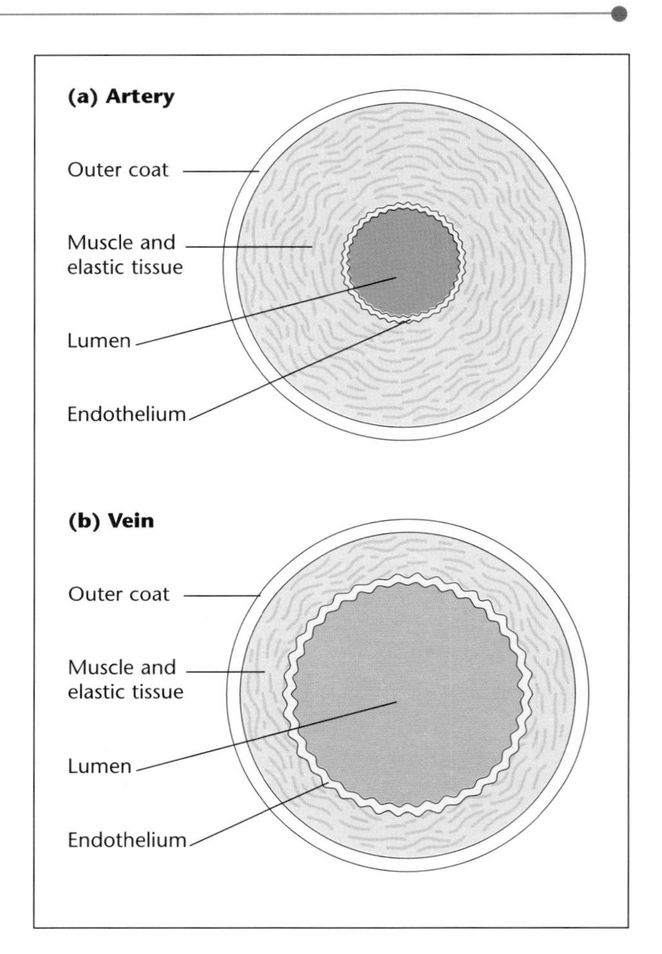

Figure 1 *Section through (a) an artery (b) a vein.*

1 **The number of surges per minute felt in the pulse is the same as the number of cardiac cycles per minute. Explain why.**

Figure 1(b) shows a vein. If you compare it with the artery you will see that the muscle and elastic tissue layer is much thinner in the vein. This is because veins carry blood back to the heart, so the blood inside them is at a lower pressure. Some large veins bring the blood back against gravity, for example in the legs and arms. **Valves** in the veins help keep the blood flowing towards the heart. When muscles contract, they press on veins and this helps keep the blood flowing.

There are more veins than arteries close to the surface of the body. You can see these through your skin, and they are used by doctors for taking blood samples. Drug addicts who inject drugs into veins often cause damage to the walls so they form scars, and eventually the veins collapse. Kidney dialysis also damages the veins.

Control valves

The valves in veins are semilunar valves, like those in the heart arteries shown on page 187. These valves are found all the way along veins. Figure 2(a) shows a closed valve. You can see that the valve has pockets which are filled by blood. In figure 2(b) the valve is open and the pockets are flat against the lining of the vein. Each valve has three pockets formed by the endothelium.

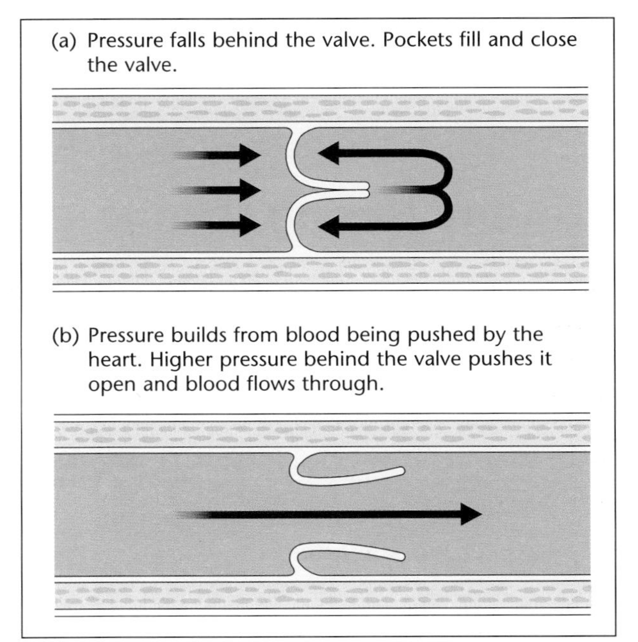

Figure 2 *Longitudinal (lengthways) section through a vein to show the action of valves.*

Leaky tubing – capillaries

Figure 3 shows a capillary. You can see that the wall is only a single layer of cells. The diameter of a capillary is 6–7 µm, which is less than that of a red blood cell. The red blood cells have to be squeezed through. Capillaries allow the exchange of materials between blood and body cells.

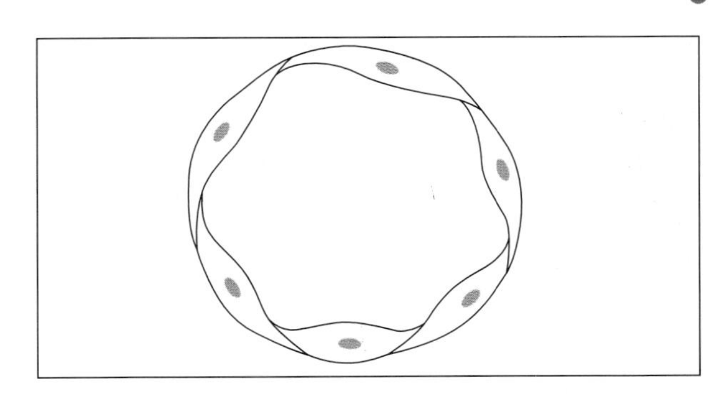

Figure 3 *Section through a capillary.*

Key ideas 196–7

The walls of different blood vessels show adaptations to their functions.

Artery walls are thicker and more elastic than veins because they carry blood under higher pressure.

Veins have valves to keep blood flowing towards the heart.

Capillaries have walls that are only one cell thick.

Changing over

At the capillaries, small molecules can enter and leave the blood. Some molecules leave the blood and enter the intercellular spaces between body cells. They form **tissue fluid**, an intercellular fluid like that described on page 78. Proteins and cells cannot leave the blood, as they are too big to pass through the gaps in capillary walls.

Pressure forcing change

Figure 1 shows how the pressure changes as blood flows out of the heart in the aorta and returns in the vena cava. The small changes in pressure inside arteries gradually fade away further away from the heart.

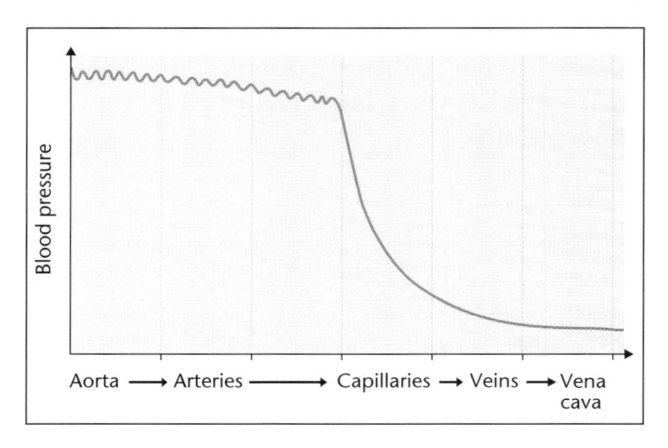

Figure 1 *Pressure changes in the blood vessels.*

1. **What causes these small pressure changes in arteries?**
2. **What is the relationship between blood pressure and distance from the heart?**

Figure 2 shows body cells and capillaries. Blood arrives at the cells in an **arteriole**, which is a branch of an artery. The arterioles branch to form a **capillary network** between all the cells. The blood in these arterial capillaries is under high pressure from the heart. The capillary network rejoins to form small vessels called **venules**, which leave the cells. The blood in the capillaries at the venous end is under much lower pressure because it is further away from the heart.

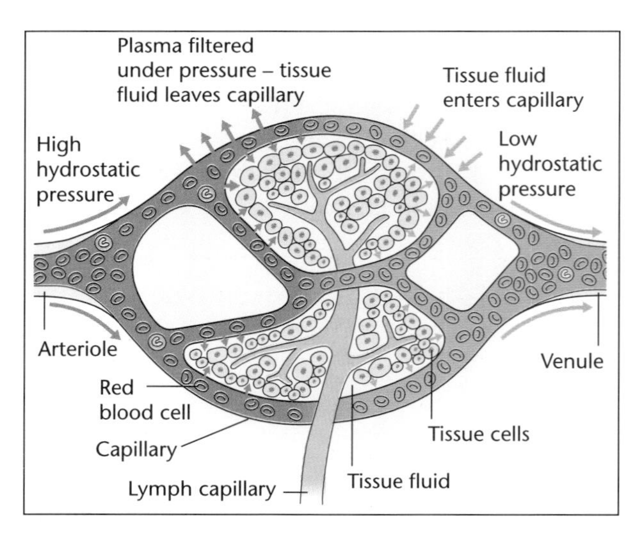

Figure 2 *Ultrafiltration in the capillaries.*

The heart pushes the blood, creating **hydrostatic pressure**. Molecules small enough to pass through the pores in a capillary are squeezed out by this pressure. This is **ultrafiltration**. It results in a drop in hydrostatic pressure from the arterial end of the capillaries to the venous end.

The fall in hydrostatic pressure means that ultrafiltration slows down. The water potential inside the capillaries falls, because water and small molecules have left but proteins remain in the blood. Therefore water re-enters the blood down a water potential gradient. Other small molecules move down diffusion gradients.

Spot the difference

Substances passing out of the capillaries into the intercellular fluid form a solution called **tissue fluid**. Cells exchange molecules with tissue fluid. As a result tissue fluid has a different composition from blood plasma.

3 On page 182 you can see the range of substances carried by the blood. Use this and the information on these two pages to copy and complete table 1.

Table 1 *The composition of tissue fluid and blood.*

Component	Plasma	Tissue fluid
Water	Present	Present
Large proteins		Absent
Glucose	High concentration	Lower concentration
Amino acids		
Chylomicrons		
Oxygen		Lower concentration
Carbon dioxide		
Wastes		Higher concentration
Red blood cells		

The back drains

Some substances in tissue fluid do not return directly to the blood. A separate set of vessels called the **lymph system** collects these substances and carries them to the blood. The liquid in the system is called **lymph**. The lymph system starts as capillaries in tissue fluid. You can see these in figure 2. The lymph capillaries join together to form **lymph vessels** all over the body. These join to form a large vessel on each side of the body and these open into the blood circulation at a vein in the neck.

In some parts of the body such as the intestines, neck and armpits there are **lymph nodes**. These produce white blood cells and antibodies, which are carried by lymph vessels to the blood. Some cells secrete proteins that cannot easily enter vein capillaries, but can enter lymph capillaries. At the small intestine, absorbed lipids enter lymph vessels called **lacteals** in the villi.

4 Look back at your table from question 3 and add another column for lymph.

In some people the lymph system becomes blocked, so excess fluid builds up and causes swelling in the tissues. Some pregnant women develop swollen ankles because hormone changes affect blood pressure. This swelling is called **oedema**.

Key ideas 198–9

Pressure in blood vessels falls the further away the blood is from the heart.

The pressure from the heart causes ultrafiltration of small molecules from capillaries into tissue fluid.

Osmosis and diffusion allow exchanges between the cells, tissue fluid and blood.

The lymph system drains excess tissue fluid from cells.

1 Transporting oxygen

As blood circulates, it collects oxygen in the lungs and gives it up to respiring cells in other body organs. **Red blood cells** carry the oxygen. Blood contains around 5 000 000 red blood cells per mm^3, each packed full of a protein called **haemoglobin**. Haemoglobin allows each cell to carry very large amounts of oxygen at a time.

Shape shifter

On page 67 you saw that proteins have a tertiary structure, formed by folding of the polypeptide chain. Haemoglobin has a more complex structure. You can see in figure 1 that it has four polypeptide chains, each with an extra iron-containing molecule called a **haem** group. The iron in the haem group gives blood its red colour, and allows haemoglobin to combine with oxygen. Each haem group can carry one oxygen molecule.

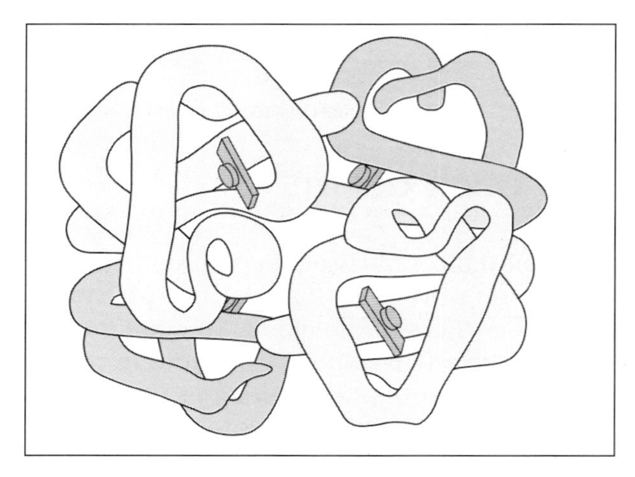

Figure 1 *The haemoglobin molecule has four polypeptide chains, coloured blue and purple above, and four haem groups, coloured grey.*

1 How many oxygen atoms can one molecule of haemoglobin carry?

Oxygen fits into a complementary slot on the haemoglobin. This is like the way a substrate fits into an enzyme's active site. Every time a molecule of oxygen attaches, the haemoglobin changes shape, making it easier for the next oxygen molecule to attach.

Haemoglobin has an **affinity** (attraction) for oxygen. Haemoglobin with oxygen attached forms **oxyhaemoglobin**. Look at figure 2 and you can see that this reaction is reversible. Oxygen **associates** with (attaches to) haemoglobin where the concentration of oxygen is high. Where the concentration of oxygen is low, oxygen **dissociates** (falls away) from haemoglobin. The association between oxygen and haemoglobin is not a chemical reaction, but it causes the blood to change colour from a dark red to the bright red you can see when you cut the skin.

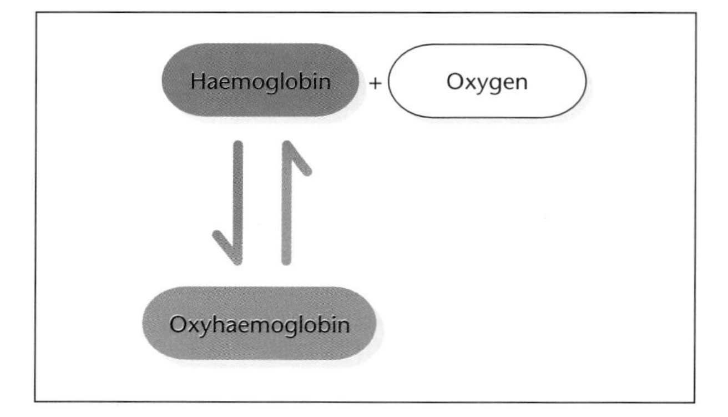

Figure 2 *Haemoglobin and oxygen associate to form oxyhaemoglobin.*

Q

2 Explain why the blood from a cut is always bright red, but a blood sample from a vein is dark red.

Transport blockers

Some molecules have a similar shape to an oxygen molecule, for example, carbon monoxide and cyanide. They can compete with oxygen for the oxygen-carrying site of haemoglobin. Like oxygen, they form a link with the haem group and cause a colour change. Carbon monoxide gives the blood a bright red colour, while cyanide turns it blue-red. These changes make the face, lips and tongue a different colour, which is used to diagnose poisoning by these molecules. People who burn gas in poorly ventilated rooms may die of carbon monoxide poisoning, formed from the partial burning of the gas.

Loading up

The amount of haemoglobin in the blood that is bound as oxyhaemoglobin is called the **percentage saturation**. As oxygen is a gas, its concentration in a mixture of gases is measured as **partial pressure** in units of **kilopascals (kPa)**. The concentration of oxygen dissolved in a solution in the body is also measured as partial pressure.

Look at figure 3 showing the amount of haemoglobin combined with oxygen in different concentrations of oxygen. This is an **oxygen dissociation curve**. You can see that at high partial pressures of oxygen, almost all the haemoglobin is combined with oxygen. As the partial pressure of oxygen decreases, so does the percentage of haemoglobin combined with oxygen.

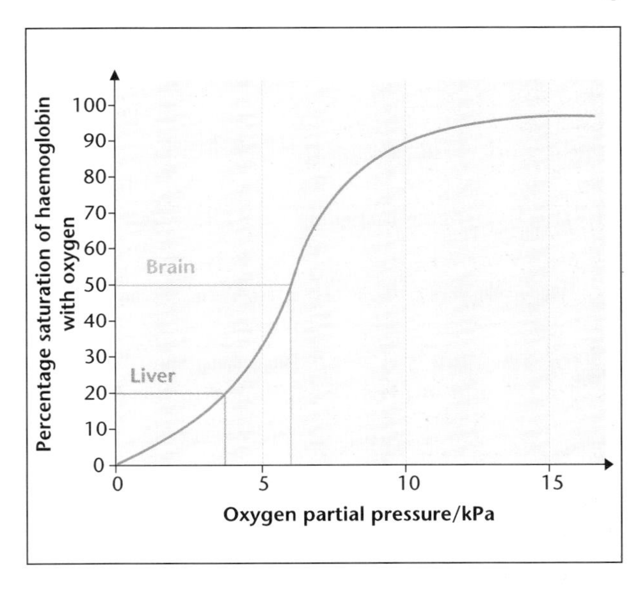

Figure 3 *Oxygen dissociation curve for haemoglobin.*

3 **Why do different tissues have different partial pressures of oxygen?**

4 **The partial pressure of oxygen in the brain and liver are shown on the graph. How much extra oxygen does the liver receive compared with the brain?**

Key ideas 200–201

Oxygen is carried by haemoglobin as oxyhaemoglobin.

Molecules with a shape similar to that of oxygen can block oxygen transport.

Oxygen is loaded onto haemoglobin in high partial pressures of oxygen.

Oxygen is unloaded from haemoglobin in low partial pressures of oxygen.

12 Changing the odds

The dissociation of oxygen from haemoglobin depends on the oxygen partial pressure. It is also affected by carbon dioxide concentration in organs. Carbon dioxide lowers the affinity of haemoglobin for oxygen. It causes the haemoglobin molecule to change shape so that oxygen is released more easily. This means that in regions of high carbon dioxide, haemoglobin will unload more oxygen.

Acid maker

Carbon dioxide decreases the oxygen-carrying ability of the blood because it reacts with water in blood to form an acid. Figure 1 shows this reaction, which forms hydrogen ions. These are acidic and would cause the pH of blood to become very low. However, haemoglobin takes up the hydrogen ions. This is called **buffering**. As haemoglobin takes up hydrogen ions it changes shape, and oxygen is released.

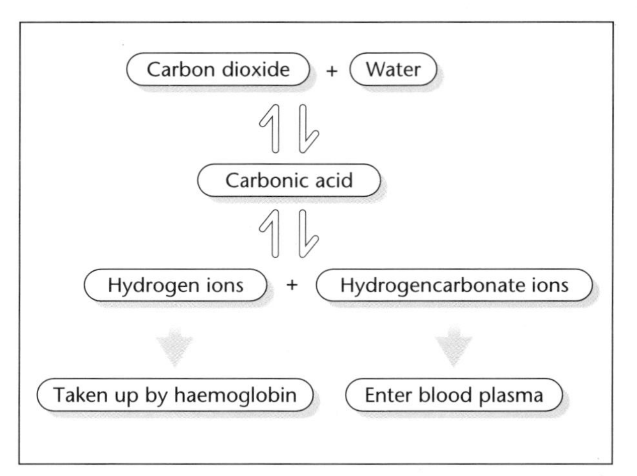

Figure 1 *The reactions of carbon dioxide in the blood.*

1 **Why is it important to prevent blood pH from falling too low?**

2 **What would be the effect of a high carbon dioxide concentration on the loading of oxygen in the lungs?**

Look at figure 2 which shows the effect of a low concentration of carbon dioxide on the dissociation curve of haemoglobin.

Compare the two curves. On the red curve, when no carbon dioxide is present, find the oxygen partial pressure at which there is 50% saturation of haemoglobin (50% is still loaded). Now read up from the same partial pressure on the blue curve, when carbon dioxide is present. You can see that the percentage saturation of haemoglobin has decreased – it has given up more oxygen.

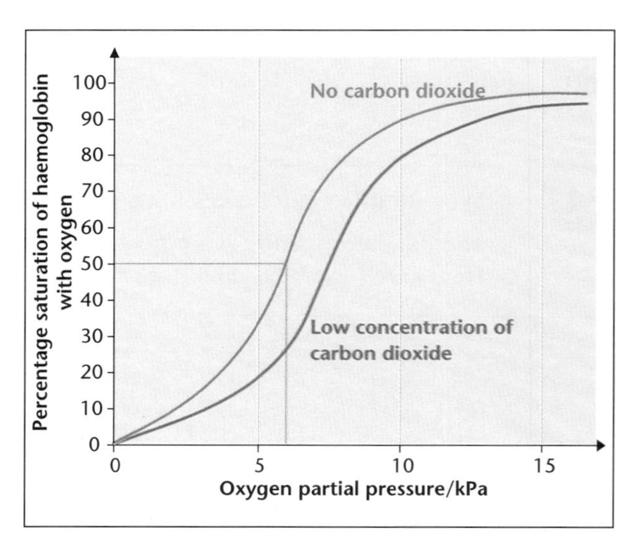

Figure 2 *The effect of carbon dioxide on haemoglobin loading.*

3 **Sketch figure 2 and draw another curve on your graph to show the effect of an even higher concentration of carbon dioxide.**

Controlling supply

On page 180 you saw how an increase in muscular activity needs an increased oxygen supply. Muscles and also other organs with high metabolic activity like the liver produce more carbon dioxide than organs like the brain. The oxygen supply to different organs is controlled according to the amount of carbon dioxide they produce.

The process of respiration uses oxygen and releases carbon dioxide, so the rate of respiration itself controls the amount of oxygen released to the cells from the blood. This is an example of **feedback control**. Look at figure 3 which shows how this works.

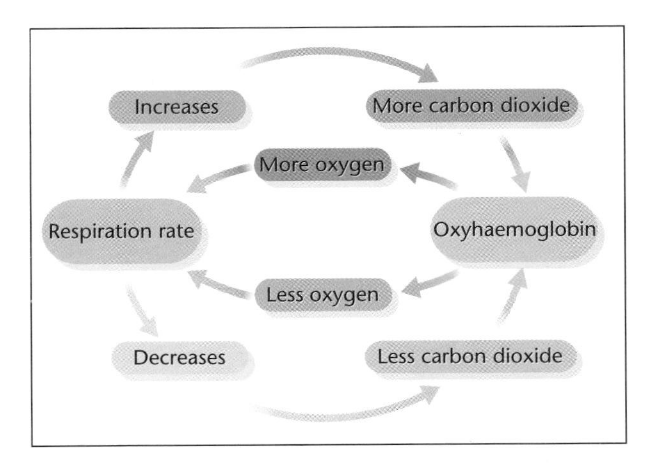

Figure 3 *Controlling the oxygen supply.*

4 Identify the stimulus in the control system in figure 3.

5 What is the advantage of this control system to the body?

Coping with change

If you travel by air, at the beginning of the flight there is always a demonstration of how to use an oxygen mask in case of emergency. This is because at high altitude the partial pressure of oxygen is very low. An aircraft flies around 10 000 m above sea level, where the partial pressure of oxygen in the air outside is about 5.5 kPa.

6 Look at figure 3 on page 201. How much oxygen could you load into haemoglobin at an oxygen partial pressure of 5.5 kPa?

The air inside an aircraft is pressurised, so it is the same as air at ground level. In an emergency there may be a sudden depressurisation, so the oxygen masks prevent passengers from becoming breathless and then unconscious.

7 Why would depressurisation cause people to become breathless and then unconscious?

People who go deep-sea diving have a different problem with pressure. Normally, nitrogen gas in air does not diffuse into the blood. Under the sea the pressure is high. When the diver breathes in air from the tanks, nitrogen gas from the air is able to diffuse across alveoli and dissolve in the blood. In an emergency a diver may have to come to the surface very quickly, and the rapid depressurisation causes the nitrogen to bubble in the blood. This is similar to the depressurisation when you remove the lid from a bottle of fizzy drink. The gas bubbles can cause capillaries to burst, leading to brain damage.

Key ideas 202–3

Carbon dioxide decreases the affinity of haemoglobin for oxygen.

This effect of carbon dioxide on haemoglobin controls oxygen supply to different tissues.

Changes in pressure affect the diffusion of gases into the blood.

13 Energy supplies

Many activities within the body, such as muscle contraction, need energy. In living organisms the main process for releasing energy is **respiration**. Respiration consists of a series of enzyme-controlled reactions that release energy from digested food. Most of an organism's energy requirements are met by breaking chemical bonds in the carbohydrates glucose and glycogen to release stored energy. However, lipids and proteins can be used to provide alternative energy sources when needed.

Meeting energy demands

The energy produced in the body depends on the level of exercise and how long it lasts. Compare the two athletes shown in figure 1.

The sprinter can only maintain this high level of activity for a short period of time. The jogger can maintain this level of activity for a longer period of time. Sports scientists divide the running needs of different sports like these into different energy pathways. These energy pathways involve the following substances:

- **ATP** is a compound formed when energy is released from food. It is stored in all cells, particularly muscle. When ATP is broken down the stored energy is released and the cells can perform work.
- **Creatine phosphate** is a compound stored in muscle. When creatine phosphate is broken down, it helps in the production of ATP.
- **Lactic acid** or **lactate** is produced from the incomplete breakdown of glucose. The build-up of lactate helps cause muscle fatigue.
- **Oxygen** may be used in the production of ATP from digested food. Carbohydrates and lipids are the main food sources used in respiration using oxygen.

Some energy pathways can only be used for a certain length of time, and different energy pathways can be used together.

Figure 1 *The sprinter is producing energy by respiration more quickly than the jogger.*

With or without oxygen

Different energy pathways make up **energy systems**. There are two main types of energy system used – **aerobic respiration** and **anaerobic respiration**. Aerobic respiration occurs in the presence of oxygen and anaerobic respiration in the absence of oxygen.

Let's look at respiration, which you studied at GCSE. Respiration is a metabolic process that takes place in all cells, providing the energy that living organisms need to survive. In respiration, food is broken down into carbon dioxide and water, and the energy in the food is released. The energy released is not used directly by the cell, but is used to make the cell's energy carrier, **ATP**. ATP carries energy around the cell to where it is needed. ATP supplies energy for the processes that take place in all living organisms, such as muscle contraction, the transmission of nerve impulses and active transport.

The main food substance used in respiration is glucose. To release all the available energy in the glucose molecule, oxygen is needed and the process is known as **aerobic respiration**. It is summarised in figure 2. The complete breakdown of one molecule of glucose using aerobic respiration yields a maximum of 38 molecules of ATP.

Glucose $C_6H_{12}O_6$ + Oxygen $6O_2$ → Carbon dioxide $6CO_2$ + Water $6H_2O$ + Energy 38ATP

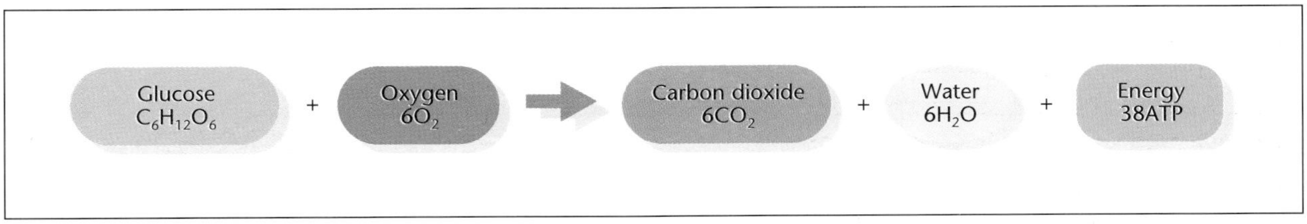

Figure 2 *Aerobic respiration.*

Respiration can also occur without oxygen, and this is known as **anaerobic respiration**. The process is summarised in figure 3.

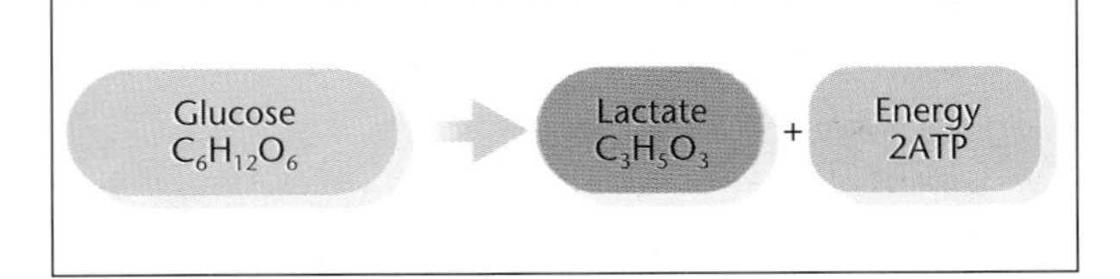

Figure 3 *Anaerobic respiration in animal cells.*

You can see that in anaerobic respiration in animal cells, the products are lactate and ATP. Glucose has not been broken down completely, as it is in the presence of oxygen, so the maximum number of 38 molecules of ATP cannot be produced. In anaerobic respiration, only two molecules of ATP are produced from one molecule of glucose.

The two equations show the importance of oxygen in energy production. This is especially important when energy demands are high, for example during exercise when muscular activity increases and oxygen levels are low.

Key ideas 204–5

Glucose can be used as a source of energy for muscle contraction.

ATP is the cell's energy carrier.

The products of aerobic respiration are carbon dioxide, water and a maximum of 38 molecules of ATP per glucose molecule.

The products of anaerobic respiration in animals are lactate and 2 molecules of ATP per glucose molecule.

14 Energy for exercising muscles

Most cells have a steady energy demand met by aerobic respiration. However, in skeletal muscle (muscle used to move the skeleton), where ATP plays an essential role in muscle contraction, there can be sudden and extreme changes in ATP demands.

Alternative energy sources

Under normal conditions the energy for muscle contraction comes from aerobic respiration of glucose. The ATP produced can then be used directly in muscle contraction. During exercise, glucose or oxygen supplies may not be enough and alternative ways of providing ATP can be used, depending on how the muscles are being used and for how long. Table 1 shows some of these alternatives.

Table 1 *ATP sources other than the aerobic respiration of glucose may be used under different exercise conditions.*

Duration of activity/seconds	Energy system	Energy source
1–4	Anaerobic	ATP in muscles
4–20	Anaerobic	ATP and creatine phosphate
20–45	Anaerobic	ATP, creatine phosphate and muscle glycogen
45–120	Anaerobic	Muscle glycogen
120–140	Aerobic and anaerobic	Muscle glycogen
140–600	Aerobic	Muscle glycogen and fatty acids

You can see in table 1 that several energy sources other than glucose can be used during exercise. When ATP is broken down to release energy, **ADP** is produced. **Creatine phosphate** can be coupled with ADP to regenerate ATP, as shown in figure 1.

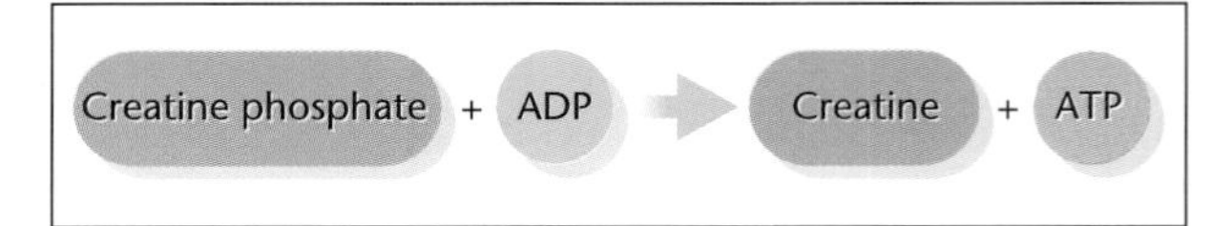

Figure 1 *Regeneration of ATP using creatine phosphate.*

Excess glucose is stored in liver and muscle cells as **glycogen**. When the demand for energy is high, glycogen can be converted back to glucose for use in respiration.

Fatty acids can also be used as an energy source. Respiration using fatty acids yields high levels of energy. The body's carbohydrate store lasts for about 90 minutes, whereas the fatty acid store will last for several days.

1 **Summarise aerobic respiration and anaerobic respiration.**
2 **Draw diagrams to show the structure of the following:**
   a **glucose**
   b **glycogen**
   c **fatty acid.**

Recovering after exercise

When the demands for glucose exceed the supply in the blood, your muscles have to rely on stored reserves of glycogen and fatty acids. If oxygen cannot be provided quickly enough, anaerobic respiration must be used. One drawback of this is the build-up of lactate, which is a mild poison. This leads to a feeling of discomfort or cramp, which occurs during and for some time after vigorous exercise. Look at figure 2. The footballer is feeling the intense pain associated with a build-up of lactate.

The footballer feels the pain of cramp because his muscles have been contracting vigorously for a long time. His circulatory system could not deliver enough oxygen for aerobic respiration, so anaerobic respiration was taking place. The lactate produced in the muscles is transferred into the blood and carried around the body. This causes the body to function less efficiently and the muscles **fatigue** (tire) very quickly.

The build-up of lactate leads to a lowering of blood pH (the blood becomes more acidic). The muscles, being starved of oxygen, take the body into a state called **oxygen debt**. After the exercise is over, this oxygen debt has to be repaid and the energy supply must be replenished. This recovery stage is shown in figure 3. The lactate is carried in the blood to the liver, where some is converted to carbon dioxide and water and most is converted to glycogen.

During recovery from strenuous exercise, skeletal muscle can also use fatty acids from lipid digestion to obtain ATP. This can then be used to replenish the exhausted supply of glycogen and creatine phosphate.

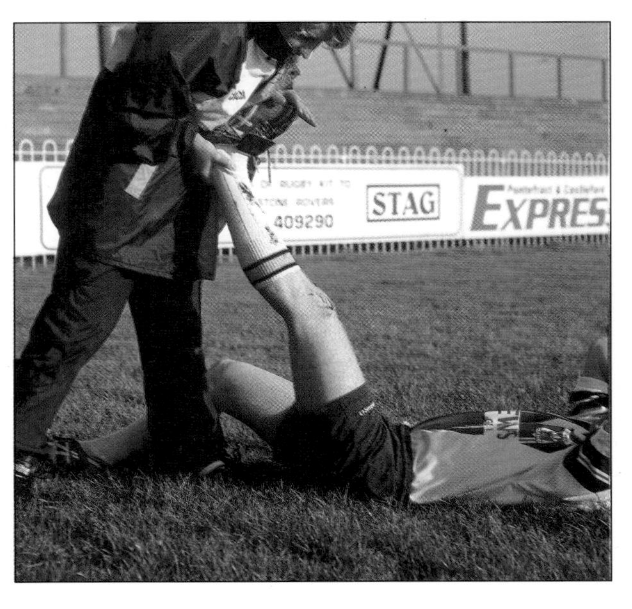

Figure 2 *The result of excess lactate is cramp.*

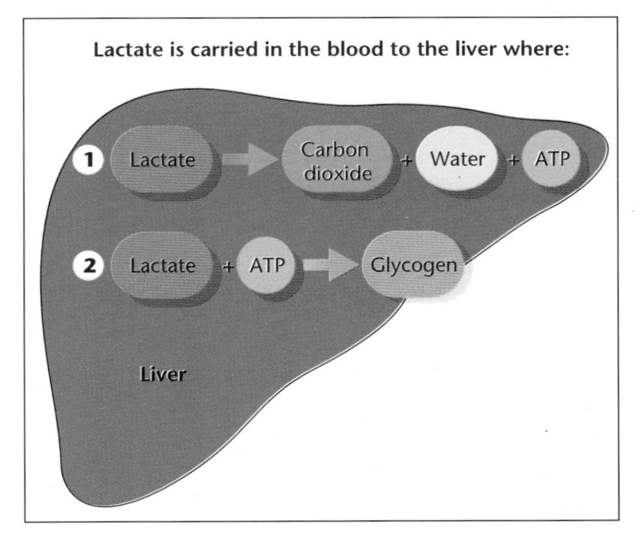

Figure 3 *Recovery after exercise. These reactions need oxygen.*

Key ideas 206–7

Glycogen and fatty acids can be used as alternative energy sources for muscle contraction.

During anaerobic respiration, blood lactate levels rise and the blood pH falls, causing muscle fatigue.

Lactate is carried to the liver where it is converted to carbon dioxide and water or to glycogen.

Unit 10 – Questions

15

① Figure 1 shows the changes that take place in the left side of the heart during a cardiac cycle.

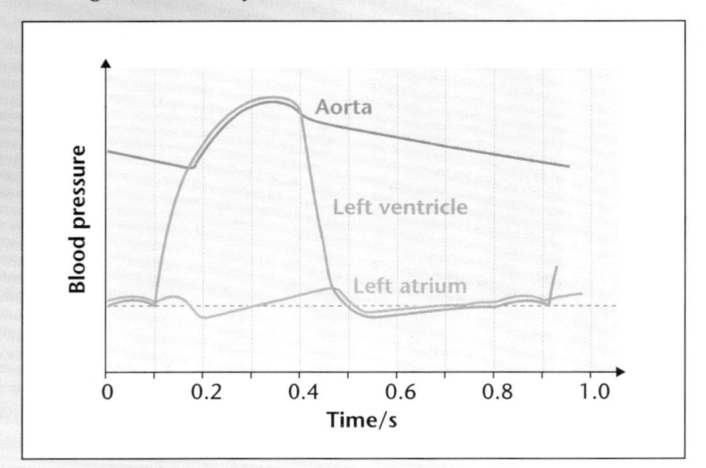

a) i) How long does one cardiac cycle last? (1 mark)
ii) Calculate the heart rate in beats per minute. (1 mark)
iii) At what time does the semilunar valve close? (1 mark)

b) Explain why the blood pressure in the pulmonary artery is lower than in the aorta. (2 marks)

(Total 5 marks)

② The graphs in figure 2 show the pulse rate and output of blood from the left side of the heart over a 7-minute period.

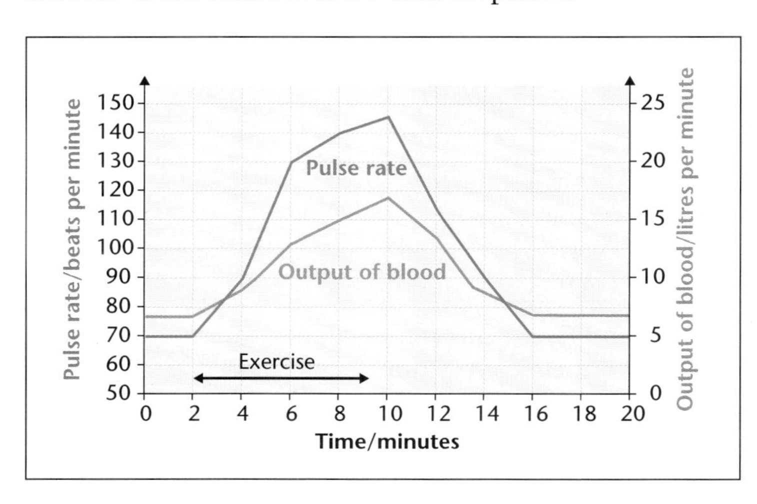

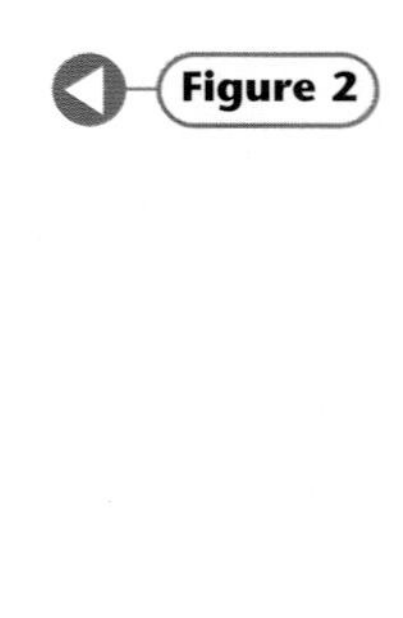

a) i) What is the relationship between pulse rate and blood output during exercise? (1 mark)

ii) Calculate the output of blood per beat from the left side of the heart at the start of exercise and 2 minutes after exercise has started. (3 marks)

b) Explain the reasons for the change in output per beat during exercise. (4 marks)

(Total 8 marks)

3) Table 1 shows the concentrations of some compounds in the muscle of a person at rest and after a period of exercise.

Compound in muscle	Concentration/μmol per gram of tissue	
	At rest	After exercise
Glycogen	78	42
Creatine phosphate	15	4.1
ATP	4.9	3.7
Lactate	0.9	29.5

a) Give one reason for the change in concentration of each of the compounds in muscle. (4 marks)

b) What happens to lactate during recovery from exercise? (3 marks)

c) How does muscle replace its glycogen store? (2 marks)

(Total 9 marks)

4) The bar chart in figure 3 shows the order and duration of diastole and systole in atria and ventricles.

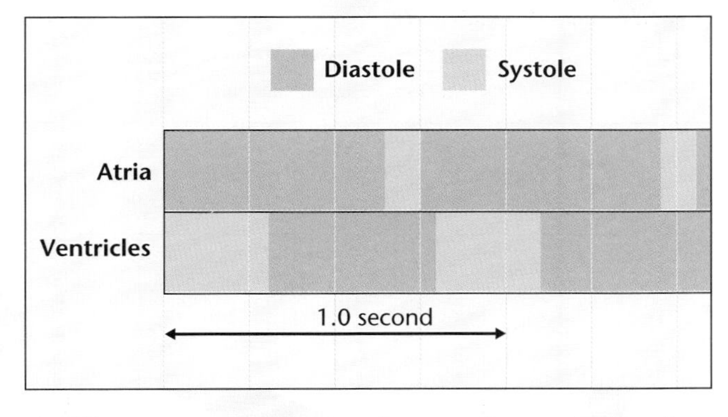

Figure 3

a) How many cardiac cycles are shown in the bar chart? (1 mark)

b) State what is happening to each of the following during ventricular systole:

i) the atria

ii) the atrioventricular valves

iii) blood in the atria. (3 marks)

(Total 4 marks)

1 The structure of a plant root

A plant root is designed to anchor the plant in the soil, and to absorb water and dissolved mineral ions from the soil.

Inside the root

Look at figure 1. You can see that the **root cap** covers the tip of the root. This is a tough layer of cells that are able to withstand the pressure of the root growing through the soil. Behind the root cap is the **apical meristem**, which contains a group of actively dividing cells. Behind this there is a region of **cell elongation**, where the new cells get longer, and then a region of **cell differentiation**. In the region of cell differentiation, plant cells develop into specialised kinds of cells. Near the root tip, **root hairs** grow from the outer layer of root or **epidermis**. They are only found in a small area of the root, after the cell elongation zone.

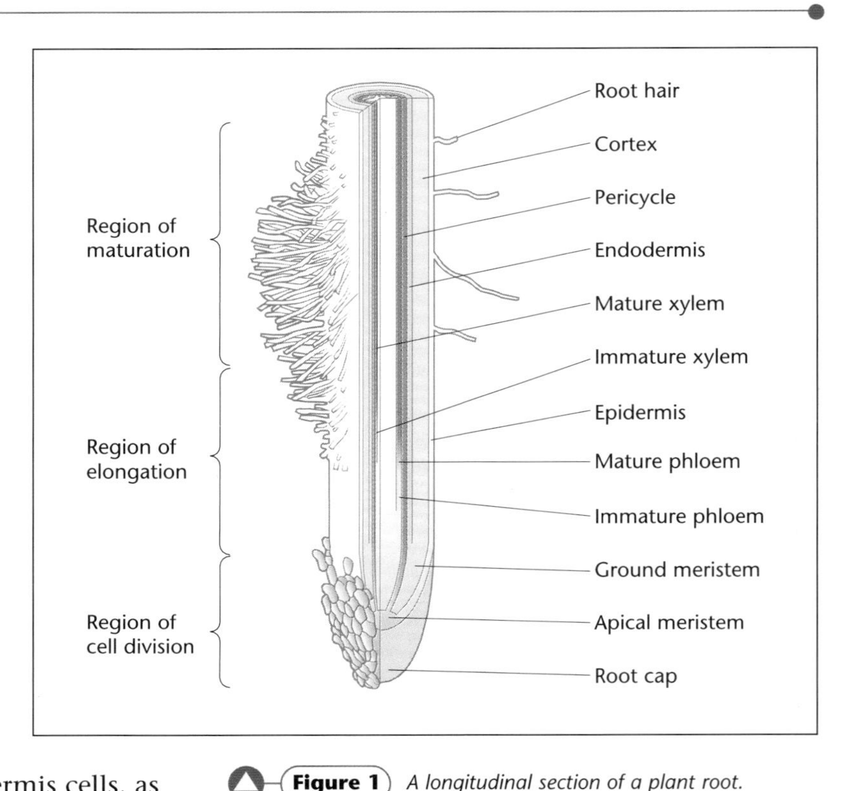

Figure 1 *A longitudinal section of a plant root.*

Root hairs are very enlarged epidermis cells, as figure 2 shows. They have a large surface area to absorb water.

1. **Explain why there is a protective layer of cells around the root tip.**
2. **Explain the purpose of the root hairs.**

Root hair
Epidermis cell

Figure 2 *A root hair cell.*

In figure 1 you can see a layer called **endodermis**. Endodermis cells have a layer of a waxy substance called **suberin** around them. This forms a **Casparian strip**, which waterproofs the side walls of the endodermis cells. As the endodermis cells get older, suberin is also laid down on their inner walls. This is important for the movement of water and ions through the root.

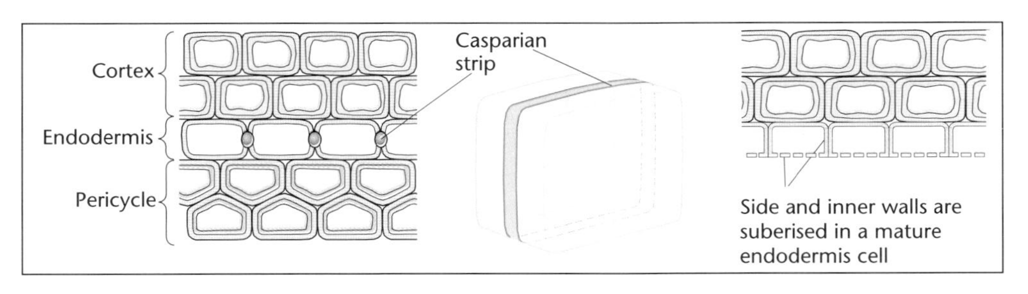

Figure 3 *The structure of endodermis cells.*

A different view

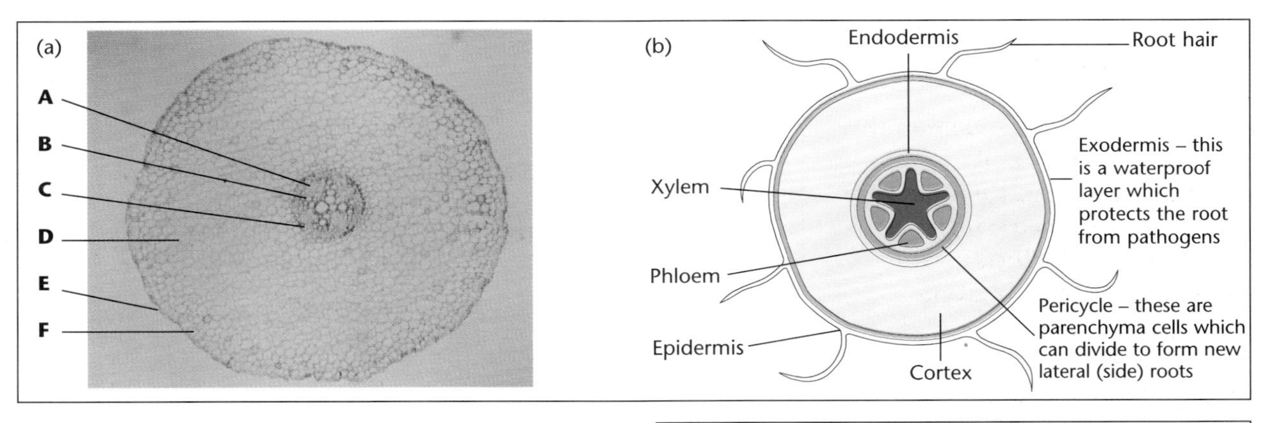

Figure 4 *(a) Photomicrograph (×15) and (b) diagram of a transverse section through a plant root.*

> **Q**
>
> **3 Look at figure 4. This shows a transverse section through a root. Name structures A–F on the photomicrograph.**

You can see the **cortex** in figures 1 and 4, outside the endodermis. The cortex is made of cells called **parenchyma cells**. It may store starch.

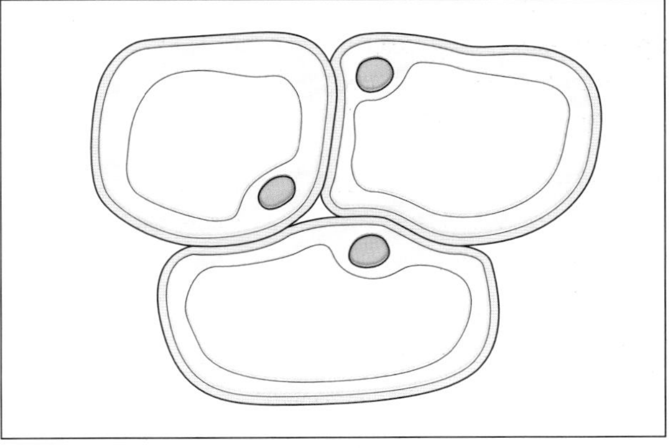

Figure 5 *Parenchyma cells in the root cortex.*

Making transport tissues

Meristems are regions in the plant where simple, non-specialised cells divide. These can then differentiate into specific types of cell. The **cambium** is a meristem tissue. Cells from the cambium can divide to form new **xylem** or **phloem** cells as the plant grows. Xylem and phloem are the plant's transport tissues.

Transport structures

2

Xylem transports water and dissolved minerals around the plant. **Phloem** transports dissolved organic substances such as sugars. The structures of xylem and phloem are suitable for their transport functions in the plant.

Xylem – carrying water

Xylem cells are long, tubular cells with no living contents when they are mature. They have cell walls that are strengthened and waterproofed by a woody substance called **lignin**. Most of the tissue is made up of large cells called **vessels**, with thickened, strengthened walls.

(a)

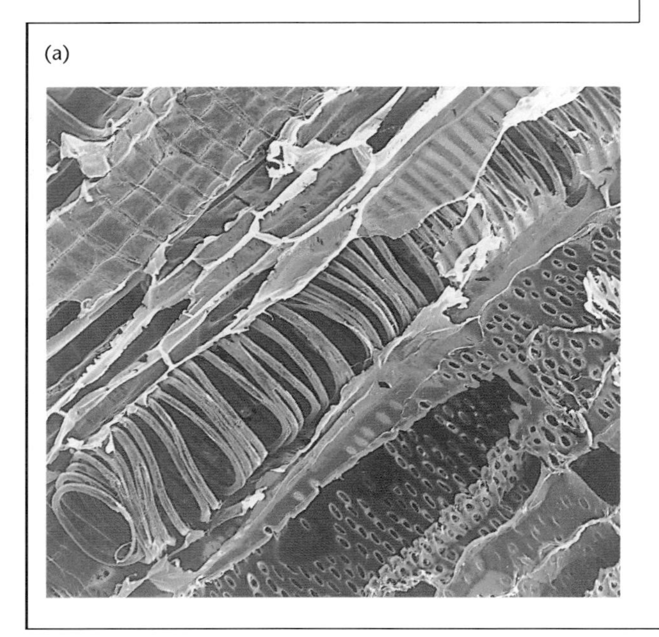

(b) Xylem (brown) and parenchyma cells (white)

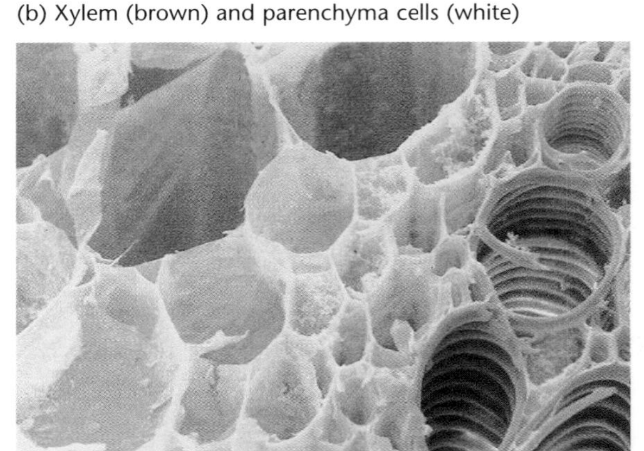

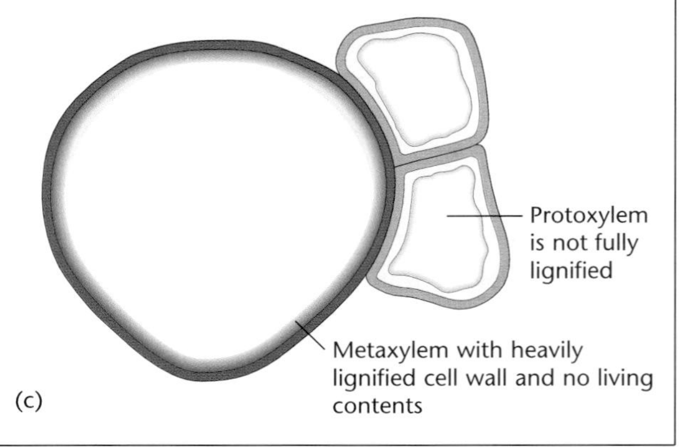

Figure 1 *Photomicrograph of (a) longitudinal and (b) transverse section of xylem cells (× 300). (c) Diagram of a transverse section of xylem cells.*

Phloem – carrying dissolved substances

Phloem tissue is made up of two kinds of cells. **Sieve tubes** are long, thin cells. They join together to form long tubes with **sieve plates** connecting them. When mature, sieve tubes have very few cell contents. Their main purpose is transporting organic solutes (such as sugars and amino acids) through the plant. Next to the sieve tubes are **companion cells**, which are very active, and help with loading and unloading of the sieve tube with solutes.

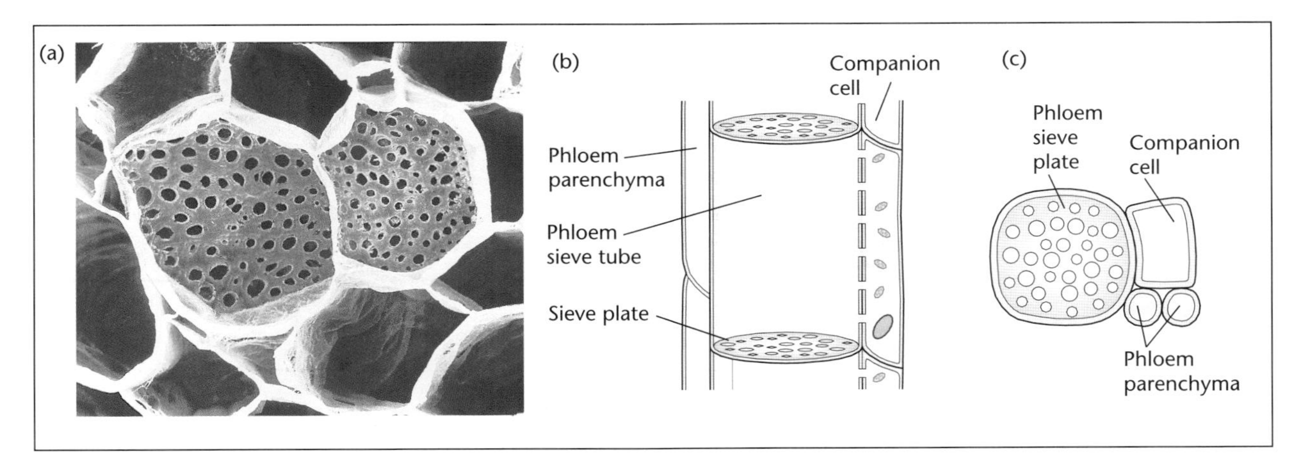

Figure 2 *(a) Photomicrograph of longitudinal section of phloem cells (×650). (b) Longitudinal and (c) transverse sections of phloem cells.*

1. **Where in the root do plant cells divide to form xylem and phloem?**
2. **Give two differences between xylem and phloem.**

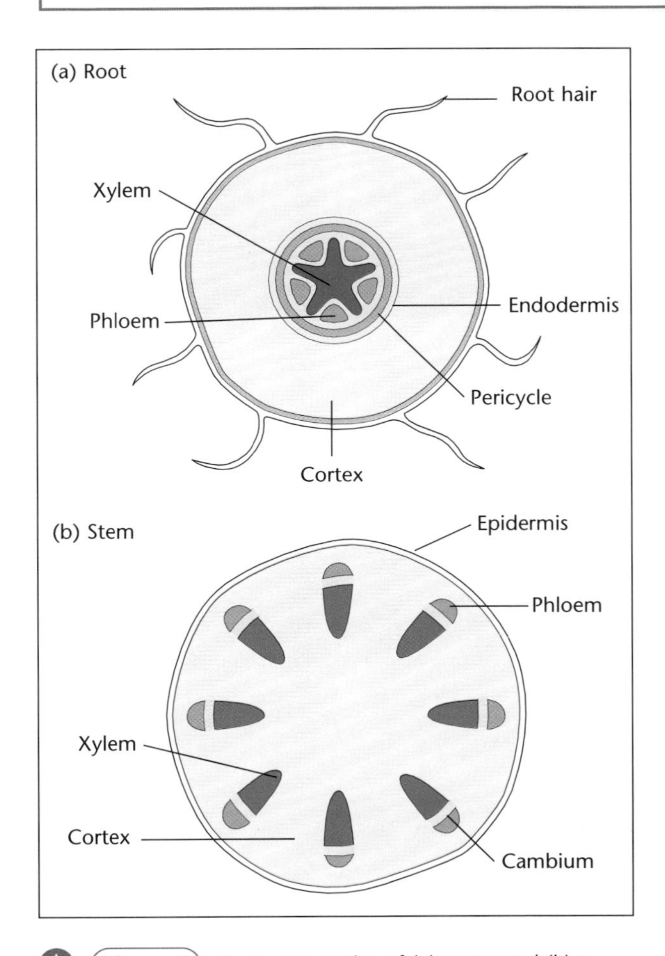

Figure 3 *Transverse section of (a) a root and (b) a stem, showing the positions of the transport tissues.*

Roots and stems

Look at figure 3 showing a transverse section of a root and a stem. You can see that the xylem and phloem are arranged differently in the two parts of the plant. In the root, the transport tissues are in the middle. In the stem, they are in groups called **vascular bundles**, further towards the edge of the stem. This helps support the stem.

Key ideas 210–13

Roots have specialised kinds of cells in them, such as endodermis and root hairs.

Xylem tissue transports water and phloem tissue transports organic solutes.

3 Specialised roots

Some plants have roots that are specialised. For example, some plants have **aerial roots**, which are produced from above-ground structures. Some plants have **prop roots** for support.

Supporting roots

Look at figure 1 showing prop roots in maize. When the roots make contact with the soil, they branch, and help to absorb water and mineral ions as well as supporting the plant.

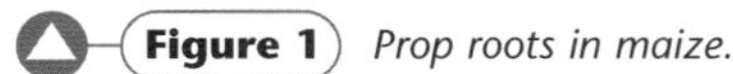

Figure 1 *Prop roots in maize.*

Living without oxygen

Roots need oxygen so their cells can respire. This is why most plants cannot live in water-logged soil where there are no air spaces. Mangroves are a group of unusual trees that not only live in water, but can even live in salt water from the oceans. Most land plants are killed by salt, but mangroves are able to get rid of the salt. The root cell membranes act as 'superfilters' to keep out the salt ions. They also have salt-secreting glands on the leaves that pump out excess salts.

Most plants die if their roots are drowned in water and have no oxygen, and in the mud of mangrove swamps, saprophytes feeding on rotting leaves usually use up all the oxygen. However, black mangrove trees have developed special kinds of roots called **pneumatophores** (air roots) that stick up out of the mud into the air to get oxygen. You can see these in figure 2.

Red mangroves have prop roots and also **drop roots**. Drop roots are like prop roots, but they grow not from the stem but from the branches of the tree into the ground, going only a few centimetres into the ground. Drop, prop and pneumatophore root systems are all covered in small pores called **lenticels** which allow oxygen to diffuse in.

Figure 2 *Pneumatophores (air roots) of the black mangrove.*

Storage roots

Most roots are storage organs, but some roots are specialised for storage. For example, the roots of the sweet potato are fleshy because they have a large amount of storage parenchyma. The parenchyma cells are full of starch grains, which are bigger than the starch grains in most plant cells.

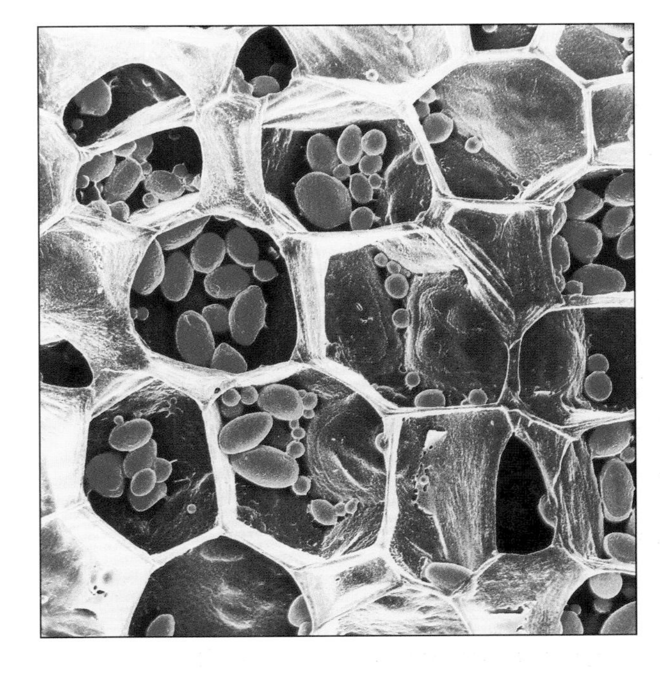

Figure 3 *Section through the root of potato (×160). The photograph shows starch grains (shown red) stored in parenchyma cells. Although potato is a stem tuber, starch grains like these are present in many different kinds of storage root.*

Photosynthesising roots

Photosynthesis is usually carried out by the leaves of a plant, not the roots. **Epiphytes** are plants that grow on other plants, but they are not parasites. They make their own food by photosynthesis. For example, orchids have aerial roots that are several layers thick and are able to photosynthesise. In some species, this is the only part of the plant that can photosynthesise.

1 Look at figure 4. How can you tell that the roots of this epiphyte can photosynthesise?

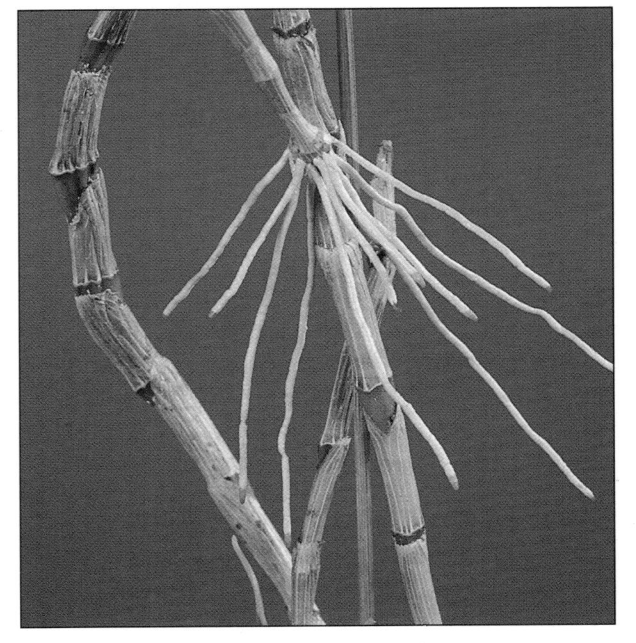

Figure 4 *The aerial roots of an orchid are able to photosynthesise.*

Key ideas 214–15

Some plants have specialised roots. In some plant species the roots may support the plant, absorb oxygen, store food materials or even photosynthesise.

4 Getting water in

Plants need water for photosynthesis, and to keep their cells turgid, which is important for supporting the plant. Water is also needed to transport mineral salts and organic solutes around the plant. The roots take in water for the rest of the plant.

Osmosis again

A thin film of water, containing tiny amounts of dissolved mineral ions, covers the particles of soil surrounding the roots. Most of the water absorbed by the plant enters in the region of the root hairs. As you can see in figure 1, water enters the root hair from the soil by osmosis, down a water potential gradient.

1 Which has the higher water potential, the solution of water in the soil or the root hair cell? Explain your answer.

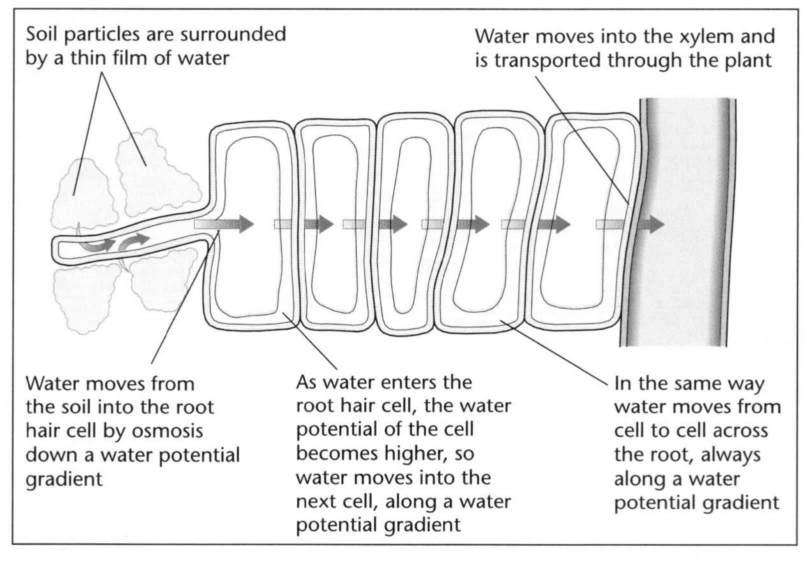

Figure 1 *The path of water from the soil to the xylem.*

As water enters the root hair cell, this raises its water potential, so it is now higher than that of its neighbouring cell. This means water passes from the root hair cell to the cortex cell next to it. This process is repeated across the root, until the water enters the xylem. However, this is just a simple way of looking at the process.

Water can, in fact, move across the root in different ways. Figure 2 shows two routes it can take.

The symplast pathway

The watery film surrounding the soil particles has a higher water potential (it is a more dilute solution) than the root hair cells. This means water enters the root hair cell by osmosis, passing through its cell wall and membrane.

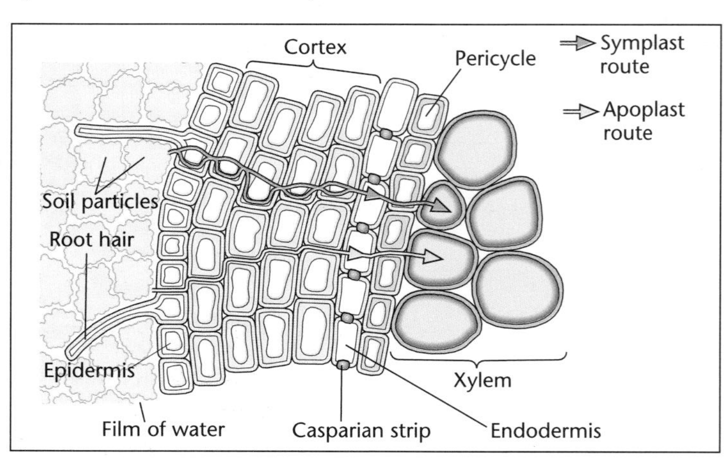

Figure 2 *Two pathways for water to move through the root of a plant.*

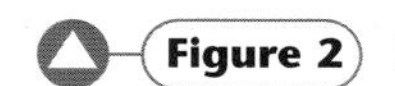

Strands called **plasmodesmata**, which pass through pores in the cellulose cell walls, connect the cytoplasm of neighbouring plant cells. You can see these in figure 3. Water passes from the soil into the cytoplasm of root hair cells, then passes from the cytoplasm of one cell to another via the plasmodesmata, down a water potential gradient. This is the **symplast pathway**.

There is a water potential gradient pulling water across the root, because water is constantly moved up the xylem, and is replaced by water from the neighbouring cells. As water leaves the cells surrounding the xylem, this reduces their water potential, so water enters them by osmosis from their neighbours. This continues across the root system, so there is a continuous movement of water from the watery film in the roots, across the root, and into the xylem.

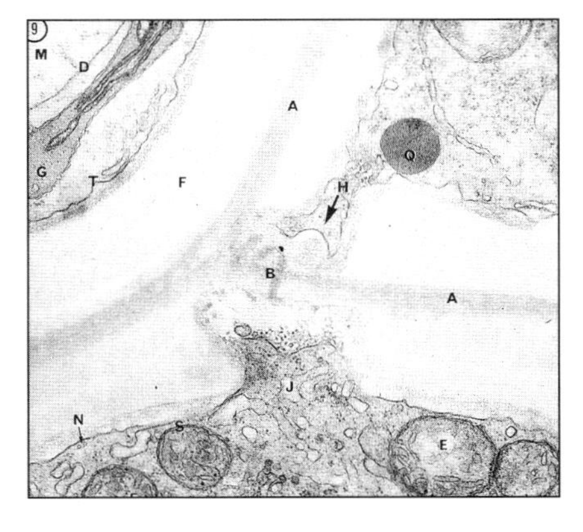

Figure 3 *Electron micrograph showing a plasmodesma (**B**) connecting two cells (×8000).*

The apoplast pathway

The cellulose cell wall is made up of a loose mesh of cellulose fibres, so there is plenty of space in the wall for water molecules. Some of the water entering the root moves across the root in the cell walls and extracellular spaces between the cells. Hydrogen bonding attracts water molecules to each other, so as water is taken up into the xylem, this draws water across the root. Mineral ions dissolved in the water can move by this **apoplast pathway** too.

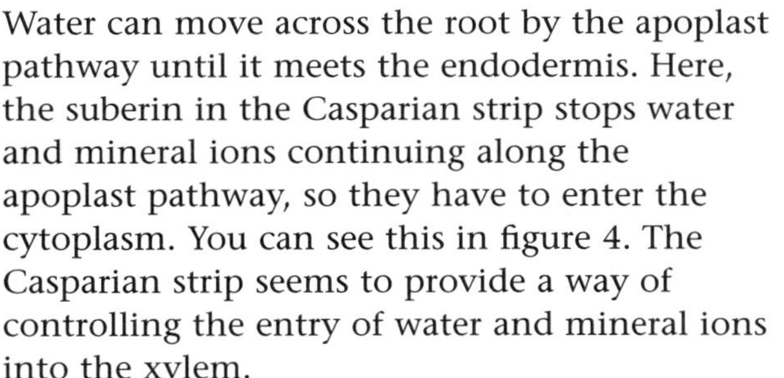

Water can move across the root by the apoplast pathway until it meets the endodermis. Here, the suberin in the Casparian strip stops water and mineral ions continuing along the apoplast pathway, so they have to enter the cytoplasm. You can see this in figure 4. The Casparian strip seems to provide a way of controlling the entry of water and mineral ions into the xylem.

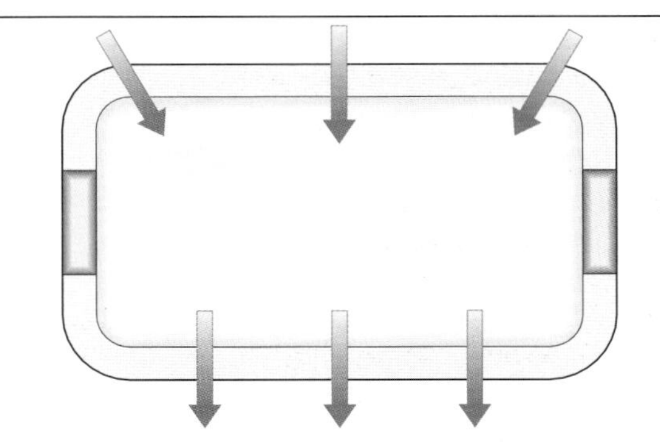

In a young endodermis cell, the strip of suberin (the Casparian strip) stops water and ions moving sideways

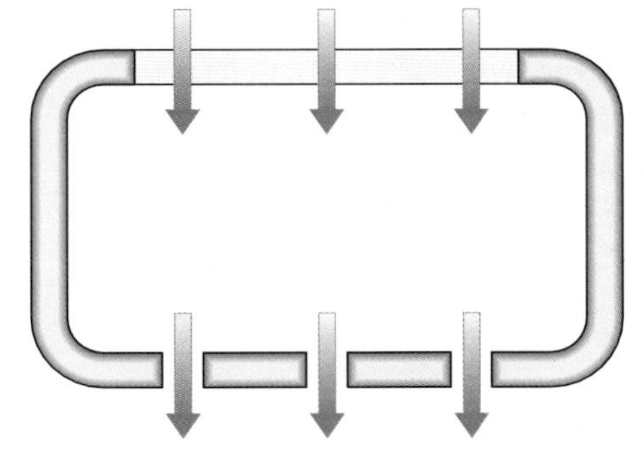

The cell wall of a mature endodermis cell is heavily suberised, so water and ions can only move onwards through the plasmodesmata

Figure 4 *The endodermis and Casparian strip – the end of the apoplast pathway.*

Key ideas 216–17

Water enters the root by osmosis, mainly into the root hairs.

Water moves across the root by osmosis from cell to cell (the symplast pathway) or by movement through cell walls and the intercellular spaces (the apoplast pathway).

5 Moving through

The movement of water in the xylem of plants depends on **transpiration.** Transpiration is the evaporation of water vapour from the surface of a plant, mainly its leaves. Most of the water that is lost from a plant evaporates through the stomata, which are open for gas exchange, providing the carbon dioxide the plant needs for photosynthesis. However, water is also lost through the cuticle and from the lenticels (pores in the bark of woody plants).

Pulling ...

In figure 1 you can see the air spaces inside the leaf of a plant. They are always saturated with water vapour, which has evaporated from the cell walls of the spongy mesophyll cells. As this water evaporates, it causes more water to be drawn into the cell by osmosis from its neighbouring cell, and so on, back to the xylem itself. As water is drawn out of the xylem by osmosis, this creates a **tension** (a 'pull') on the column of water in the xylem. Molecules of water show **cohesion** – they are held together by hydrogen bonds. This makes the column of water in the xylem very strong and unlikely to break. This means that as transpiration causes water to move out of the xylem in the leaves, the whole column of water in the xylem is pulled upwards. This explanation for the movement of water through a plant is called the **cohesion–tension theory.**

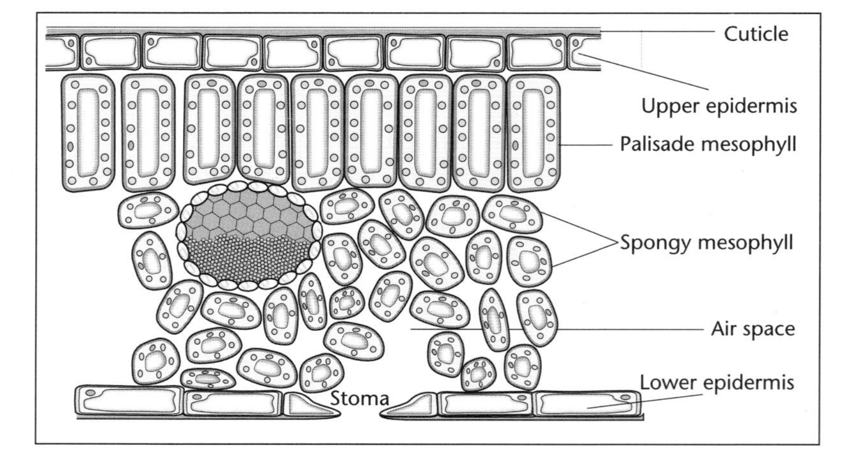

Figure 1 *The structure of a leaf.*

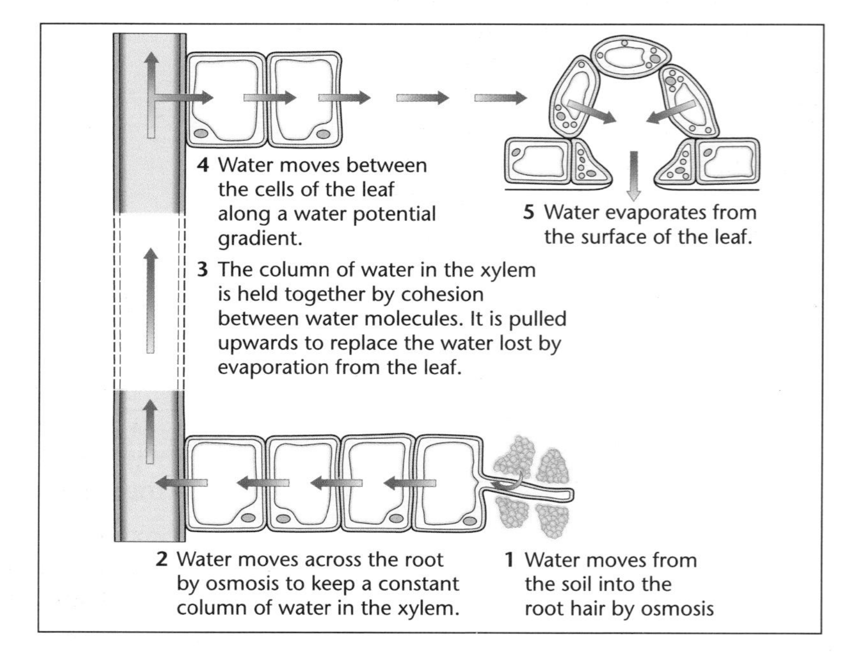

Figure 2 *How water moves through a plant by cohesion–tension.*

Another factor which helps to pull the water in the xylem upwards, and stops the column of water breaking, is that water molecules are attracted strongly to the walls of the xylem vessels. This is called **adhesion**.

1 In 1893 Josef Bohm carried out the experiment shown in figure 3 to demonstrate the cohesion–tension theory. Explain what the different parts of the apparatus represent.

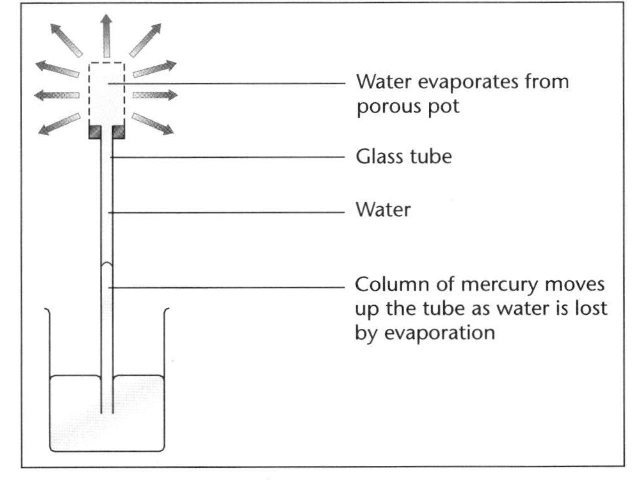

Figure 3 *Josef Bohm's experiment to demonstrate the cohesion–tension theory.*

… and pushing

If you cut off a pot plant just above the root, and connect a glass tube to it, water will gradually build up in the glass tube. You can see this in figure 4. The water is pushed up by **root pressure**.

2 How do we know that this rise is not due to transpiration?

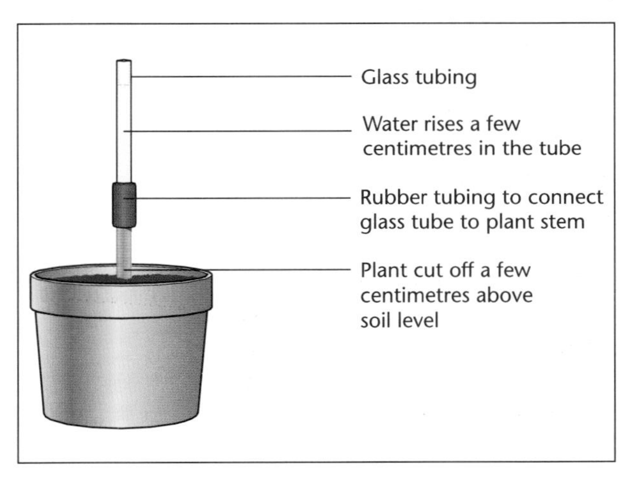

Figure 4 *Demonstrating root pressure.*

Look at figure 1 on page 210. Inside the endodermis is a layer called the **pericycle**. Dissolved mineral ions are actively transported out of the pericycle cells and into the xylem. This lowers the water potential of the xylem and helps water to pass into the xylem. It is the movement of these mineral ions into the xylem that creates root pressure.

3 At night, when transpiration is very low, you can sometimes see drops of water being forced out of the leaves. This is called guttation. Can you explain what causes this?

Key ideas 218–19

Water moves through the xylem by cohesion between water molecules and tension created by the 'pull' of transpiration.

Root pressure helps water move up in the xylem, and is caused by ions being actively transported into the xylem.

6 Transpiration

Transpiration is the loss of water from the above-ground parts of a plant. Most water is lost through the stomata in the leaves, but water can be lost through other parts of the plant, such as the leaf cuticle.

Measuring water loss

You can show that transpiration happens by enclosing the pot of a potted plant in a plastic bag and putting the plant on a top-pan balance. The mass gradually falls as water evaporates off the surfaces of the plant.

1 Look at figure 1. Why is the pot enclosed in a plastic bag?

2 This method does not measure transpiration very accurately. Can you suggest why?

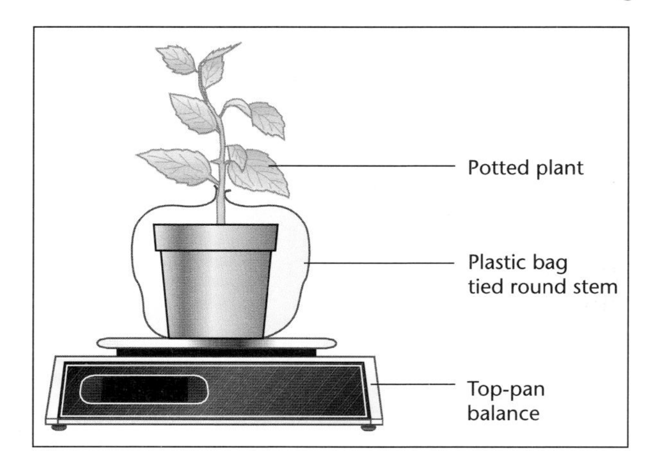

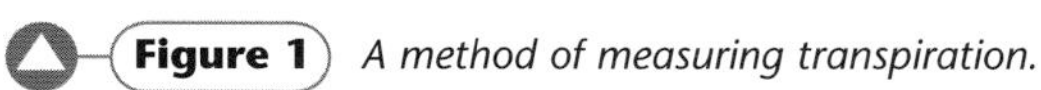

Figure 1 *A method of measuring transpiration.*

It is very difficult to measure transpiration, the loss of water from a plant, accurately. It is much easier to measure the uptake of water by a plant. This can be done using a **potometer**. Figure 2 shows a typical potometer.

3 Over a period of 5 minutes, a student noticed that the air bubble moved 2 cm along the scale on the potometer. How can the student find the volume of water taken up by the plant in 5 minutes?

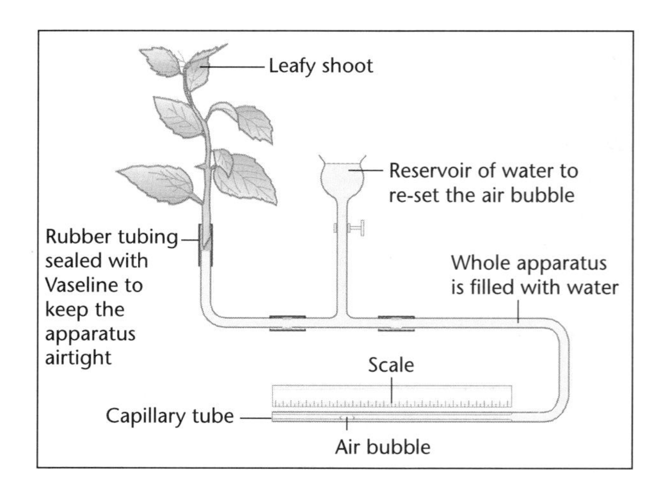

Figure 2 *A potometer demonstrates the uptake of water by a plant.*

Changing the rate of water loss

The rate of water loss from a plant is affected by a number of factors, including light intensity, temperature, air movement and humidity.

Light intensity: the stomata in the leaf usually open in the light, to allow carbon dioxide into the leaf for photosynthesis. The stomata close in the dark when photosynthesis is not occurring. This means that the transpiration rate increases as the light intensity increases, until the stomata are fully open and transpiration is at a maximum. Figure 3 shows this relationship.

Temperature: a higher temperature increases the kinetic energy of molecules, and therefore increases the rate of evaporation of water from the leaf. It also means the surrounding air can hold more water vapour, and this also increases the rate of transpiration.

Air movement: in still air, a layer of moist air builds up around the surface of the leaf. This reduces the rate of transpiration by reducing the water potential gradient. In windy conditions, the layer of moist air is blown away, and very moist air in the leaf meets the much drier air directly outside the leaf. This gives a much bigger water potential gradient, and increases the rate of transpiration. You can see this in figure 4.

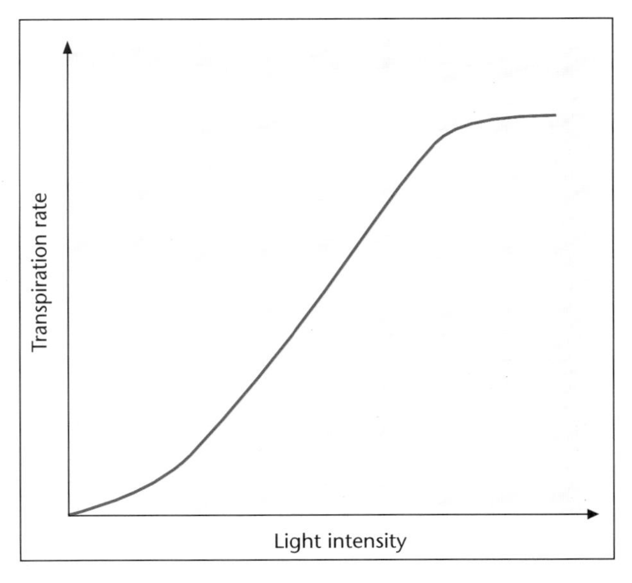

Figure 3 *The effect of light intensity on the rate of water loss by a plant.*

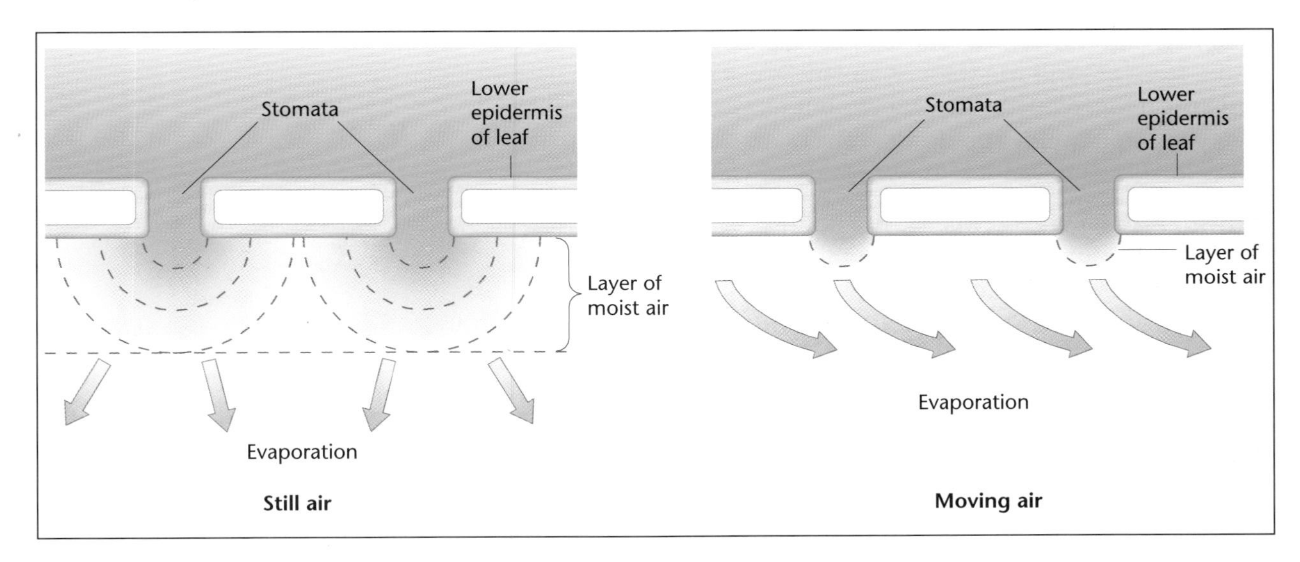

Figure 4 *The effect of air movement on the rate of transpiration from a leaf.*

Air humidity: this is the concentration of water vapour in the air. If the air is very humid, for example, on a rainy day, transpiration is reduced because the water potential gradient between the leaf and the air is very small. Very dry air, with a low humidity, causes the transpiration rate to rise.

Key ideas 220–21

Transpiration is the evaporation of water from the surface of a plant.

Water uptake can be measured using a potometer.

Transpiration is affected by a number of factors, including light, temperature, air movement and humidity.

7 Experimenting with xylem

You have seen that water and mineral ions are transported in the xylem. How do we know this? There are several ways of looking at the xylem and finding out how water and mineral ions are transported.

Experimental techniques

Using dyes: if you place a plant in a solution of a dye such as eosin, you can see the dye moving up the stem in the xylem. This is particularly easy to see if you use a plant with a colourless stem, such as celery. If you then cut a thin cross-section of the stem, and look at it under the microscope, you can see that the dye is present only in the xylem.

Ringing experiments: removing a strip of tissues from around the stem of a plant is called **ringing**. This removes the phloem but leaves the xylem in place. If you do this, the plant does not wilt, showing that it still has plenty of water.

Using radioactive tracers: if a plant is placed in a solution containing a radioactive mineral ion, such as radioactive potassium ions, you can trace the way that the ion travels through the plant by using the technique of autoradiography, as shown in figure 2.

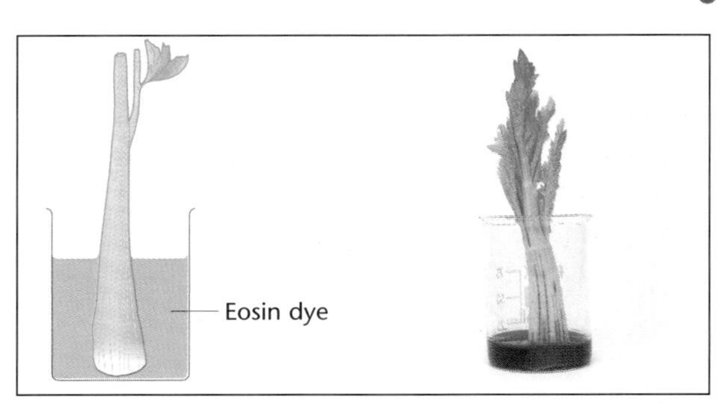

Figure 1 *A stem of celery is placed in eosin dye, and the eosin dye travels up the xylem.*

Mineral ion uptake

Mineral ions are taken into roots by a combination of diffusion and active transport. Plants live in an environment where the mineral ion availability can vary considerably, yet they can have much higher concentrations of ions in their cells than in the surrounding medium.

Look at table 1. This shows the concentrations of three different ions in sea water and in the cells of a marine alga, *Halicystis*. You can see that sea water has a higher level of sodium ions and a lower level of potassium ions than the cells of the alga. The alga must have found a way of concentrating potassium ions inside its cells and a means of keeping sodium ions out.

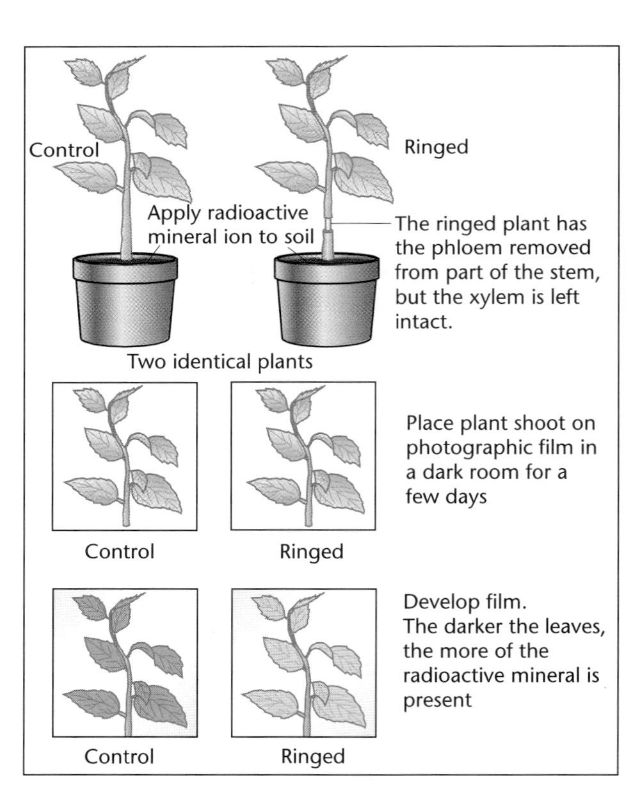

Figure 2 *Ringing and autoradiography can be used to investigate the path of mineral ions through the plant.*

1 If sodium and potassium ions are moved against a concentration gradient, how do they pass through cell membranes?

Active transport uses energy from respiration. To see if ions enter plant roots by active transport, experiments can be carried out using substances that inhibit respiration.

Look at figure 3(a). This shows the effect of DNP, a respiratory inhibitor, on the uptake of potassium ions by tobacco cells. You can see that when respiration is stopped, the plant cells do not take up potassium ions.

Figure 3(b) shows further evidence that active transport is involved in moving ions into plant roots. You can see that phosphate absorption falls almost to zero when maize plants have been kept in the dark for four days. When they are able to photosynthesise again, they start taking up phosphate ions.

2 Explain why the maize plants cannot take up phosphate ions after being in the dark for four days.

3 What effect do you think the following would have on ion uptake by roots:

a lowering the temperature from 25 °C to 5 °C

b reducing oxygen availability to the roots?

Moving ions through the plant

As you have seen, once the ions enter the root, they travel across the root dissolved in water by mass flow. From the root, most of the mineral ions enter the xylem and travel to different parts of the plant with the water. However, some of the mineral ions are transported in the phloem.

 **Table 1** *Concentrations of mineral ions in sea water and in cells of* Halicystis.

Ion	Concentration in sea water/mM	Concentration inside cell/mM
Sodium	488	257
Potassium	12	337
Chloride	523	543

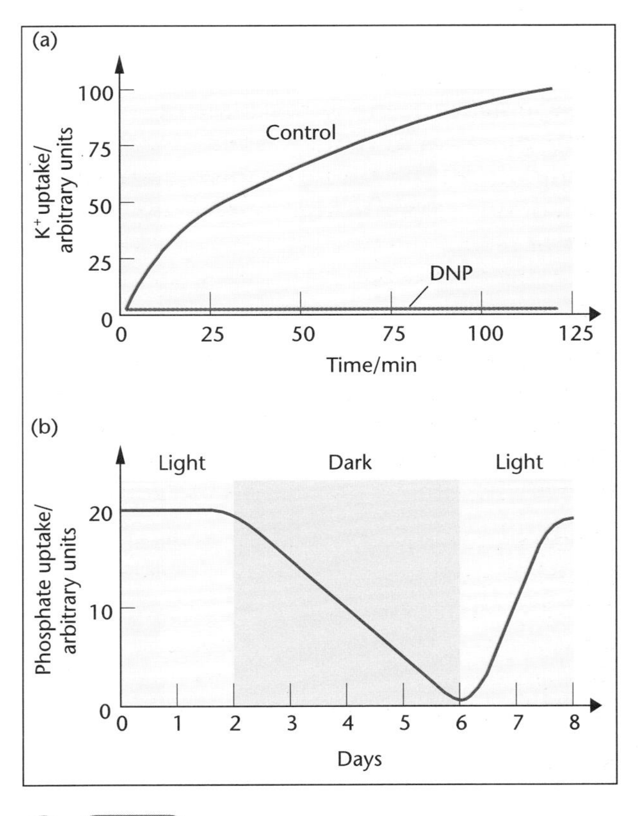

 **Figure 3** *(a) Graph showing the effect of DNP on uptake of potassium ions.*
(b) Graph showing the rate of phosphate ion absorption in light and dark conditions.

Key ideas 222–3

You can show that water and mineral ions travel in the xylem by using dyes, ringing experiments, radioactive tracers and autoradiography.

Ions enter a plant by a combination of active transport and diffusion. They travel through the plant with water by mass flow, although some ions are transported in the phloem.

8 Surviving without water

Some plants live in very dry conditions where there is very little water, for example, deserts, dry grasslands and rocky places. These plants are called xerophytes and they have special adaptations.

Dunes

Sand dunes are very hostile environments. There is no fresh water, plenty of salty water and strong winds. The sand contains little or no organic matter so it cannot retain water.

Figure 1 shows marram grass growing on sand dunes, where there is very little fresh water and there may be salt present. Look at figure 2 showing a section of a marram grass leaf. This is well adapted to living in windy, dry conditions. It has a thick cuticle to reduce water loss, and the stomata are in **pits**, surrounded by hairs. This traps a layer of moisture outside the stomata, reducing the diffusion gradient, so less water is lost in transpiration. There are also **hinge cells**. These allow the leaf to roll up when it is short of water, so the stomata are not exposed to wind or dry air.

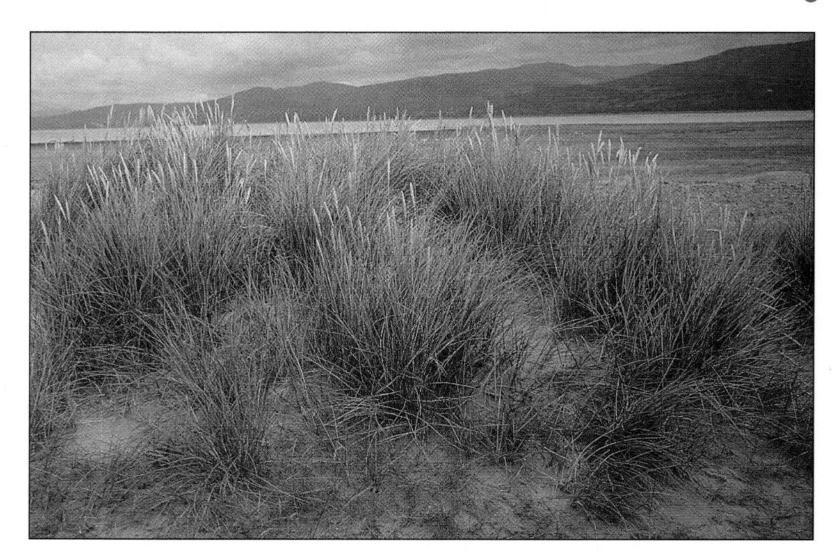

Figure 1 *Marram grass grows on dry sand.*

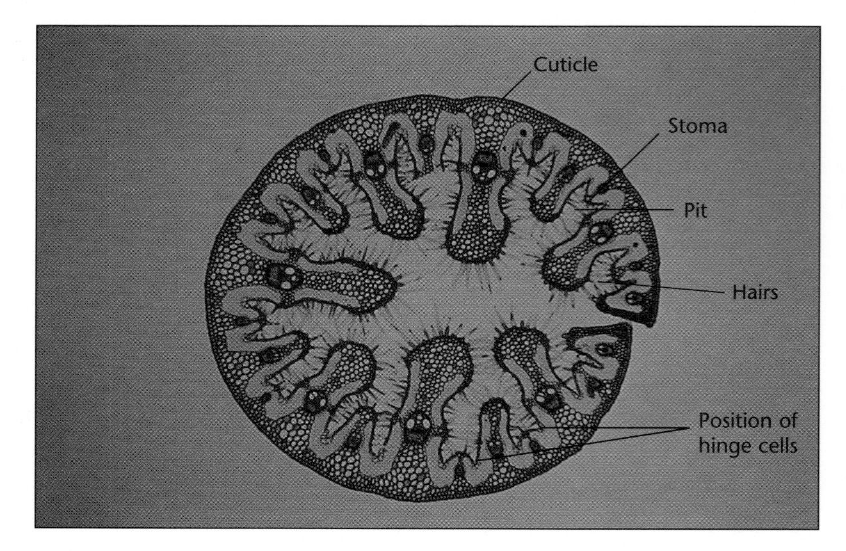

Figure 2 *Section through a marram grass leaf (× 60).*

Deserts

Look at the photograph of a cactus in figure 3. This plant has a number of features that enable it to live in very dry conditions.

1 Explain how the following features of the cactus help it to survive in very dry conditions:

a It has a very long, shallow, spread-out root system.

b It has a swollen, succulent stem.

c Its leaves are reduced to spikes.

d It has a round shape, giving it a low surface area to volume ratio.

e The stomata are sunken into pits.

f It has hairs over its surface which reflect light.

Figure 3 *Cacti have a round shape and leaves reduced to spines.*

Water water everywhere

Some plants live in an environment where there is plenty of water, but they have difficulty obtaining it because it is salty. Conditions like this are found in estuaries and salt marshes. Plants adapted to live in salty conditions are called **halophytes**. An example of a halophyte is cord grass (*Spartina*). The root system of these plants can take up water even though there is a great deal of salt in the ground, and they do this by having a very low water potential in their root cells.

Figure 4 Spartina *lives in salty estuaries.*

Key ideas 224–5

Plants adapted to dry conditions are called xerophytes. They have structural adaptations to reduce water loss.

Xerophytic adaptations include having a thick waxy cuticle, sunken stomata surrounded by hairs, succulent stems or leaves, an extensive root system and a surface covered with hairs.

Halophytes are adapted to obtain water in salty conditions. They have root cells with very low water potentials.

9 A closer look at phloem

The phloem is the tissue through which sugars and other organic solutes are transported (or **translocated**) in the plant. How do we know this? There are several ways of investigating the phloem.

Using aphids

Aphids, such as greenfly or blackfly, are insects that feed on plant sap. They have a long feeding tube called a **proboscis**. You can see this in figure 1. Scientists can anaesthetise an aphid which is feeding on a plant, and then cut across its mouthparts. This leaves a tiny sampling tube through which drops of phloem sap soon appear. The sap can be collected and studied.

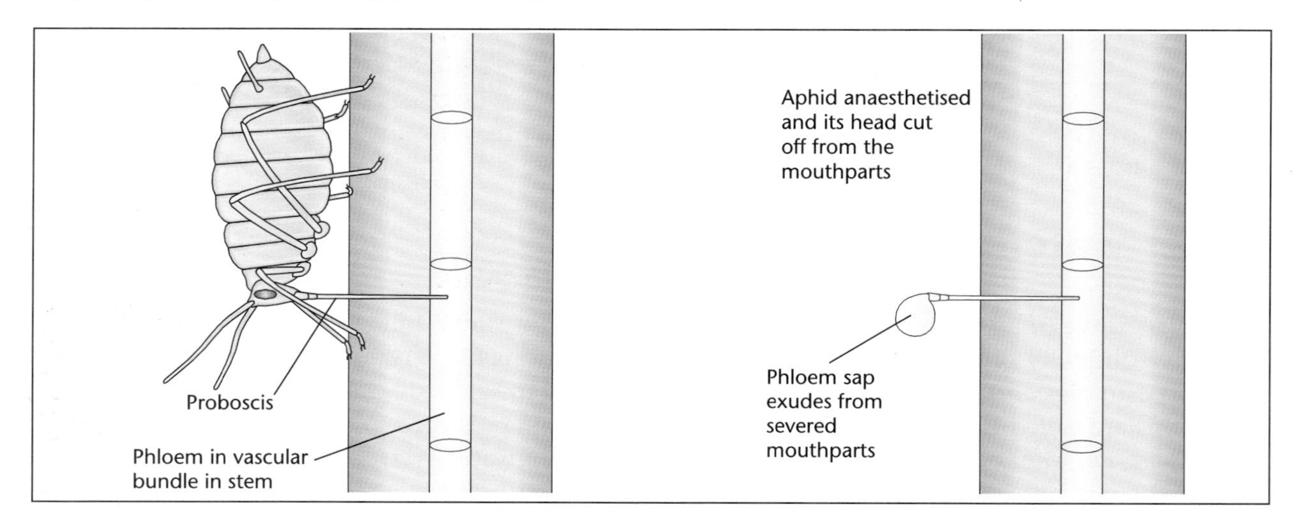

Figure 1 *Aphids feed by inserting their mouthparts into the phloem. Cutting off the aphid's head makes a sampling tube for phloem sap.*

Ringing experiments

Cylinders of bark can be removed from plant stems. This removes the phloem and outer layers of cells from a region of the stem, but leaves the xylem intact. The contents of the phloem can be sampled above and below the ring using aphid mouthparts.

1. **Why is it important to leave the xylem intact in a ringing experiment?**
2. **In the experiment shown in figure 2, explain why sugar is not found below the ring in diagram (a), but sugar is found both above and below the ring in diagram (b).**
3. **Sugars are able to move both up and down the plant in the phloem. Explain how you could show this experimentally.**

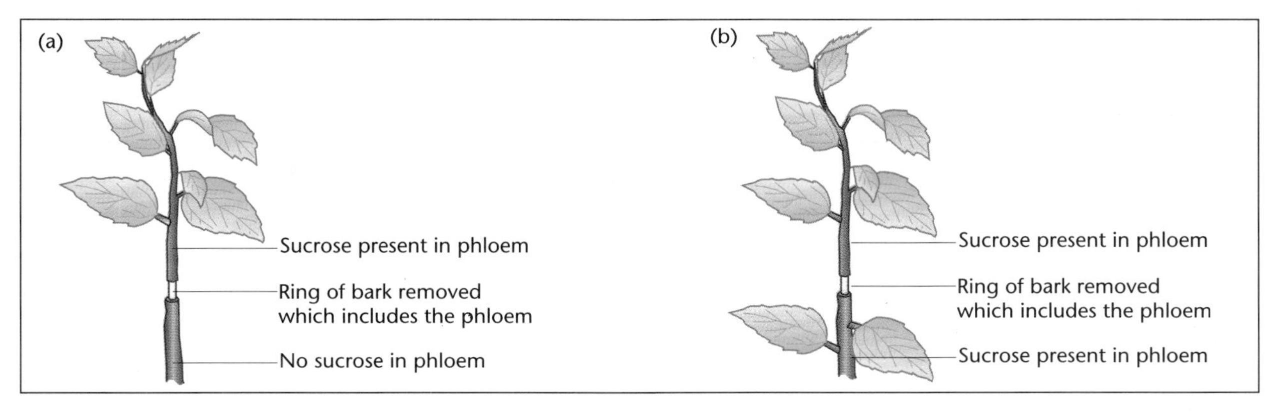

Figure 2 *A ringing experiment.*

Using radioactive tracers

The plant makes organic substances during photosynthesis, which travel in the phloem. If a plant is supplied with carbon dioxide containing radioactive carbon, ^{14}C, then this becomes incorporated in the organic substances in the plant. It is then possible to trace what happens to the organic substances made in photosynthesis.

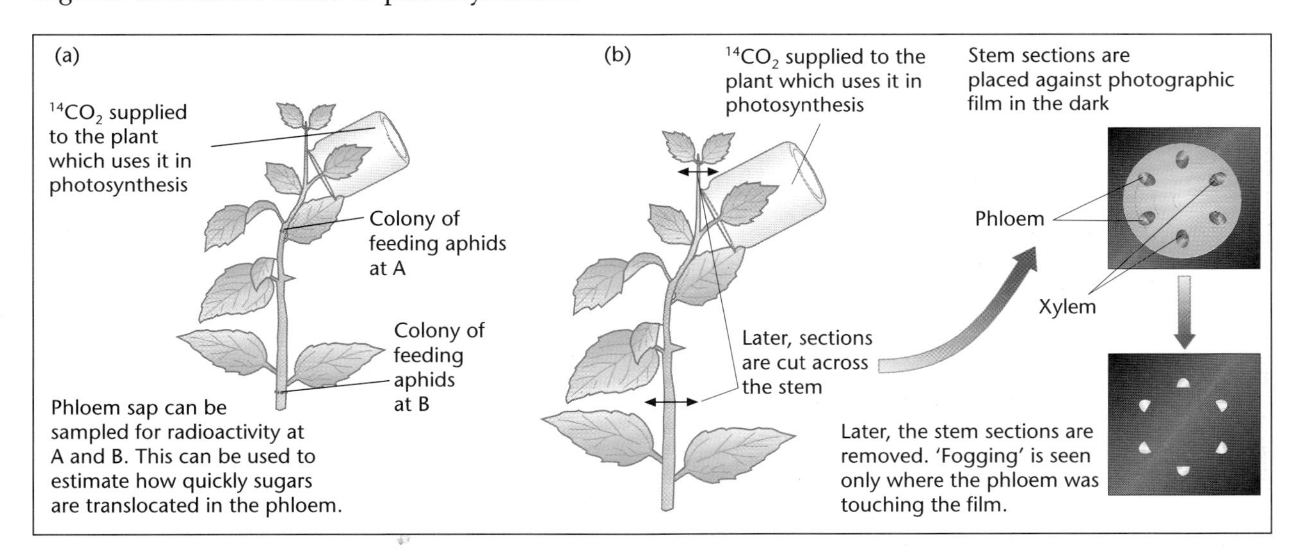

Figure 3 *How radioactive tracers can be used to investigate translocation.*

Key ideas 226–7

Translocation can be investigated using various methods.

Aphids can be used to make tiny phloem sap sampling tubes.

Ringing experiments remove sections of phloem tissue, allowing us to sample the phloem above and below the ring.

Radioactive tracers allow us to trace what happens to the organic materials made in photosynthesis.

4 How could you use a radioactive tracer to find out how quickly sugars move through the phloem?

10 The mass flow hypothesis

The leaves of a plant make a great deal of sugar during photosynthesis. This needs to be translocated around the plant, to places where it is needed. It may be used in respiration, stored in the form of starch, or used to make other substances the plant needs.

Sources and sinks

Cells that photosynthesise and make sugars are called **sources**. The sugars produced are converted into sucrose, which is transported around the plant. One way of explaining how sugars move around a plant is the **mass flow hypothesis**.

According to this theory, sugars build up in source cells, causing water to enter these cells from the xylem by osmosis. The sugars are then actively transported into the phloem sieve tubes. Specialised parenchyma cells called **transfer cells** carry out this active transfer. Water follows the sugars by osmosis.

The solution in the phloem can move either up or down the plant to a sink. A **sink** is the name given to any part of the plant that removes sugar from the phloem. A sink either uses the sugars for respiration because it is growing (such as a flower bud), or converts the sugars to a storage substance (such as a potato tuber which converts the sucrose to starch). In figure 1, the sink is a storage organ where the sucrose is removed from the phloem and converted to starch.

1 **Is each of the following a source or a sink?**
   a **a developing fruit**
   b **a palisade mesophyll cell**
   c **a spongy mesophyll cell**
   d **an onion bulb**

2 **Which way would the solutes in the phloem be moving between:**
   a **leaf and developing root**
   b **flower and leaf?**

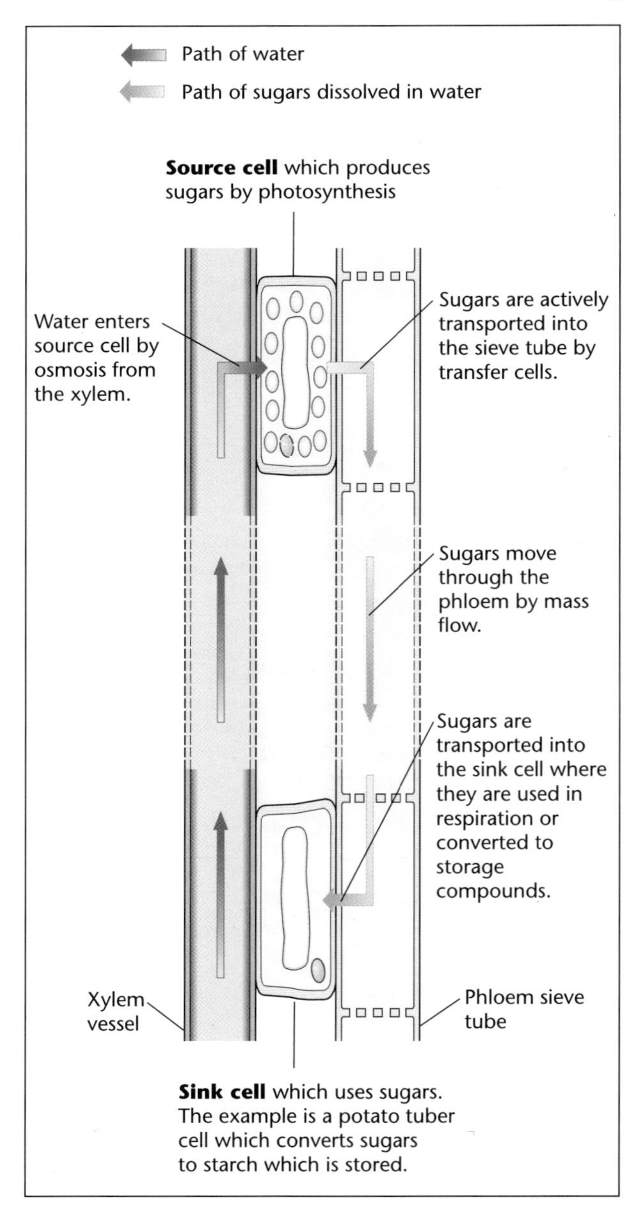

Figure 1 *The movement of sugars through a plant from source to sink.*

How mass flow works

In figure 1, sugars are said to move from source to sink by mass flow. It is possible to make a model that shows how the mass flow theory works.

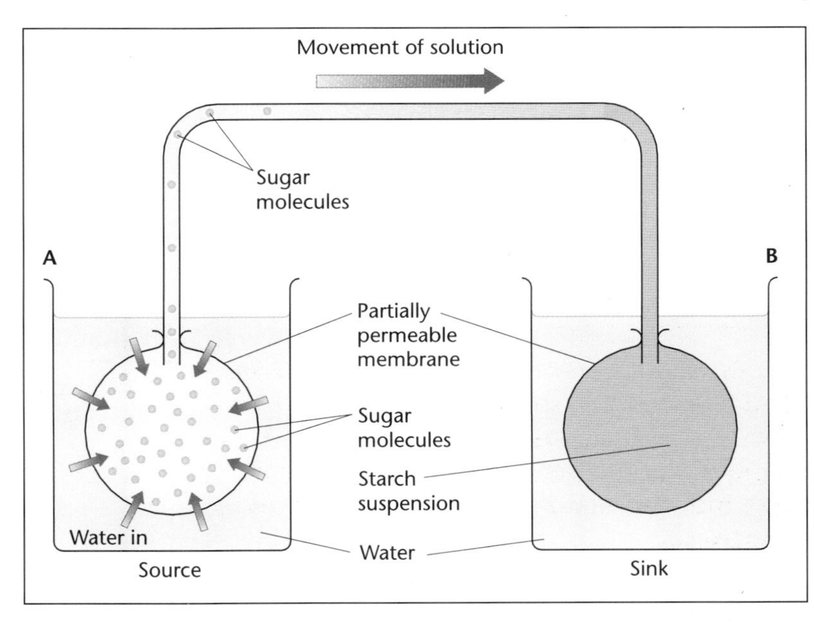

Figure 2 *Model to demonstrate mass flow.*

Look at figure 2. **A** is a container with a partially permeable membrane filled with a concentrated sugar solution, to represent a source. **B** is a container with a partially permeable membrane filled with a starch suspension, to represent a sink. The two containers are placed in beakers of water and are linked by a tube. Water moves from the beaker into **A** (the source) by osmosis. Pressure builds up in **A**, causing the sugary solution to move along the tube linking **A** to **B**. Only a little water enters **B** from the beaker. This is because starch is insoluble and so the water potential in **B** is high and osmosis cannot occur.

In this way sugar moves from **A** to **B**. This movement stops after a while in this model, but supporters of the mass flow theory say that if you could continually add sugar to **A**, and remove sugar from **B**, copying what happens in a plant, then the model would continue to work indefinitely.

Is the mass flow hypothesis right?

Scientists are not sure that the mass flow hypothesis is completely right. Sucrose and amino acids move through the phloem too fast to be moving simply by the passive means of the mass flow model. It has also been noticed that different solutes can travel at different speeds and even in different directions in the phloem. It is possible that the companion cells, which have many mitochondria, supply the energy needed to move organic solutes actively through the phloem sieve tubes.

Key ideas 228–9

The sugars made in photosynthesis are translocated through the phloem in the form of sucrose, along with amino acids and other organic solutes.

Transfer cells actively transport sugars into the phloem.

The mass flow hypothesis is the main theory to account for the movement of organic solutes in the phloem.

Unit 11 – Questions

11

1. The roots of twelve bean plants were placed in a nutrient solution containing radioactive phosphate (^{32}P) for 24 hours. After this, the plants were removed and placed in a non-radioactive nutrient solution, and the leaves of six of the plants were covered with aluminium foil to exclude light.

   The graph in figure 1 shows the daily measurement of radioactivity in the leaves.

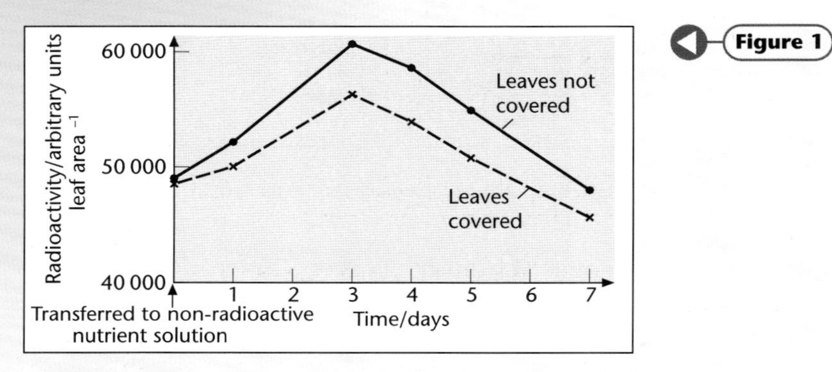

Figure 1

   a) Explain how the ^{32}P passed from the nutrient solution to the leaves. (4 marks)

   b) How would the amount of ^{32}P in the uncovered leaves have been affected if the plants had been exposed to moving air? Give a reason for your answer. (2 marks)

   c) Suggest *one* reason for the difference in the amount of radioactivity in the two sets of leaves. (1 mark)

   d) i) In which tissue would compound containing ^{32}P have been transported out of the leaves? (1 mark)

   ii) Outline an experiment which could be carried out to support your answer. (3 marks)

   (Total 11 marks)

2. Figure 2 shows a cross section through a young root.

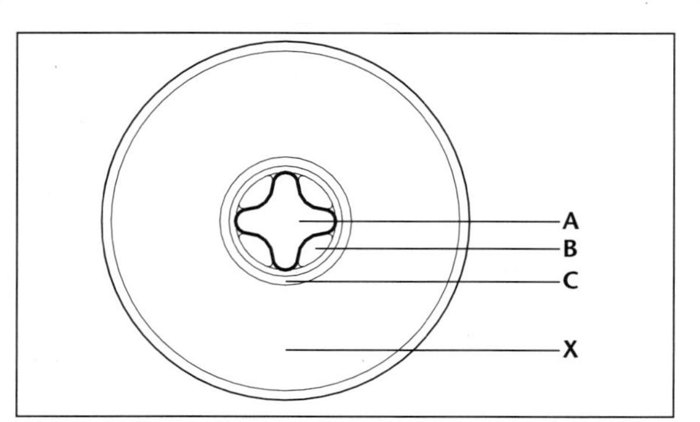

Figure 2

a) Name the tissues **A**, **B** and **C**. (3 marks)

b) In the region labelled **X** water and ions move through both apoplast and symplast pathways.
Which part of the cells in region **X** form the:
i) apoplast pathway?
ii) symplast pathway? (2 marks)

c) In the cells of tissue **C**, why can water and salts pass only through the symplast? (1 mark)

(Total 6 marks)

③ Figure 3 shows two pathways along which water can pass from the soil into the xylem of a root.

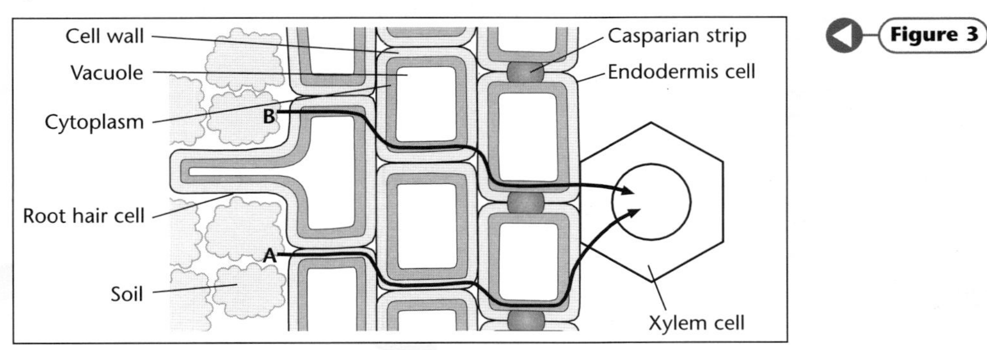

Figure 3

a) Name the pathway labelled **B**. (1 mark)

b) The Casparian strips shown in the endodermal cells are made of a waterproof material. Suggest the importance of the Casparian strip in the movement of water through the root. (2 marks)

c) Explain in terms of water potential how water enters a root hair cell. (2 marks)

(Total 5 marks)

④ The graph in figure 4 shows the rates of transpiration and water absorption in a herbaceous plant over a 24 hour period in the summer.

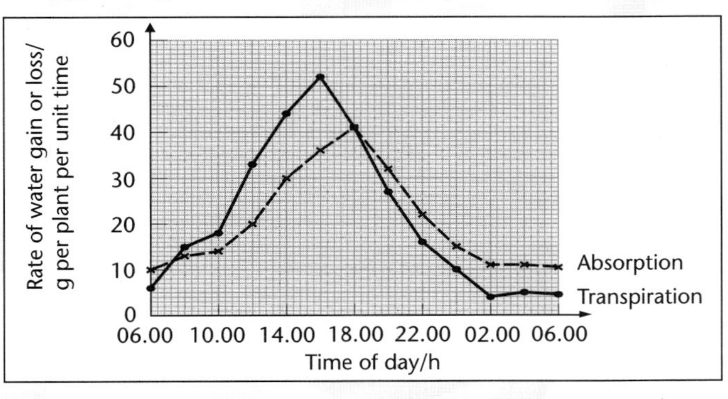

Figure 4

a) At what time of day is the difference between the rates of the two processes at its greatest? (1 mark)

b) Account for the rate of transpiration:
i) between 12.00 h and 20.00 h (2 marks)
ii) between 2.00 h and 6.00 h. (1 mark)

c) Suggest why gardeners are advised to transplant young seedlings in the evening. (1 mark)

(Total 5 marks)

Module 3 – Test yourself

1

(1) Figure 1 shows a section through the heart showing the position of the pacemaker.

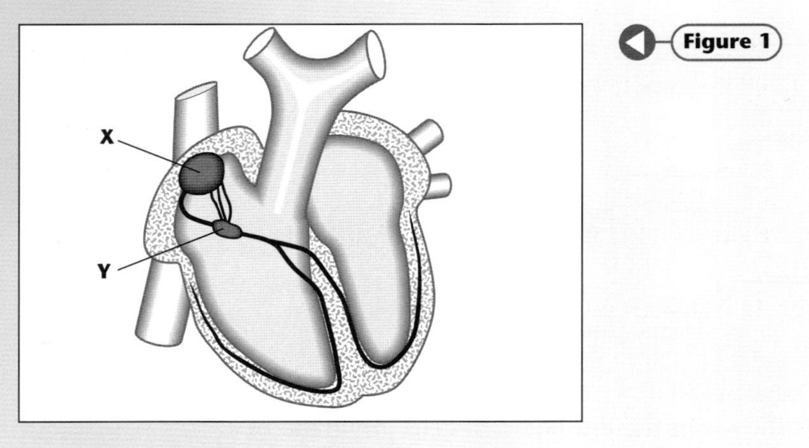

Figure 1

a) Which letter, **X** or **Y**, represents:
   i) the sinoatrial node?
   ii) the atrioventricular node? (2 marks)

b) i) Describe how the sinoatrial node controls heart rate. (4 marks)
   ii) Explain how exercise causes an increase in heart rate. (3 marks)

(Total 9 marks)

(2) The graph in figure 2 shows an oxygen dissociation curve for adult haemoglobin.

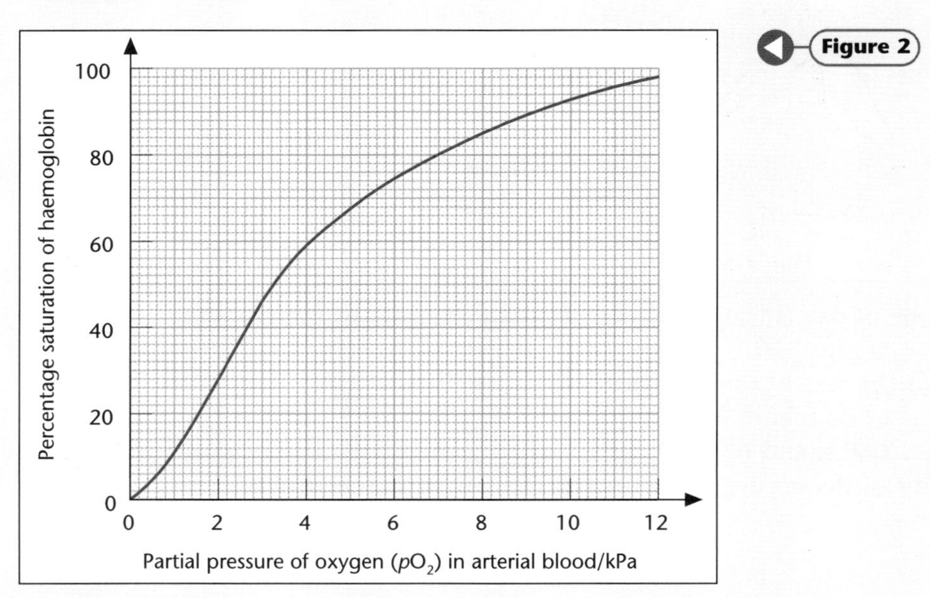

Figure 2

a) The partial pressure of oxygen in the lungs is 12 kPa. The liver has a partial pressure of oxygen of 2 kPa.

i) How much oxygen is unloaded from the haemoglobin in the liver? (1 mark)

ii) Sketch the graph and draw a curve on your sketch to show the effect of carbon dioxide on the unloading of haemoglobin. (1 mark)

b) At high altitude the partial pressure of oxygen in an athlete's arterial blood may be as low as 8 kPa. Use the graph to explain why the athlete can still perform well. (2 marks)

(Total 4 marks)

(3) Describe the role of the nervous system in:

a) the maintenance of regular breathing whilst the body is at rest (4 marks)

b) increasing the rate of ventilation of the lungs during exercise. (4 marks)

(Total 8 marks)

(4) **a)** Give *two* differences between plasma and tissue fluid. (2 marks)

b) i) Describe how tissue fluid forms. (3 marks)

ii) Explain why some tissue fluid is returned to the blood via the lymph system. (2 marks)

iii) Give *one* difference between plasma and lymph. (1 mark)

(Total 8 marks)

(5) The graph in figure 3 shows how the pressure of blood in two arteries in a healthy person varies with time. The carotid artery supplies blood to the brain.

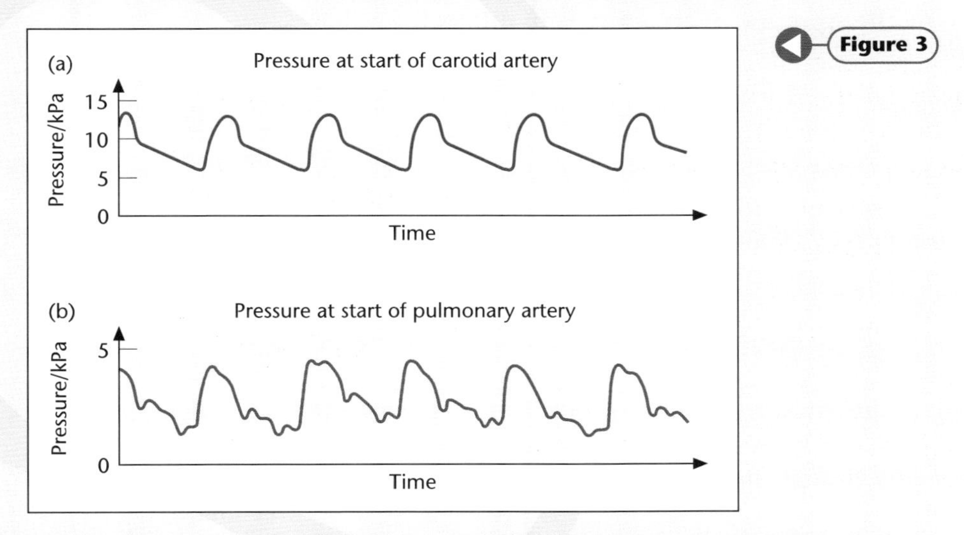

Figure 3

a) Which chamber of the heart pumps blood into the pulmonary artery? (1 mark)

b) i) Sketch the graphs and label one point on graph (a) when the heart pressure is at its greatest. (1 mark)

ii) Explain why graph (b) shows changes in pressure. (2 marks)

iii) How can these changes in pressure be used to measure the heart rate? (2 marks)

(Total 6 marks)

Module 3 – Test yourself

2

6 The diagrams show sections across an artery and a vein.

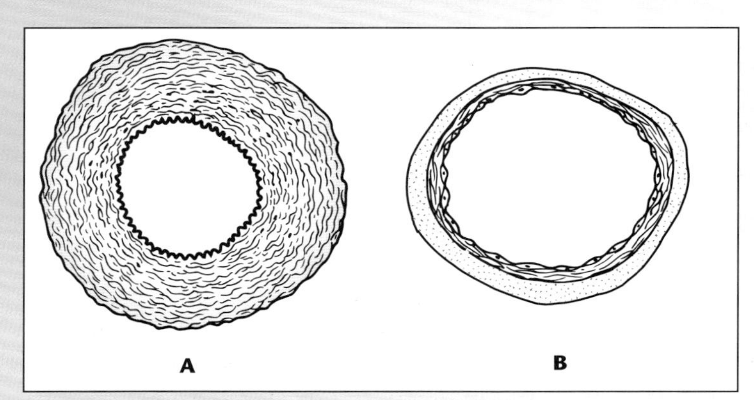

a) Which diagram shows an artery? Give a reason for your answer. (1 mark)

b) Explain why the structure of an artery wall differs from that of a vein. (2 marks)

c) Explain how valves in the veins help blood flow towards the heart. (3 marks)

(Total 6 marks)

7 Two plants were grown in culture solution. This method is commonly known as 'hydroponics'. Plant I was grown in a complete mineral salt solution, and plant II was grown in an identical mineral salt solution that lacked potassium.

a) i) Suggest why the plants were grown in a solution, rather than in soil. (1 mark)

ii) The plant grown in the complete nutrient solution grew better. Use your knowledge of biology to suggest *one* reason why this plant grew better than the plant lacking potassium. (1 mark)

The way in which mineral ions travel through plants can be investigated using radioactive mineral ions. You are supplied with a solution containing radioactive potassium ions.

b) i) Outline an experiment you could carry out to find out whether potassium ions travel through the plant in the xylem or the phloem. (4 marks)

ii) Outline an experiment you could carry out to investigate whether potassium ions are absorbed into a plant by diffusion or active transport. (4 marks)

(Total 10 marks)

8 **a)** Give two normal functions of a root. (2 marks)

Figure 5 shows a mangrove tree growing in a swamp. The roots of the mangrove grow in waterlogged soil, so the air spaces in the soil are always filled with sea water. They are specially modified to overcome this.

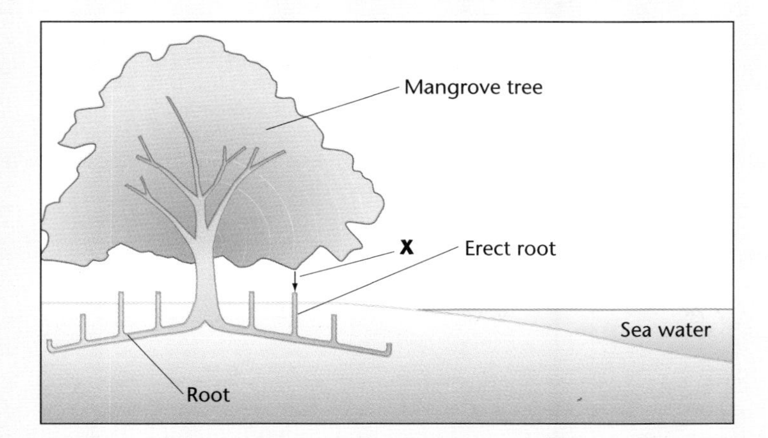

b) Normal roots actively transport mineral ions into the plant. Suggest why the mangrove may have difficulty in carrying out this process. (2 marks)

c) The arrow shows a gas, **X**, entering the modified roots of the mangrove. Name this gas and explain the process in the plant for which it is needed. (2 marks)

(Total 6 marks)

9 Two identical plants were taken. One had a ring of phloem removed below its leaves. Radioactive phosphorus (^{32}P) was supplied to the roots of both plants, and both plants were placed in an atmosphere containing radioactive carbon dioxide ($^{14}CO_2$).

The concentrations of ^{32}P and ^{14}C after 24 hours are given in table 1.

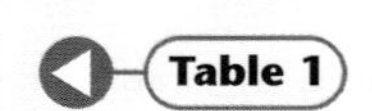

	Unringed plant	Ringed plant
^{32}P in roots	100	100
^{32}P in leaves	2.2	1.7
^{14}C in roots	0.9	0
^{14}C in leaves	0.1	0.99

a) From these results explain:

i) how ^{14}C travels through the plant

ii) why no ^{14}C is found in the roots of the ringed plant. (2 marks)

b) Explain the results obtained for ^{32}P. (3 marks)

(Total 5 marks)

Module 1 Core Principles

Unit 1 Enzymes

1 Similar yet different (pages 4–5)

1 Glucose from food; oxygen from gas exchange
2 Excreted in air breathed out
3 Helps build up proteins used for muscles

2 Helping reactions occur (pages 6–7)

1 Substrate – maltose; product – glucose
2 Enzyme and substrate have complementary shapes, other molecules do not fit the specific 3D shape of the active site.
3

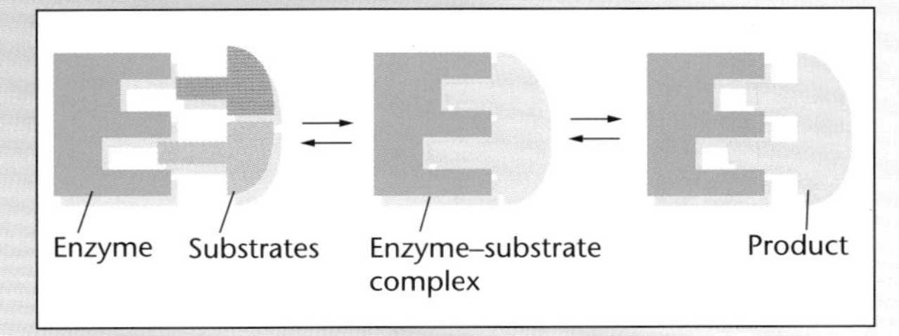

3 Ready for action (pages 8–9)

1 The shape of the enzyme's active site is no longer complementary to the substrate so no enzyme–substrate complexes are formed.
2 Zinc could be an activator or a prosthetic group.

4 Shaping up (pages 10–11)

1 Above 50 °C the enzyme has too much kinetic energy so hydrogen bonds vibrate too much and break. Below 40 °C there is less kinetic energy so the reaction is slower than the maximum rate.
2 a As the kinetic energy increases, there are more collisions between the enzyme and substrate so more enzyme–substrate complexes are formed. Therefore the rate increases.
b The graph rises for the reason given in (a) above until it reaches the optimum temperature. Above the optimum temperature the rate falls quickly because the enzyme loses its shape and becomes denatured as hydrogen bonds break.
3 40 °C
4 The shape of the enzyme's active site is no longer complementary to the substrate therefore no enzyme–substrate complexes form and no product is made.
5 a Below the optimum pH, in more acidic conditions, ionic and hydrogen bonds break and the enzyme denatures.
b Above the optimum pH, in more basic (alkaline) conditions, ionic and hydrogen bonds break and the enzyme denatures.
c An enzyme has an optimum pH at which the rate of reaction is at a maximum, because the bonds holding the active site in shape are not disrupted. Above or below this pH the enzyme becomes denatured.
6 pH 7

6 Reaching a maximum (pages 14–15)

1 a The substrate concentration is limiting, therefore there are spare active sites available.
b The enzyme concentration is limiting – all active sites are occupied so excess substrate molecules 'have to wait' until active sites are available.
2

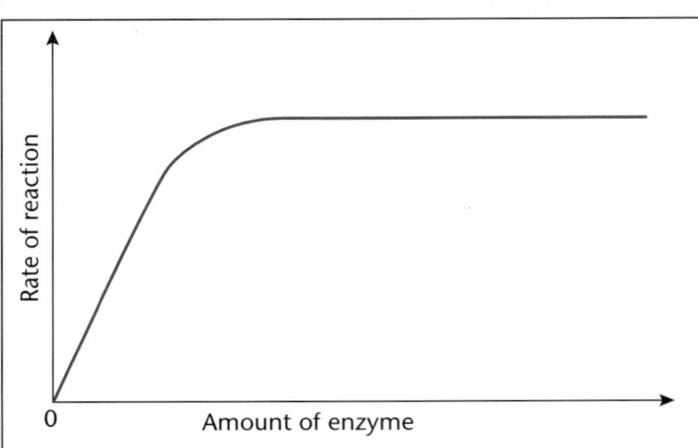

3 The trypsin inhibitor has a similar shape to the substrate.
4 The inhibitor competes for the active site. If the inhibitor binds to the active site, substrate molecules are prevented from binding. No enzyme–substrate complexes form and no product is made.

7 Being obstructive (pages 16–17)

1 The shape is not complementary to that of the active site.
2 To save energy

8 Unit 1 – Questions (pages 18–19)

1 a i The place on an enzyme where the substrate binds
ii The shape of an active site is complementary to that of its substrate so only specific molecules fit.
iii The inhibitor has a shape similar to that of the substrate so it enters and blocks the active site.
iv The inhibitor binds to another part of an enzyme molecule, causing it to change shape and preventing the substrate from binding.
b i Between 15 °C and 40 °C the rate of reaction increases with temperature because the substrate and enzyme molecules have more kinetic energy so collide more frequently and with more energy.
ii From 50 °C to 60 °C the rate of reaction decreases with temperature because the enzyme has started to denature so the shape of the active site no longer fits the substrate.

2 a Activation energy

b

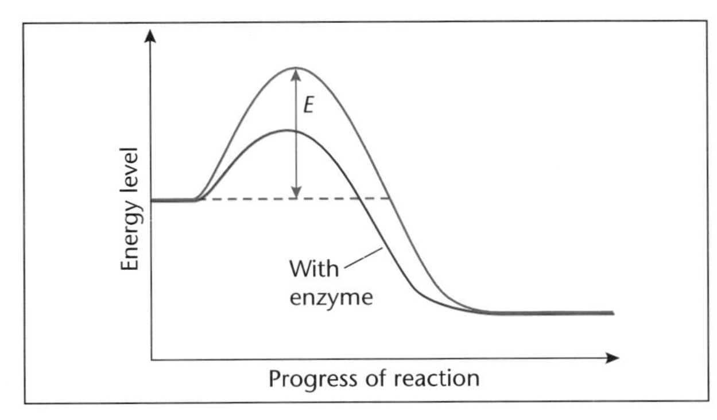

3 a Four of:
- catalyst/speeds up reactions
- lowers the activation energy of a reaction
- is unchanged at the end of the reaction
- cannot change the substrate or products of the reaction
- to catalyse a reaction the substrate binds to the active site.

b At the optimum pH, the active site has the best shape for binding to the substrate. At pH values on either side of the optimum, the bonds holding the enzyme start to break. The shape of the active site is lost and the substrate no longer fits the active site, so the reaction slows down.

4 a pH 7

b Extremes of pH have caused bonds holding the enzyme to break. The active site no longer fits the substrate so there is no reaction.

c A similar set of wells containing solutions at different pH without enzyme, or a similar set of wells with boiled enzyme instead of active enzyme.

5 a Succinate dehydrogenase has an active site on its surface and only fumarate fits/complements the active site.

b Malonate has a similar shape to fumarate. It partially fits/blocks the active site so fumarate cannot bind.

6 a At low substrate concentration there are spare active sites so the rate is lower; as the substrate concentration increases, more enzyme active sites are used, so the rate increases until all the active sites are in use.

b

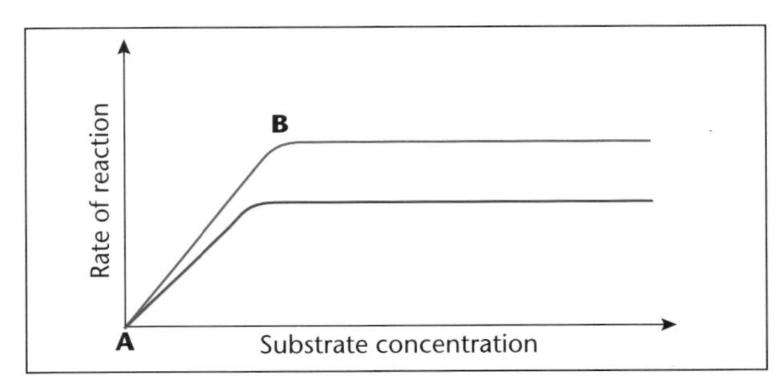

Unit 2 Digestion

1 Food in humans (pages 20–21)

1 It provides a large surface area of food for enzyme action.

2 It provides a large surface area and allows stretching of the gut wall.

2 Adapted for work (pages 22–3)

1 The muscle layers and elastic submucosa enable peristalsis to occur, which pushes the food along. Mucus secretions help food 'slide' through. The thick epithelium protects the oesophagus from damage.

2 Allows expansion when food passes along in the oesophagus; allows expansion for storage in the stomach

3 Enables churning of food and mixing with digestive juices

4 The secretions contain protease enzymes which could digest body cells and acid which could damage the mucosa.

5 To provide the optimum pH for pepsin; to help break bonds in proteins

3 Specially adapted (pages 24–5)

1 Microvilli and villi; the cell surface membrane of epithelial cells contains maltase and exopeptidase enzymes used in digestion, so an increased surface area allows digestion to happen more quickly. The increased surface area allows digested food molecules to be absorbed more quickly.

2

Region of the gut	Functions	Adaptations
Oesophagus	Peristalsis of solid food	Thick muscle layers to push food Mucus-secreting glands to prevent friction Folded and elastic walls to allow expansion Replaceable lining to prevent damage from food
Stomach	Temporary storage of food and mixing of contents Some digestion	Three layers of muscle for churning Glands producing digestive juices
Duodenum	Digestion	Receives secretions via ducts from liver and pancreas Produces alkaline secretions to neutralise acid from the stomach
Ileum	Digestion Absorption	Glands producing digestive juices Villi and microvilli to increase surface area Many blood and lymph vessels to transport absorbed food

Module 1 Core Principles

Unit 2 Digestion (continued)

4 Making smaller (pages 26–7)

1 Similarities: enzymes are used; occur in the small intestine; large molecules are broken down to smaller molecules.
Differences: Carbohydrase enzymes for carbohydrates, peptidase enzymes for proteins; carbohydrates are also digested in the mouth.

2 Lipase enzymes for lipids; lipids are digested better after emulsification by bile.

5 More about digestion (pages 28–9)

1

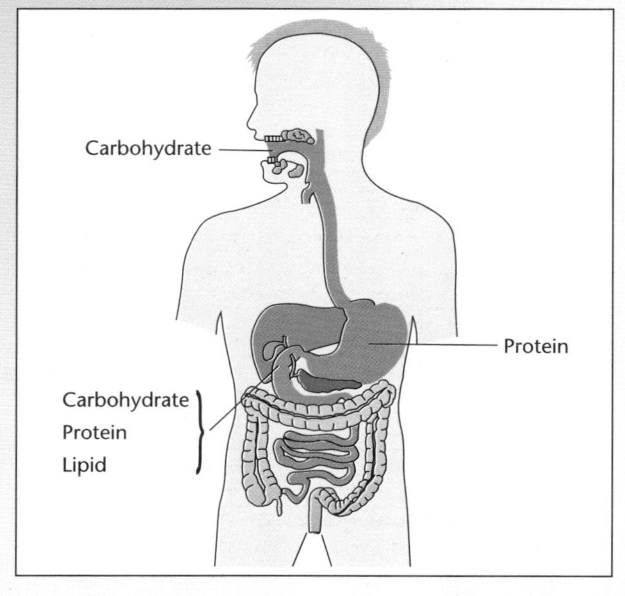

2 a

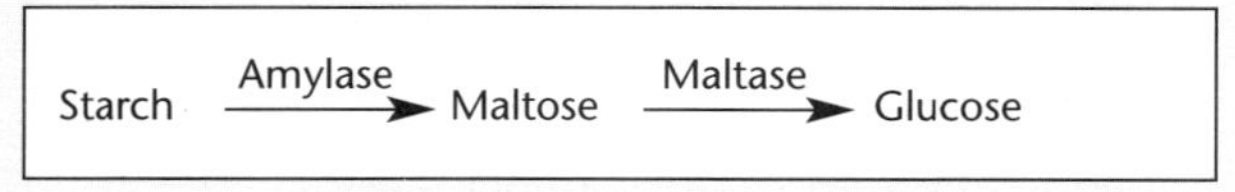

b

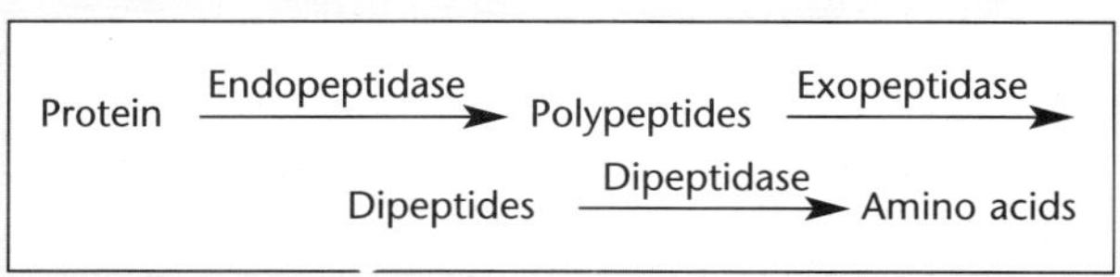

c

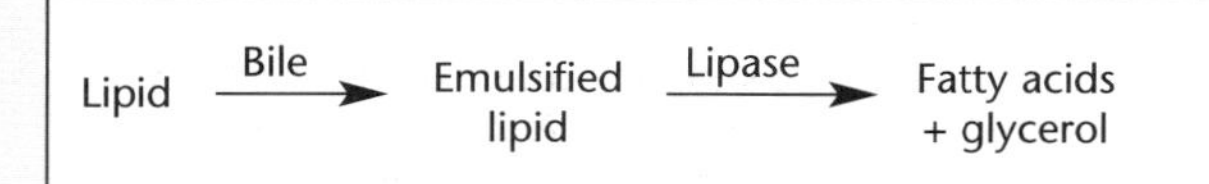

6 Absorbing food (pages 30–31)

1 Increases the surface area, therefore increases the amount of absorption that can take place

7 When something goes wrong (pages 32–3)

1

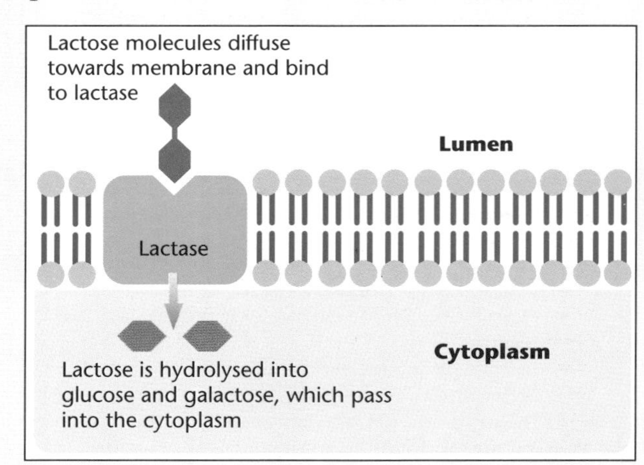

2 Decreases the surface area, so decreasing the amount of absorption

8 Feeding from dead organisms (pages 34–5)

1 Carbohydrases – carbohydrate; proteases – protein; lipases – lipids

9 Looking for enzyme activity (pages 36–7)

1 The well at the top left

2 The enzyme amylase and substrate starch have complementary shapes so they can form enzyme–substrate complexes. The more enzyme is present in a well, the more enzyme–substrate complexes can form and the more reactions can take place, making a larger colourless area.

3 Grow the fungus on starch agar; after 48 hours pour over iodine solution; measure the clear zone.

10 Unit 2 – Questions (pages 38–9)

1 a An organism/plant that feeds on dead organic matter
b Enzymes are secreted onto the surrounding food source; large/insoluble molecules are digested outside the fungus/extracellular digestion; small/soluble molecules are absorbed.
c Transfer some fungus onto the centre of a nutrient medium containing starch; leave to grow/incubate for 2–3 days; pour iodine on the surface of the plate. A clear area around the fungus shows that carbohydrase has digested some of the starch.

2 a Microvillus/brush border
b Provides an increased surface area on the villi for absorption/allows a greater number of molecules to cross the membrane per unit time/increases the rate of diffusion

3 a

Enzyme	Site of action	Substrate	Product
Endopeptidase	Stomach	Protein	Polypeptides
Exopeptidase	Small intestine	Polypeptides	Amino acids

b Endopeptidase cuts the longer chain into several smaller chains; this allows exopeptidases to work on several ends (two ends per short chain instead of only two for one long chain).

4 a Fatty acids; glycerol

b Six of:

- digested in the small intestine
- bile emulsifies fat/breaks up large fat droplets into small fat droplets
- lipase produced by pancreas/small intestine
- enzyme hydrolyses the bonds between glycerol and each fatty acid
- small fatty acids diffuse into blood
- longer chain fatty acids and glycerol diffuse into epithelial cells and recombine
- triglycerides packaged to make chylomicrons
- passed into lymph by exocytosis.

5 a Small intestine

b Presence of villi

c Large surface area to absorb digested food; good supply of blood vessels and lymph vessels

Unit 3 Cells

1 Keeping order (pages 40–41)

1 About 4 μm

2 Finding out about cells (pages 42–3)

1 Because electron microscopes use a vacuum, and living organisms cannot survive in a vacuum because they need oxygen for respiration; living organisms would not survive the complex staining and preparation procedures.

2 Advantage: greater resolution. Disadvantage: cannot view living organisms; picture is only black and white or false colour.

3 Cells with a nucleus (pages 44–5)

1 Chloroplasts; large central vacuole; cell wall

2 a Plant cell

b Cell wall

4 Hives of activity (pages 46–7)

1 Transmission EM

2 To control their growth and development

3 Because muscle cells use a lot of ATP/energy, and need many mitochondria to supply this energy

5 Making and transporting substances (pages 48–9)

1 Microvilli to increase surface area and mitochondria to provide energy

6 Only found in plants (pages 50–51)

1 Cellulose forms long fibres which don't stretch very much, so they form a rigid and strong framework around the cell.

2 A cell in a root

7 Different densities (pages 52–3)

1 a Ribosomes, RER

b Chop up leaf tissue as shown for liver cells. Homogenise and filter to remove cell wall and other debris. Centrifuge at a low speed for a short time to remove nuclei, then centrifuge the supernatant at a higher speed to deposit the chloroplasts.

8 Cells without a nucleus (pages 54–5)

1 About 2 μm

2 Prokaryotes do not have a nucleus; eukaryotic cells have a nucleus with a nuclear membrane around it. Prokaryotes have a circular chromosome; eukaryotes have DNA in linear chromosomes. Prokaryotes have naked DNA; eukaryotes have DNA that is complexed with protein. Prokaryotes do not have membrane-bound organelles; eukaryotes have membrane-bound organelles such as mitochondria and endoplasmic reticulum. Prokaryotes have ribosomes that are smaller than eukaryotic ribosomes. Bacteria have flagella of a different type from those in eukaryotes. Prokaryotic cell walls are made of a different material (murein) from eukaryotic cells walls (cellulose). These are the main differences, but you may have listed even more.

3

Structure	Function
Cell wall	Stops cell bursting when it takes in water by osmosis
Cell membrane	Selectively allows materials into and out of the cell
Genetic material	Carries the genetic information of the cell, coding for bacterial enzymes, etc.
Ribosomes	Protein synthesis
Flagellum	Locomotion
Plasmid	In some bacteria, carries additional genes to those in the main DNA, e.g. coding for antibiotic resistance
Capsule	Protects against phagocytosis and drying out

9 Unit 3 – Questions (pages 56–7)

1 a **A** cell wall; **B** nuclear membrane

b Discrete nucleus; presence of organelles/named organelle

c Plant cell; cell wall present or chloroplast present

2 **A** smooth endoplasmic reticulum/Golgi body; **B** mitochondrion; **C** rough endoplasmic reticulum

3 Prokaryotic cell: no nucleus, circular DNA, no organelles, cell wall of murein. Eukaryotic cell: nucleus with a membrane, DNA linear/not circular, organelles/named organelles present, plant cell wall of cellulose.

4 Two of:

- light microscope – low resolution/detail limited/objects close together not seen separately; electron microscope – high resolution/greater detail/objects close together seen separately
- light microscope has lower magnification/only magnifies to ×1000; electron microscope gives high magnification
- light microscope shows natural colour; electron microscope gives no colour/computer image.

5 Similarities – both have: a nucleus; a cell surface membrane; mitochondria; endoplasmic reticulum. Differences – plant cells have: a cell wall; a large central vacuole; chloroplasts in some cells; plasmodesmata between cells; smaller Golgi body.

Module 1 Core Principles

Unit 3 Cells (continued)

6 a Traps light and uses it for photosynthesis
b Modifies substances before they are secreted by cells/transports substances through cells
c Controls the activities of the cell/contains DNA of the cell
d Prevents the cell from bursting when water enters by osmosis/supports the cell

7 a **A** flagellum – used for movement of the bacterium; **B** circular DNA/chromosome – carries genes/genetic information; **C** slime capsule – prevents drying of cell/protects the cell; **D** cell wall – supports the cell/prevents the cell from bursting when water enters by osmosis.
b Prokaryotic DNA: has no proteins; is not inside a nucleus; is circular.

8 **A** nuclear envelope/membrane – encloses DNA/separates DNA from cytoplasm/allows RNA to leave. **B** ribosome/rough endoplasmic reticulum – used in the synthesis of proteins.

9 Four of:
- cells crushed/homogenised to extract organelles
- spun at a low speed in a centrifuge to settle out nuclei/dense organelles
- pellet at the bottom contains the organelle
- supernatant/liquid transferred into another tube and centrifuged at a higher speed to settle mitochondria/organelles of the next highest density
- supernatant transferred and centrifuged at a higher speed to settle the organelles of the next highest density
- keep repeating at higher speeds until all organelles are separated.

Unit 4 Biological molecules

1 Biomolecules (pages 58–9)

1 a To break open the cells so that all the contents of the cells are released
b To get rid of any debris such as pieces of potato skin, pieces of cell wall and starch grains
c To see if there was starch present already
d The test shows that there are no starch grains present in the filtered potato juice.
e An enzyme
f Repeat the experiment, but boiling the potato juice. If an enzyme is responsible for turning glucose into starch, you would expect no starch to be produced in the control experiment as the enzyme would be denatured. Alternatively, repeat the experiment substituting buffer or water for potato juice. If an enzyme is responsible for turning glucose into starch, you would expect no starch to be produced in the control experiment.

2 Carbohydrate polymers (pages 60–61)

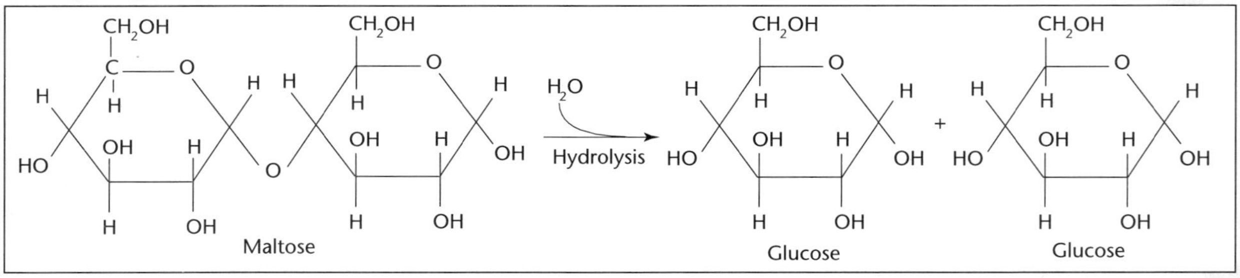

1 By using an enzyme
2 a Glucose
b (See figure above)
3 Insoluble; compact – many branches

3 New arrangements (pages 62–3)

1 (See figure below)

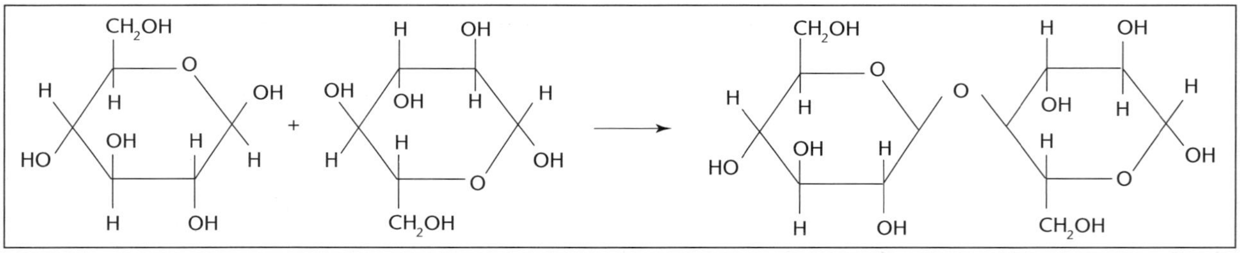

4 Proteins (pages 64–5)

1 Protease/peptidase/exopeptidase

2 a Amino group

b 5

c

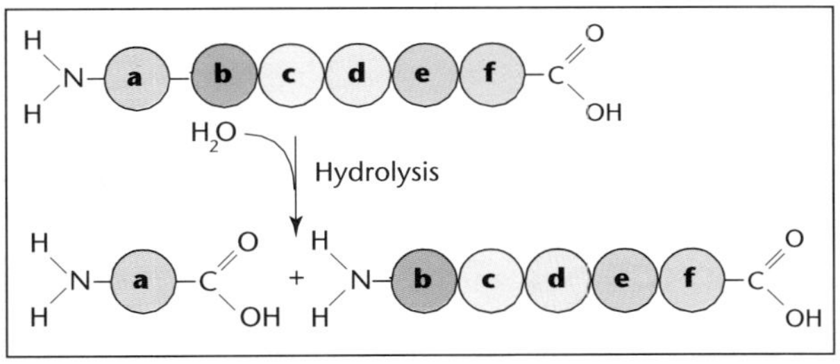

5 Getting into shape (pages 66–7)

1 Because they form part of body structures

6 Body building (pages 68–9)

1 a Fibrous

b Fibrous

2 So that it can be transported in the blood

7 Greasy substances (pages 70–71)

1 **B**

2

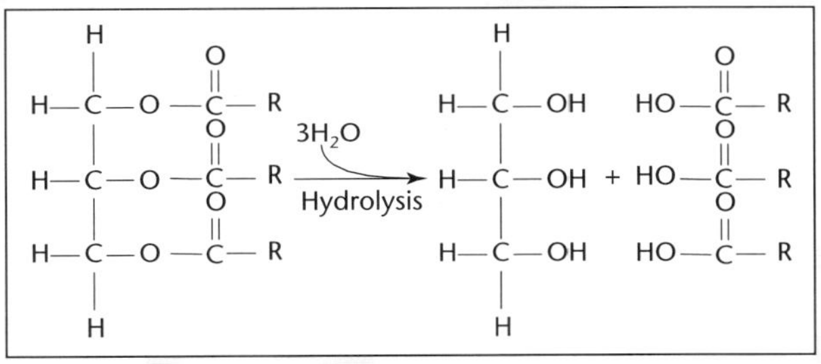

8 Wonderful water (pages 72–3)

1 Buoyancy – water supports some of the body mass.

2 The temperature remains fairly stable while the air temperature changes more.

3 A lot of heat is removed from the body to evaporate a small amount of water.

9 Colour writing (pages 74–5)

1 To separate the spots – if the same solvent was used, the spots would not separate as they have similar solubilities in that particular solvent.

10 Unit 4 – Questions (pages 76–7)

1 a (See figure below)

b i Order and number of amino acids

ii Coiling of the chain into an alpha helix/beta-pleated sheet

iii Folding of a molecule into a specific shape

2

Statement	Glucose	Starch	Amino acid	Polypeptide	Protein	Lipid
Contains carbon	✓	✓	✓	✓	✓	✓
Contains hydrogen	✓	✓	✓	✓	✓	✓
Contains oxygen	✓	✓	✓	✓	✓	✓
Contains nitrogen			✓	✓	✓	
May contain sulphur			✓	✓	✓	

3 a **A** glycerol; **B** fatty acids

b

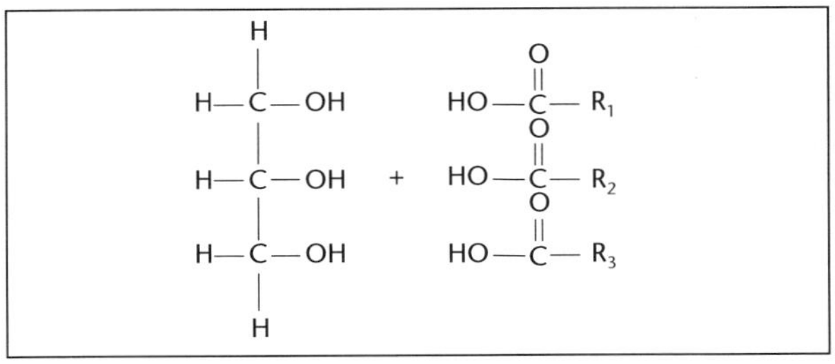

4 a Dipeptide

b Peptide bond

c

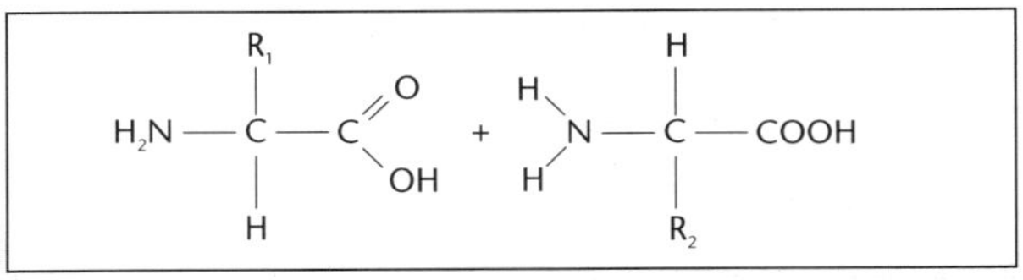

5 a Glucose

b Glycerol

c Fatty acid

6 a Add Benedict's solution and heat; red colour/precipitate indicates reducing sugar (glucose).

b Add dilute acid and heat for 1 minute (only valid if Benedict's test is negative); cool and repeat Benedict's test – red colour indicates sucrose.

c Add iodine (in potassium iodide solution); blue-black colour indicates starch.

d Add Biuret solution (sodium hydroxide and copper sulphate); lilac colour indicates protein.

e Add an alcohol and shake for 1 minute; pour top layer off and add water; milky colour indicates fat.

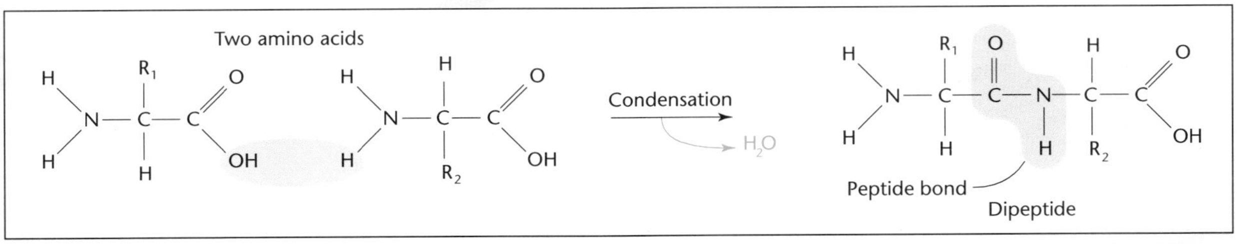

Module 1 Core Principles

Unit 5 Cell transport

2 Membrane molecules (pages 80–81)

1 A phospholipid has two fatty acid chains while a triglyceride has three. The third fatty acid in a phospholipid has been replaced by a phosphate group. The phosphate group makes part of the phospholipid molecule charged.

2 The double bonds cause kinks or bends in the tails, which prevent the molecules packing together closely.

3 Membranes at work (pages 82–3)

1 The shape of the hormone is complementary to the shape of the receptor protein in the same way as a substrate is complementary to the shape of the enzyme's active site.

2 Tertiary structure allows a protein to have a specific shape.

3 The structure of cimetidine is very similar to that of histamine, so it can fit onto the receptor in its place.

4 From side to side (pages 84–5)

1 The hydrophobic part of the phospholipid will repel (push away) water molecules. Any molecules dissolved in the water will also be pushed away.

2 The shape of the protein forming the channel allows only molecules with a complementary shape to pass through.

6 Unit 5 – Questions (pages 88–9)

1 a **A** phospholipid; **B** protein

b

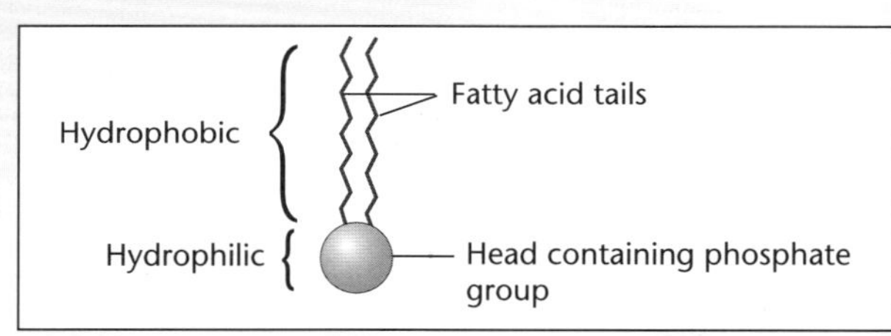

c Molecules are able to move (fluid); molecules/proteins constantly change position (mosaic).

d Receptor for other molecules/hormones; transport across the membrane

e

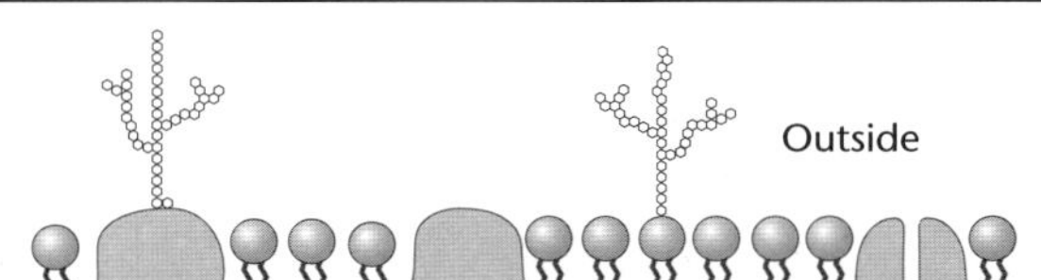
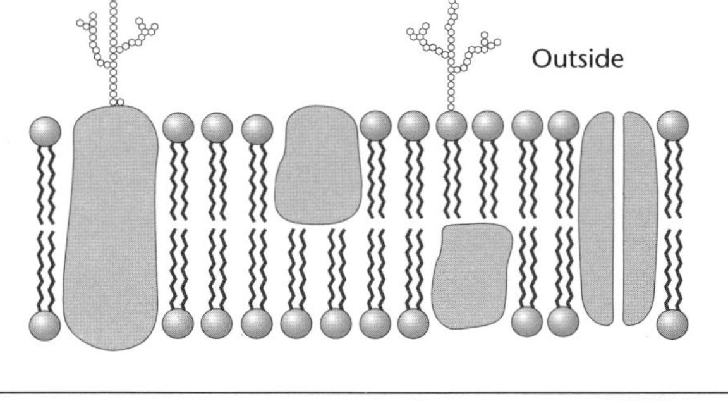

Carbohydrate is only present on the outside of a membrane.

2 a Diffusion; facilitated diffusion; active transport

b i Diffusion and facilitated diffusion

ii Active transport

c Active: moves substances against a diffusion gradient/from low to high concentration; passive: moves substances with a diffusion gradient/from high to low concentration. Active: uses energy/ATP; passive: does not use energy/ATP.

3 a They both have a specific shape which only complements one molecule.

b Active transport occurs against a concentration gradient and diffusion goes with the concentration gradient; active transport uses energy and diffusion is passive; active transport uses carriers and simple diffusion does not use carriers.

4 a

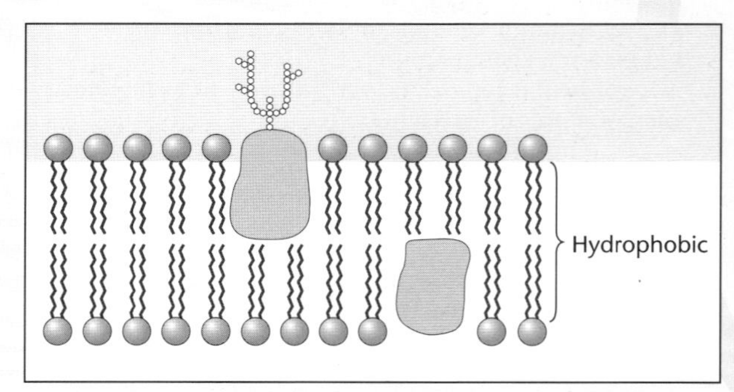

b i **A** proteins

ii **B** carbohydrates

iii **C** phospholipids

iv **C** phospholipids

5 a Active transport – the concentration of the ions inside the cells is higher than that outside the cells.

b The amount inside the cells varies/the concentration of phosphate is higher than that of the others.

Unit 6 Exchanging materials

1 Supply and demand (pages 90–91)

1 a 1 cm: surface area is $1 \text{ cm} \times 1 \text{ cm} \times 6 = 6 \text{ cm}^2$
2 cm: surface area is $2 \text{ cm} \times 2 \text{ cm} \times 6 = 24 \text{ cm}^2$
b 1 cm: volume is $1 \text{ cm} \times 1 \text{ cm} \times 1 \text{ cm} = 1 \text{ cm}^3$
2 cm: volume is $2 \text{ cm} \times 2 \text{ cm} \times 2 \text{ cm} = 8 \text{ cm}^3$
c 1 cm: ratio is 6 : 1
2 cm: ratio is 24 : 8 = 3 : 1
d The ratio decreases as the size increases.

2 Adaptations relate to the function of the surface in which the cells are found. In the small intestine and an alveolus, molecules are passing through the cells. In the leaf, molecules are passing into the cell.
a Small intestine epithelial cell – microvilli on the surface of cell
Alveolus epithelial cell – cell is flattened
Mesophyll cell – limited contact with other cells
b Small intestine epithelial cell – part of a single cell layer, although cells are not especially thin. This is because the processes involved in active uptake by these cells use mitochondria to provide ATP. Many mitochondria take up more space inside a cell.
Alveolus epithelial cell – flattening of the cell reduces the distance from one side to the other.
Mesophyll cell – large vacuole pushes cytoplasm very close to cell wall, so the distance through the wall to the cytoplasm is very short.

2 Exchanging gases in mammals (pages 92–3)

1 Blood has a higher concentration of carbon dioxide than the air in the alveolus. Carbon dioxide diffuses from the plasma, through the capillary wall and alveolus wall into the layer of liquid inside the alveolus. It then diffuses into the air in the alveolus.

3 Moving air – ventilating the lungs (pages 94–5)

1 (See figure opposite)

2 Cartilage allows stretching as the neck moves/allows more flexibility in the neck region/allows food to be pushed through the oesophagus more easily.

3 Narrowing of the airways decreases ventilation (the volume of gas moving in and out of the lungs). It makes breathing out more difficult, so a smaller volume of air can be inhaled with each breath. As a result there is a lower diffusion gradient in the lungs, so less oxygen is exchanged for carbon dioxide. Coughing caused by sensitive airways also reduces the ventilation and may result in damaged alveoli, reducing the total surface area for gas exchange.

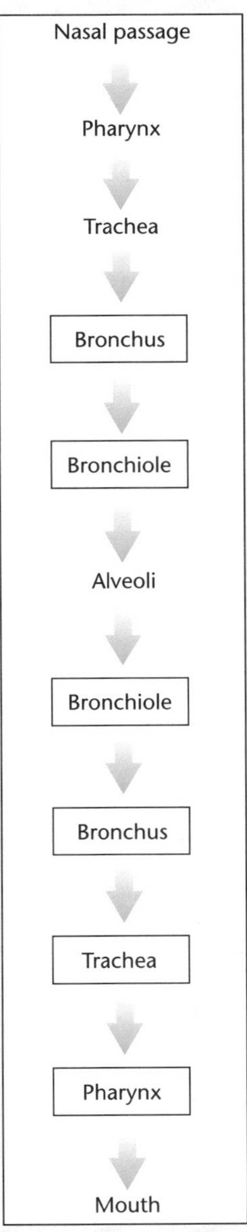

5 Moving water – ventilating the gills (pages 98–9)

1 a Expansion of the buccal cavity lowers the pressure inside the buccal cavity in comparison to the surrounding water. Water flows in through the open mouth, down the pressure gradient.
b Expansion of the operculum lowers the pressure inside the opercular cavity in comparison to the buccal cavity. Contraction of the buccal cavity when the mouth closes raises the pressure in the buccal cavity. The water flows from the higher pressure in the buccal cavity to the lower pressure in the opercular cavity.
c Contraction of the opercular cavity when the operculum valve opens raises the pressure in the opercular cavity above the pressure of the surrounding water. Water flows out of the opercular cavity down a pressure gradient.

2 Water supports the gill lamellae and holds them apart. In air they stick together, reducing the surface area so less oxygen can diffuse through.

6 Exchanging gases in plants (pages 100–101)

1 Carbon dioxide taken in, oxygen given out

2 Photosynthesis uses up carbon dioxide so its concentration inside the leaf remains lower than in the outside air. Photosynthesis releases oxygen so its concentration inside the leaf remains higher than in the outside air.

Module 1 Core Principles

Unit 6 Exchanging materials (continued)

3 Oxygen produced by photosynthesis inside the cells can be used directly.
4 Respiration uses up oxygen so its concentration inside the leaf remains lower than in the outside air. Oxygen diffuses through the surface of the leaf, into the intercellular spaces and then into the cells down a diffusion gradient. Respiration releases carbon dioxide so its concentration inside the leaf remains higher than in the outside air. Carbon dioxide diffuses out of the cells, into the intercellular spaces and out through the surface of the leaf down a diffusion gradient. At night stomata are closed, so most gas diffuses through the epidermis.

7 Efficient exchange surfaces (pages 102–3)

1 The surface of the alveolus is an epithelium.
The epithelium cells are flattened.
The capillary wall is a single layer of flattened cells.
The two surfaces are next to each other.
2 The branching of the lamellae to form gill plates gives a large area in contact with the outside water.
There are four pairs of gills, each with millions of gill plates.
Water supports the filaments so both sides are in contact with the water.
3 Both ventilate the surface to maintain a flow of oxygen-rich air or water towards the exchange surface and a flow of air or water with increased carbon dioxide away from the exchange surface.
Both circulate blood next to the exchange surface to maintain a flow of oxygen-rich blood away from the exchange surface and a flow of blood with increased carbon dioxide towards the exchange surface.
4 In fish the blood circulation flows through the gill lamella. In mammals the blood circulation flows across one side of the alveolus.
5 Mesophyll cells use gases from the air for biochemical reactions. In light, carbon dioxide is used in photosynthesis so there is a lower concentration of carbon dioxide in cells than in intercellular air. The intercellular air in turn has a lower carbon dioxide concentration than the air outside the leaf. This gives a gradient of carbon dioxide between the inside of the leaf and the air outside.

8 Waterways – osmosis (pages 104–5)

1 Similarities: molecules move along diffusion gradients; the movement is from a high to a low concentration of the same molecule.
Differences: osmosis occurs through a partially permeable membrane; osmosis applies only to water.
2 From **C** to **B** to **A**
3 Between **C** and **B**, because there is a greater water potential gradient between these cells
4 **E** (–2 kPa)
5 The solution around cell **D** (it has the lowest water potential)
6

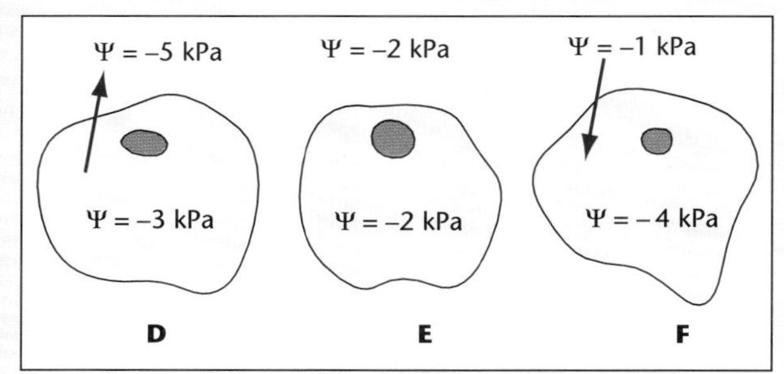

7 **E**
8 a The solution around cell **F**
b The solution around cell **D**
c The solution around cell **E**

9 Cells and osmosis (pages 106–7)

1 a Isotonic solution: there is no net movement of water as the cells and solution have the same water potential so cells stay the same size. Hypotonic solution: the cells have a lower water potential than the solution so they gain water and increase in size. Hypertonic solution: the cells have a higher water potential than the solution so they lose water and decrease in size.
b A red blood cell has a lower water potential than the hypotonic solution. As water enters the cell along a water potential gradient, the cell expands. The cell membrane stretches and eventually the cell bursts.
c Red blood cells lose water to a hypertonic solution. As water is lost, the cytoplasm reduces in volume, so the molecules of the cell membrane move closer together. As the molecules in the bilayer cannot overlap, the membrane folds over the smaller cell surface.
2 The intercellular fluid around all body cells is formed by blood. If the water potential of the blood is regulated, then that of the intercellular fluid will also be regulated. This will prevent cells being damaged by osmotic changes.
3 a Water potential measures the kinetic energy of water. As there is an increased amount of water in the cell, then water can move more freely, so the water potential is less negative.
b The vacuole has a greater volume so it exerts more outward pressure on the wall.
4 The cells lose water to the solution so the size of the vacuole decreases. As a result, the pressure of the cell wall decreases as the vacuole is no longer pushing against the cell wall. The cell wall has no support from inside, so the cellulose fibres in the walls can bend.
5 The dissolved ions decrease the water potential of the cell so water will enter the cell and keep it turgid.

6 a The surfaces of leaf cells have a layer of water on them. This water evaporates into the intercellular air spaces because the air has a lower concentration of water than the cell surface. The air outside the leaf has a lower concentration of water than the intercellular air spaces, so water diffuses from the inside of the leaf to the outside, down a diffusion gradient. This happens more quickly when the stomata are open.

b The water lost from the intercellular air spaces is replaced by water from the cells. If the cells lose too much water, the vacuole shrinks. This causes the pressure against the cell wall to fall so the cell wall is no longer supported from inside.

10 Unit 6 – Questions (pages 108–9)

1 a

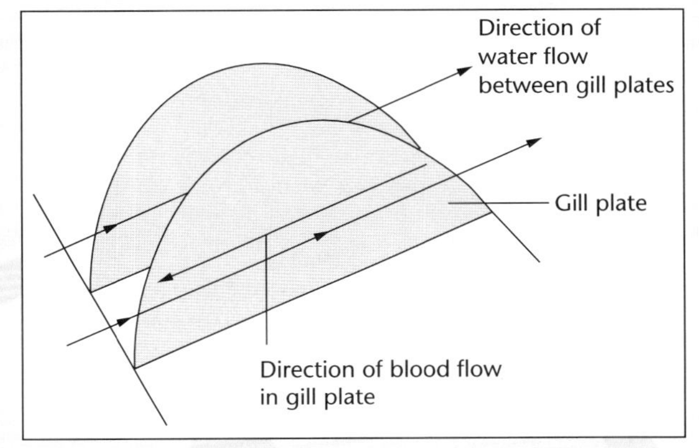

b It increases the distance across which diffusion occurs; water always flows towards blood that has a higher carbon dioxide/lower oxygen level than the water; blood always flows towards water with a higher oxygen/lower carbon dioxide concentration than the blood.

c Two of:
- the thinner the gill, the more active the fish, as gas exchange is faster through a thinner surface
- the smaller the distance between blood and water, the more active the fish, as there is less distance for diffusion
- the greater the number of lamellae, the more active the fish, as there is a larger surface area for gas exchange
- the smaller distance between lamellae, the more active the fish, as there is a greater surface exposed to water.

2 a Eight of:
- intercostal muscles contract and raise the rib cage
- diaphragm muscle contracts and lowers the diaphragm
- volume in thorax increases
- lungs pulled out by expansion of thorax
- pressure in lungs falls below atmospheric pressure so air enters
- relaxation of diaphragm and intercostal muscles
- volume of thorax decreases
- elastic recoil of lungs
- increases pressure in lungs above the atmosphere so air leaves.

b Six of:
- operculum valve closes, mouth opens and buccal cavity expands
- pressure in buccal cavity falls below external water pressure so water enters
- opercular cavity expands so pressure falls below that in buccal cavity
- mouth closes and buccal cavity contracts
- pressure in buccal cavity rises above that in opercular cavity
- water flows from buccal cavity into opercular cavity
- operculum valve opens and opercular cavity contracts
- pressure in opercular cavity rises higher than external water pressure so water leaves through opercular valve.

3 a Diffusion

b Two of:
- thin wall/single layer of cells/epithelium forming the wall
- blood capillaries close to alveolus wall
- alveoli folded to increase surface area.

c Four of:
- oxygen in alveolus dissolves in liquid lining the alveolus
- diffuses down a diffusion gradient into the blood/description of a concentration gradient for oxygen
- carbon dioxide in blood plasma
- diffuses down a diffusion gradient into the alveolus/description of a carbon dioxide concentration gradient
- gases diffuse through the cells of the alveolus and capillary walls.

4 a i **A** palisade cell; **B** intercellular air space; **C** (spongy) mesophyll cell

ii, iii

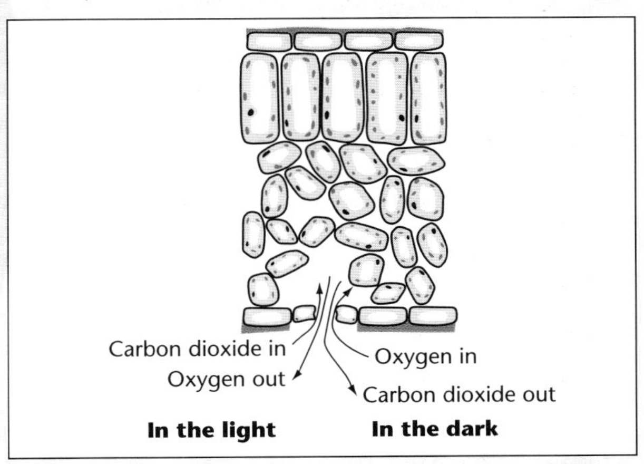

b They make the leaf surface more porous; increase the rate of entry of gases.

5 a The movement of water from a solution with a higher water potential to a solution with a lower water potential; through a partially permeable membrane

b From **A** to **B** and **C**; from **B** to **C**; **C** has the lowest water potential; **A** has the highest water potential.

Module 2 Genes and Genetic Engineering

Unit 7 The genetic code

1 Looking similar (pages 116–17)
1 21

2 Storing information (pages 118–19)
1 a A polymer is a large molecule made up of many similar repeating units joined together.
b A monomer is the basic unit of which a polymer is made.
2 Ribose has one more oxygen atom than deoxyribose.
3

	DNA	RNA
Sugar	Deoxyribose	Ribose
Purine bases	Adenine and guanine	Adenine and guanine
Pyrimidine bases	Cytosine and thymine	Cytosine and uracil
Inorganic component	Phosphate	Phosphate

4 A reaction in which two molecules join together and a molecule of water is removed in the process

3 DNA structure (pages 120–21)
1 TACGGTCAG
2 35%
3 Cytosine 19, thymine 31

4 Copying DNA (pages 122–3)
1 Because half the original molecule is kept intact (conserved) and the other half is newly synthesised. Each molecule has one new strand and one old strand.

5 How genes work (pages 124–5)
1 a 4^2 or 16
b 4^4 or 256
2 16 is not enough to code for 20 amino acids, while 256 is far too many. A triplet code gives 64 which is enough, with not too many excess codons and some 'spare' codons that can be used as stop and start codes.
3 Glutamine–asparagine–valine–phenylalanine–tryptophan

6 Copying the code (pages 126–7)
1 Hydrogen bonds
2 This shows the enzyme where the beginning of the gene is. Without this, more than one gene could be transcribed which is unnecessary.
3 Unwinding exposes the bases, so that a complementary RNA nucleotide can base pair.
4 UAACGGUUC
5 At least 20

7 Reading the message (pages 128–9)
1 AUC
2 It is single stranded so that mRNA can carry a copy of the DNA code with unpaired bases; it forms base pairs with the correct tRNA molecule; it is smaller than DNA so it can travel out of the nucleus and move around the cell.
3 Because more protein can be made on each mRNA strand, so fewer strands of RNA need to be transcribed for the same amount of protein to be synthesised

8 Changed codes (pages 130–31)
1 The 'wrong' amino acid could change the shape of the protein by affecting the way it folds. This could affect the shape of the active site, especially if the 'wrong' amino acid is in the part of the molecule that forms the active site.

10 Unit 7 – Questions (pages 134–5)
1 a AAAAGUCCAUCACUUAAUGCUGCU
b i AAAGUCCAUCACUUAAUGGCUGCU
ii A at position 1, 2, 3 or 4 deleted
iii G inserted between bases 18 and 19 or 19 and 20 on original strand/between bases 17 and 18 or 18 and 19 on new mRNA strand
c It has a different amino acid sequence; this may change the active site/shape so substrate no longer binds correctly.
2 a Three of: **H**, **I** and **K** are purines; **H** pairs with **J**; **I** pairs with **M**; **K** pairs with **L**.
b i 3; because there are 21 bases coding for seven amino acids
ii ywwxxwz
3 a i $(100 - [2 \times 17.5]) \div 2 = 32.5\%$
ii The order of the bases is different; this produces genes which code for different products so the organisms are different.
b $249 \div 3 = 83$ (3 bases for every amino acid)

Unit 8 Cell division

1 Understanding cell division (pages 136–7)
1 Nitrogen-containing base, deoxyribose sugar, phosphate group (see figure at top of page 247)
2 Enzymes unwind the double strand and it 'unzips'. DNA polymerase attaches to each strand. DNA polymerase base pairs free nucleotides against each DNA strand. Each strand of the original DNA acts as a template for the new strand.

3 Splitting up (pages 140–41)
1 End of interphase – 16 polynucleotide strands (2 per chromosome, each original chromosome has replicated); prophase – 16 polynucleotide strands; metaphase – 16 polynucleotide strands; anaphase – 8 polynucleotide strands at each pole of the cell; telophase – 8 polynucleotide strands in each new nucleus; start of interphase: 8 polynucleotide strands

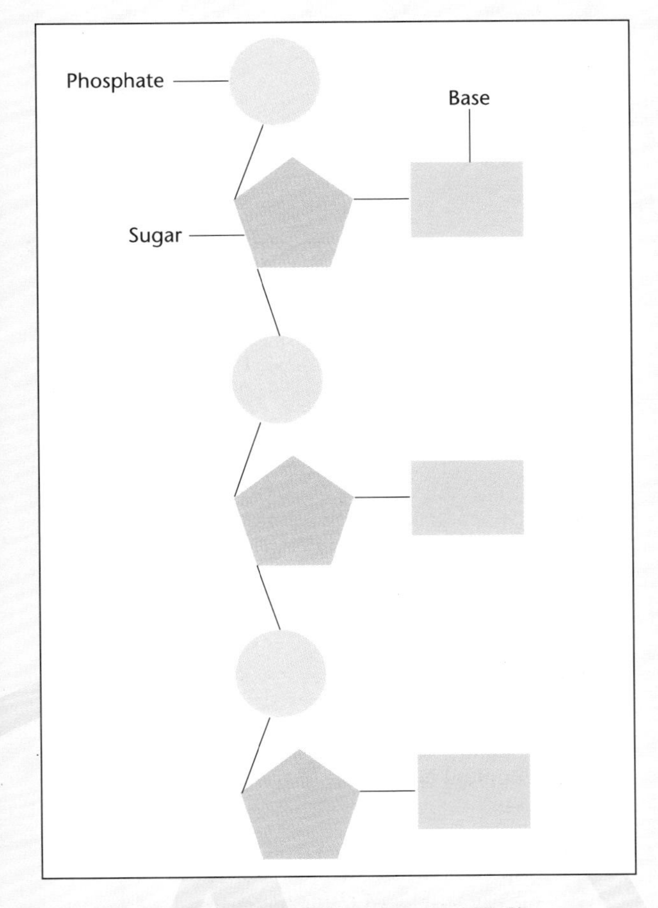

4 Generation to generation (pages 142–3)

1 In mitosis, each daughter cell has identical genes to those of the parent cell.

6 Cloning animal cells (pages 146–7)

1 Interphase – growth and synthesis of organelles and proteins; DNA replication. Mitosis – nuclear division. Cytokinesis – cell division.

7 Sexual reproduction (pages 148–9)

1 a Ova have a large amount of cytoplasm with yolk droplets containing proteins and lipid which are food reserves for the initial growth for the developing embryo.
  b Sperm have many mitochondria to provide ATP/energy for swimming and a tail for swimming.

2 This creates new combinations of DNA/genes, increasing variation.

3 a 8
  b 4
  c 8

8 Life cycles (pages 150–51)

1

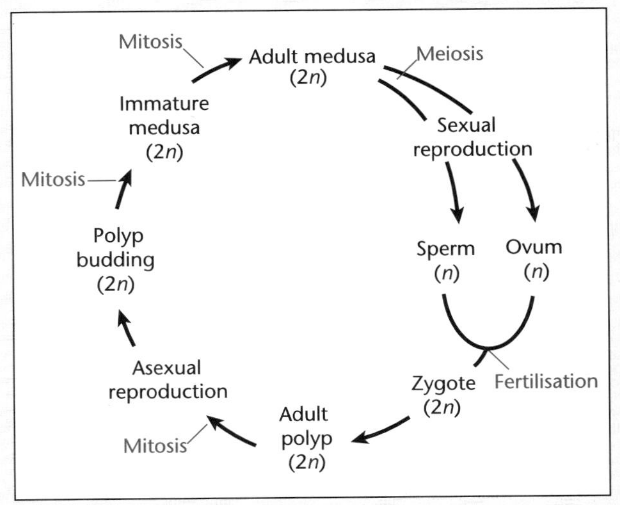

9 Unit 8 – Questions (pages 152–3)

1 a **D E B A C**
  b Ten of:
  - **D – interphase:**
  - replication of DNA
  - building up of energy reserves
  - synthesis of organelles.
  - **E – prophase:**
  - chromosomes forming/appearing
  - DNA coils around proteins/chromosomes become shorter and thicker
  - spindle forms from centrioles/nuclear envelope disappears.
  - **B – metaphase:**
  - chromosomes attach to the spindle
  - across the equator
  - held on by centromeres/spindle attachments.
  - **A – anaphase:**
  - chromosome duplicates/sisters/copies/chromatids separate
  - pulled to the poles of the spindle by the centromeres.
  - **C – telophase:**
  - chromosomes unwind
  - nuclear envelope forms around each set of chromosomes
  - cytoplasm divides between the two nuclei.

2 a $449 \div 503 \times 100 = 89\%$
  b Three of:
  - DNA replicates
  - cytoplasm accumulates energy stores
  - organelles synthesised
  - centrioles replicate.

  c Interphase requires the longest time as growth, synthesis and DNA replication take time; cell division stages are relatively short as events are all related to chromosome movement; anaphase takes the longest as the chromosomes take time to move along the spindle and uncoil.

Module 2
Genes and Genetic Engineering

Unit 8 Cell division (continued)

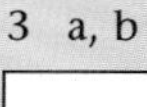

3 a, b

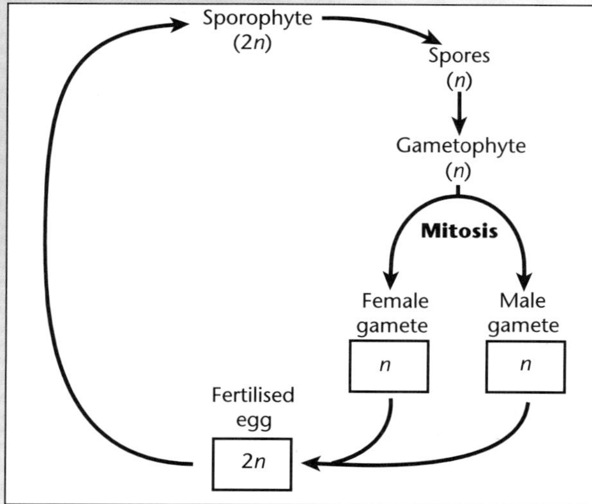

4 a 19
  b 19
  c 38

5 a i Gametes are genetically unique cells produced for sexual reproduction.
    ii They have half the total chromosome number of a body cell.
  b i Cell division in which homologous chromosome pairs are separated; producing gametes containing one member of every pair/half the total number of chromosomes
    ii It enables a constant chromosome number from one generation to the next; it gives genetic variation as all gametes are different from each other.
  c It enables the two stages to live in different environments so they do not compete.

6 a Four of:
  - part of a plant separates from the parent
  - different plants use different parts, e.g. stem, leaf, bud
  - disease-free plants used for tissue culture
  - an explant 1 cm long is cut from the tip
  - the explant is grown in sterile conditions for a period of time
  - shoots are removed and recultured before planting.

  b Adult animal cells have part of their DNA switched off so not all of the DNA is available/cells are not totipotent.
  c Four of:
  - eggs are removed from a female and fertilised in a dish
  - the cell is allowed to divide once
  - the coating around the cells which allows normal division is removed using enzymes
  - an artificial coating is placed around each cell
  - separated cells now develop independently into genetically identical embryos.

Unit 9 Gene technology

1 Engineering genes (pages 154–5)

1 The DNA of the donor gene is transcribed by recipient cells to make mRNA. The mRNA passes into the cytoplasm and the ribosomes attach to it. Transcription places the amino acids in the right order to synthesise a protein. The protein is the gene product made from the donor DNA.

2 Transferring genes (pages 156–7)

1 A reaction which breaks a bond between two molecules/monomers/nucleotides by the addition of water
2 The enzyme active site recognises a specific set of bases by their shape. It will cut the DNA wherever these bases occur.
3 The sticky ends will be complementary so the pieces of DNA can be joined.
4 Condensation

3 Putting genes into bacteria (pages 158–9)

1 2, 5, 12

4 Improving nature (pages 160–61)

1 18
2 a GGACCGTGGTAATTTCTTTTATAGTAGCCACCAAGG ATACTACTTATATCT
  b One fewer
3 It lowers the water potential of the cell compared with the intercellular fluid.
4 It increases the distance across which gases diffuse/makes the exchange surface too thick for fast diffusion.
5 The ducts from gastric glands, pancreatic duct, bile duct
6 The defence cells would attack the cells containing the virus.
7 Liposomes enter into the cytoplasm but do not go to the nucleus. The DNA only reaches the nucleus by chance/DNA is likely to be broken down in the cytoplasm before reaching the nucleus.

5 Altered animals (pages 162–3)

1 These are suggestions only, you may think of others.

Sheep and alpha-1-antitrypsin:
- Is this an acceptable use of animals bred for food production?
- Economics – a new source of income when the market for meat is falling?
- Ethics – is it acceptable to transfer human genes to sheep?
- Animal welfare – would rearing require confinement of animals?
- What happens to the animals when they die or are too old to produce milk?

Improving food quality:
- This improves the chances of poorer countries with lower quality land available to raise sufficient food for their populations.
- Ethics – transferring genes between species – is this any different from selective breeding?
- Who 'owns' the right to produce genetically modified animals – the company that developed them?

Engineering humans:
- Should gene therapy be accepted to treat genetic disease in the same way as drugs or surgery are used for other diseases?
- Should there be laws to limit the use of genetic engineering in humans?
- How could decisions about genetic modification of people be made?

6 Altered plants (pages 164–5)

1 The plants cannot synthesise amino acids needed to make proteins, so they cannot produce new cells or synthesise enzymes for metabolic reactions.

2 They are all produced by mitosis, so they have the same genes as the parent.

3 a 'Pharmed' plants, increased vitamins in crops, vaccine crops, stress-tolerant crops

b Herbicide-resistant plants, insecticide-resistant plants, slow-ripening tomatoes, pre-coloured flowers and cotton, virus-resistant plants, nematode-resistant cereals, frost-resistant plants, 'pharmed' plants, vaccine crops, oil- and plastic-producing plants

7 Chain reactions (pages 166–7)

1

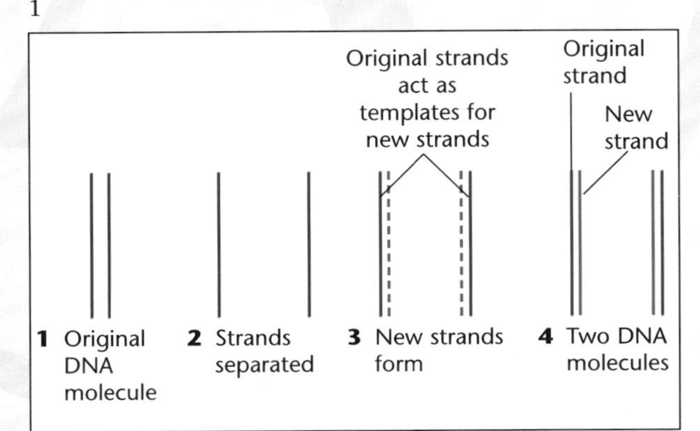

Replication is semi-conservative because each new molecule has one new and one original strand.

8 Finding genes (pages 168–9)

1 The base sequences occur randomly in the DNA. The enzyme cuts wherever these base sequences occur, so the sections are different lengths depending on the distance between the restriction sites.

2 a 10

b 11 and 13

3 DNA controls the synthesis of mRNA from which proteins are synthesised. The order of the amino acids gives the order of the nucleotides in mRNA. The triplet codes for the amino acids can be looked up and placed in order. This will give the sequence of the mRNA which was transcribed from the DNA. This gives the sequence of the gene for the protein.

9 Finding the order (pages 170–71)

1 GGCAGAT
GGCAGATCGT
GGCAGATCGTGAGT
GGCAGATCGTGAGTT
GGCAGATCGTGAGTTCGAGA

2 TGACCAGATC

10 Unit 9 – Questions (pages 172–3)

1 a Circular DNA; separate from chromosome DNA in bacteria

b i Endonuclease

ii Ligase

c CGGA

2 a i DNA from two different sources

ii Transfer of bacterial colonies from a master plate to another plate without changing the positions of the colonies

b Five of:
- plasmid containing an antibiotic resistance gene cut open
- foreign DNA spliced into plasmid
- plasmid used to transform bacteria
- bacteria grown on master plates on a medium without antibiotics
- transferred to plate with antibiotic medium
- only transformed bacteria with antibiotic resistance gene able to survive.

3 A = Bal I; B = Ava I; C = Eco RI; D = Pvu II

4 a Cytosine/C

b Thymine/T

c CAGTACGTAT

d GTCATGCATA

Module 3 Physiology and Transport

Unit 10 Transport in animals

1 Supplying cells (pages 180–81)

1 High temperature may denature enzymes/structural proteins in muscle.
2 Hormones bind to receptors on cell membranes. This sends signals to the cell to change its activity.
3 • Increased rate of respiration increases the supply of ATP for muscle contraction.
  • Increased blood flow increases the rate of supply of oxygen/glucose and of removal of carbon dioxide and heat.
  • Increased heart rate increases the blood flow through the circulation, speeding up the supply of oxygen and glucose and removal of carbon dioxide and heat.
  • Increased blood pressure increases the volumes of gases exchanged so more carbon dioxide is removed from the blood and more oxygen taken in by the blood.
  • Converting glycogen makes the supply of glucose within muscle more readily available to use for respiration.
  • Releasing oxygen provides a supply of oxygen for immediate use.

2 The supply network (pages 182–3)

1 a Twice
  b It keeps oxygenated blood separate from deoxygenated blood so that a higher concentration of oxygen reaches the body cells; it allows the systemic circulation to have a higher pressure so blood reaches cells more efficiently.

3 Pushing blood around (pages 184–5)

1 a (See diagram below)
  b Pulmonary artery and aorta

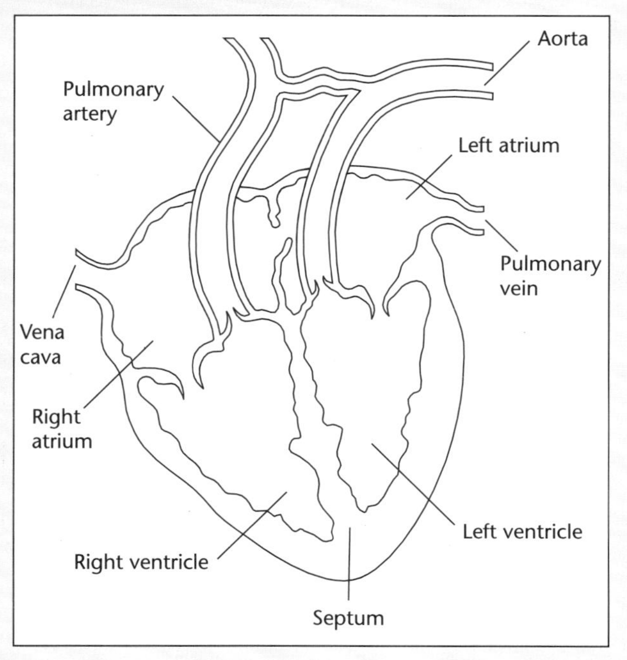

2 Deoxygenated blood from the right side of the heart mixes with oxygenated blood from the left side.
3 The blood pressure is lowered, so less blood circulates to the lungs per heartbeat to pick up oxygen and remove carbon dioxide. Breathing speeds up to ventilate the lungs more often and increase gas exchange. Less blood circulates to the body per heartbeat. The blood has a lower oxygen content, so cells receive less oxygen. As a result less respiration occurs so there is less ATP to maintain cell processes.

4 Cycling through (pages 186–7)

1 The pressure in the right atrium falls below that in the right ventricle and in the vena cava.
2 The pressures in the right side of the heart are lower than those in the left side, but follow the same patterns:

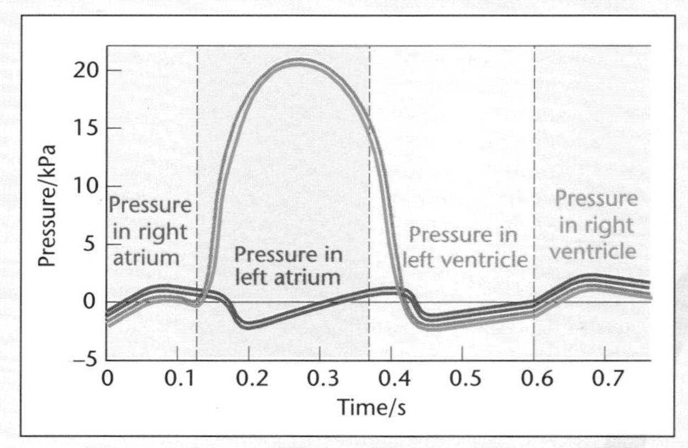

3 0.39 s (when the pressure in the left ventricle falls below the pressure in the aorta)
4 a 0.42 s (when the pressure in the left atrium rises above the pressure in the left ventricle)
  b 0.18 s (when the pressure in the left ventricle rises above the pressure in the aorta)

5 Controlling the heart rate (pages 188–9)

1 SA node excited → AV node excited → Purkyne fibres in bundle of His excited → ventricles then atria contract → heart muscle relaxes

6 Beating faster (pages 190–91)

1 a Carbon dioxide level
  b Chemoreceptors in aorta and carotid sinus
  c Cardiac centre in medulla
  d SA node, AV node and ventricle wall
  e Increase in heart rate
2 a Fewer nerve impulses to the cardiac centre; nerve impulses from the cardiac centre in the parasympathetic nerves; SA node causes heart rate to decrease.
  b More nerve impulses to the medulla; nerve impulses in the sympathetic nerves to the arterioles; muscles in the arterioles contract causing vasoconstriction.

7 Controlling the breathing rate (pages 192–3)

1

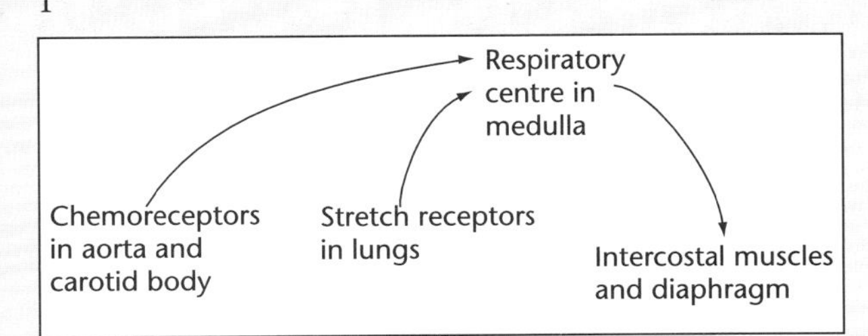

2 a Stretching/expansion of the lungs
  b Stretch receptors in the bronchi and bronchioles
  c Respiratory centre in the medulla
  d Diaphragm and intercostal muscles
  e Muscles relax

8 Breathing quicker and deeper (pages 194–5)

1 Chemoreceptors in the aortic and carotid bodies and medulla detect a fall in carbon dioxide level. Fewer impulses are sent from the medulla to the diaphragm and intercostal muscles. The rate and depth of breathing decrease.

2 a Increased levels of carbon dioxide
  b Chemoreceptors in the aortic and carotid bodies and the medulla
  c Respiratory centre in the medulla
  d Diaphragm and intercostal muscles
  e Rate and depth of breathing increase

3 There is a delay in the nerve impulses from the brain so the diaphragm and intercostal muscles do not contract so often. As a result, impulses to the medulla are less frequent and the medulla switches off.

9 Pipework (pages 196–7)

1 Each pulse is a surge of blood caused by a heartbeat.

10 Changing over (pages 198–9)

1 Elastic recoil of arteries due to each heart contraction pushing a small surge of blood through the arteries

2 The further away, the lower the pressure

3, 4

Component	Plasma	Tissue fluid	Lymph
Water	Present	Present	Present
Large proteins	Present	Absent	Present
Glucose	High concentration	Lower concentration	Lower concentration
Amino acids	High concentration	Lower concentration	Lower concentration
Chylomicrons	Low concentration	Higher concentration	High concentration
Oxygen	High concentration	Lower concentration	Lower concentration
Carbon dioxide	Low concentration	Higher concentration	Higher concentration
Wastes	Low concentration	Higher concentration	Higher concentration
Red blood cells	Present	Absent	Absent

11 Transporting oxygen (pages 200–201)

1 8 atoms/4 molecules

2 Haemoglobin combines with oxygen in the air to form bright red oxyhaemoglobin; when a blood sample is taken, air is excluded.

3 The rate of respiration varies in different tissues, so the concentration of oxygen also varies.

4 30%

12 Changing the odds (pages 202–3)

1 Enzyme activity is affected by pH; changes in pH would interfere with metabolic reactions in cells.

2 None, because the partial pressure of oxygen in the lungs is very high

3

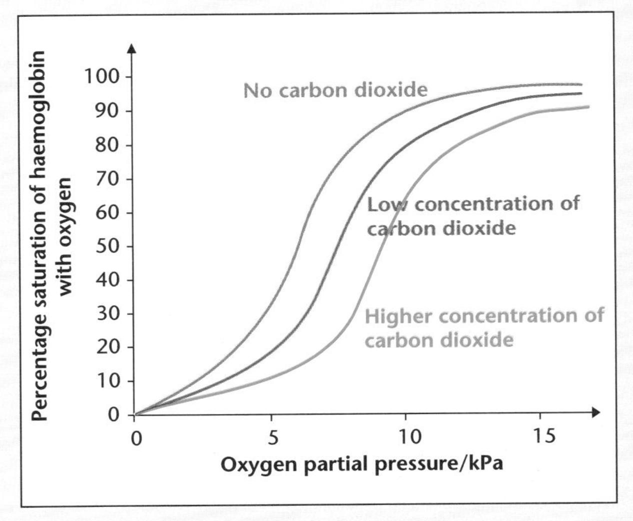

4 The carbon dioxide level in the blood

5 It allows the oxygen supply to be matched to its use by cells.

6 About 35%

7 Too little oxygen is loaded; this causes faster breathing/breathlessness ventilates the lungs more; insufficient oxygen reaching the brain causes unconsciousness.

14 Energy for exercising muscles (pages 206–7)

1 Aerobic respiration:
oxygen + glucose → carbon dioxide + water + 38ATP
Anaerobic respiration: glucose → lactate + 2ATP

2 a

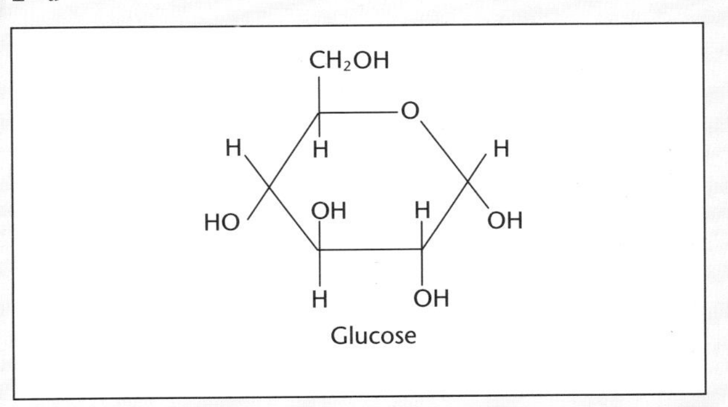

Module 3 Physiology and Transport

Unit 10 Transport in animals

b

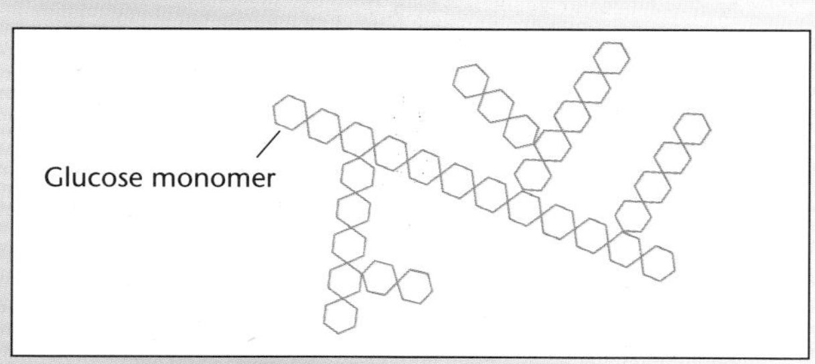

c

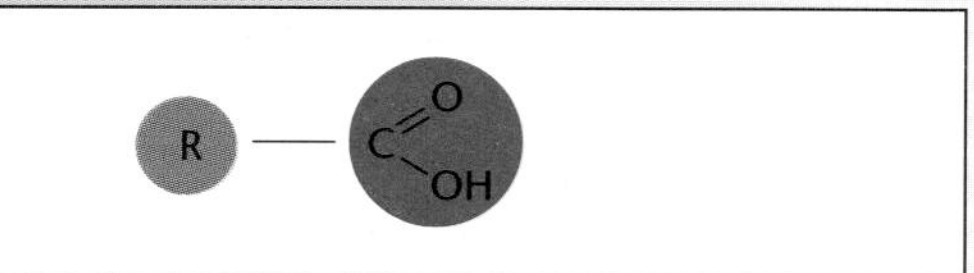

15 Unit 10 – Questions (pages 208–9)

1 a i 0.8 s
ii 60 ÷ 0.8 = 75 beats per minute
iii 0.4 ± 0.1 s
b The walls of the right ventricle are thinner than the walls of the left ventricle; they exert less force on the blood so the pressure is lower.

2 a i As pulse rate rises, the output increases.
ii 7 ÷ 70 = 0.1 litres per beat at the start; 8 ÷ 90 = 0.09 litres per beat after 2 minutes' exercise
b The respiration rate has increased in the muscle; higher carbon dioxide levels are detected by receptors in the medulla; the heart rate increases so more blood/greater output removes carbon dioxide faster; greater output supplies additional oxygen to muscles during exercise.

3 a Glycogen is converted to glucose for use in respiration/energy release/ATP production; creatine phosphate is used as an energy source with ADP to regenerate ATP; ATP has been used to supply energy for movement; lactate is a product of anaerobic respiration.
b Lactate is taken in the blood to the liver; in the liver some is converted to water and carbon dioxide; most is converted to glycogen.
c Fatty acids from lipid digestion; are used to form ATP which is then used to replace glycogen.

4 a 2
b i The atria are in diastole/relaxing.
ii The valves are closed.
iii Blood is entering the atria from the veins.

Unit 11 Transport in plants

1 The structure of a plant root (pages 210–11)

1 To prevent damage from the soil
2 To increase the surface area to absorb water and dissolved minerals
3 **A** Phloem
B Xylem
C Pericycle
D Cortex
E Epidermis
F Exodermis

2 Transport structures (pages 212–13)

1 Meristem
2 Xylem is dead tissue/no cell contents, phloem is living; xylem has no cross-walls, phloem has sieve plates formed from cross walls; phloem has companion cells.

3 Specialised roots (pages 214–15)

1 They are green/contain chloroplasts.

4 Getting water in (pages 216–17)

1 The water in the soil. It has the greater amount of water in the solution.

5 Moving through (pages 218–19)

1 The porous pot represents the leaf. Water can evaporate from its surface. The long glass tube represents the column of water in the xylem. The reservoir of mercury represents water entering the xylem from the root and the soil. Mercury is used in this experiment rather than water, because of its greater density. If water was used instead of mercury, you would need a column of water many metres high.
2 The leaves and stem have been removed, so transpiration cannot take place.
3 Root pressure – water continues to enter the xylem because it has a low water potential as a result of ions being actively pumped in.

6 Transpiration (pages 220–21)

1 This is to stop water evaporating from the soil in the pot.
2 The plant is growing, so the loss in mass is offset to a small extent by an increase in the mass of the plant tissues due to growth.
3 By finding the diameter (and hence radius) of the capillary tube, and using the formula volume = $\pi r^2 d$, where d is the distance moved by the air bubble (i.e. 2 cm) and r is the radius of the capillary tube.

7 Experimenting with xylem (pages 222–3)

1 Active transport
2 The plants have not been able to photosynthesise so there is no ATP for active transport.
3 a This will reduce ion uptake, as reducing the temperature slows down enzyme activity and hence respiration. Respiratory energy is needed for active transport.
  b This will also inhibit respiration and hence reduce active transport, slowing down the rate of ion transport into the root.

8 Surviving without water (pages 224–5)

1 a This enables it to absorb water from a very large area, so even if rainfall is very light, the cactus can absorb more of it.
  b This enables it to store water.
  c This reduces water loss from transpiration, since the surface area of the plant is reduced.
  d This minimises the surface area and hence the amount of water which can evaporate from the plant.
  e This reduces transpiration since the humidity is usually greater in the pits than in the dry air surrounding the plant.
  f This reduces the temperature at the surface of the cactus and therefore reduces transpiration.

9 A closer look at phloem (pages 226–7)

1 Otherwise the plant might die from loss of water
2 In the first experiment, sugar is present above the ring because it has been made by the leaves in photosynthesis. It is not found below the ring because the phloem has been removed. In the second experiment, sugar is found above and below the ring, because leaves are present above and below the ring. This experiment also shows that sugar (sucrose) can travel in both directions in the phloem, since above the ring, it has been transported downwards from the leaves, and below the ring, it has moved upwards from the leaves.
3 Ring one plant above the leaves and another plant below the leaves and compare with a control (unringed) plant.
4 Supply a number of plants of the same age and size with radioactive carbon dioxide. Keep them in the same conditions of light and temperature. At different times, cut sections across the stems of the plants above and below the source of carbon dioxide and monitor the radioactive carbon.

10 The mass flow hypothesis (pages 228–9)

1 a Sink
  b Source
  c Source
  d Sink
2 a Downwards
  b Upwards

11 Unit 11 – Questions (pages 230–31)

1 a Taken into roots through root hairs; by active transport from the nutrient solution; carried across the root to the xylem; carried in the transpiration stream in the xylem vessels
  b It would be increased; moving air increases the rate of transpiration, so more phosphate arrives at the leaf each second.
  c Uncovered leaves are photosynthesising and using phosphate to make new molecules in the leaf.
  d i In the phloem
    ii Allow aphids to feed on the phloem; collect the exudate; test the exudate for radioactivity.
2 a **A** xylem; **B** phloem; **C** endodermis
  b i Cell walls
    ii Cytoplasm
  c The Casparian strip in the walls of the cells does not allow water to pass/is waterproof.
3 a Symplast
  b It forces water to enter the cytoplasm of the cells; possibly controls the entry of water and minerals into the xylem.
  c Root hair cell has a lower water potential than the surrounding soil solution; water enters by osmosis from the soil solution down a water potential gradient.
4 a 15.30–16.00
  b i Stomata are open; transpiration losses increase as temperature increases.
    ii Stomata are closed, reducing transpiration losses.
  c Loss of water from leaves is low so plants have more chance of surviving while their roots recover and there is less absorption by the roots.

Glossary

Abdominal cavity The cavity below the diaphragm, containing the gut, reproductive organs and kidneys.

Absorption The passing of digested food molecules through the gut wall and into the blood.

Acidophile An 'acid-loving' organism that can thrive in a pH lower than 5.

Activation energy The minimum amount of kinetic energy required for a reaction to occur.

Activator An inorganic ion which combines with an enzyme or a substrate and acts as a cofactor.

Active site The place on an enzyme where a substrate molecule is temporarily bound during a chemical reaction.

Active transport The movement of molecules across a membrane from an area where they are at a lower concentration to an area where they are at a higher concentration, using specialised transport molecules, requiring energy from respiration.

Addition mutation A change in the nucleotide sequence of DNA, in which a nucleotide is added to the sequence.

Adenine One of the four bases in the nucleotides of DNA and RNA.

Adhesion The attraction of two different substances, one of which is usually a liquid and the other a solid. Adhesion results from intermolecular forces between the substances and is distinct from cohesion, which involves only attractive intermolecular forces within a single substance.

ADP (adenosine diphosphate) A molecule that reacts with inorganic phosphate to form ATP.

Adventitious root Root that grows from the stem, leaf or bud tissue of a plant.

Aerial root Root arising from an above-ground part of the shoot.

Aerobic A situation where there is sufficient oxygen for aerobic respiration.

Aerobic respiration A series of reactions using oxygen in which energy is transferred from organic compounds, such as carbohydrates, to the temporary energy storage molecule ATP.

Afferent blood vessels Blood vessels entering a tissue or an organ.

Affinity Having an attraction towards a specific molecule.

Albumin A protein found in blood plasma and the white of eggs.

Alkalophile An 'alkali-loving' organism that can thrive in environments with a pH higher than 9.

Allele One of two or more different versions of a gene.

Allergy A prolonged inflammatory response triggered by the binding of an allergen to a specific cell.

Alpha-1-antitrypsin An enzyme used in the treatment of cystic fibrosis.

Alpha helix A form of secondary structure in a protein. An alpha helix consists of a long polypeptide chain held in a helix by hydrogen bonds.

Alternation of generations Having a haploid gamete-producing adult and a diploid spore-producing stage in the life cycle.

Alveolus (plural alveoli) A tiny air sac in the lungs where gaseous exchange occurs.

Amino acid The monomer used as the building block of polypeptides and proteins. Each amino acid contains an amino group, $-NH_2$, and carboxylic acid group, -COOH.

Amino group $-NH_2$ group, found in amino acid molecules and some other organic molecules.

Amylase An enzyme that hydrolyses starch into sugars.

Anabolic A term describing metabolic reactions that join smaller molecules together to build larger ones.

Anaerobic A situation where there is insufficient oxygen for aerobic respiration.

Anaphase The phase of mitosis in which the chromatids separate and move towards the poles.

Antibody A chemical produced by the body to attack foreign chemicals.

Anticodon The three-base sequence in a tRNA molecule that is complementary to a particular three-base sequence (the codon) in a mRNA molecule.

Antigen A molecule, cell or organism that stimulates the immune system of an organism to produce an antibody.

Antigenicity The ability of a substance to trigger an immune response.

Aortic body A group of chemoreceptor cells next to the wall of the aorta.

Aphid Insect that feeds on plant sap, used in experiments to investigate transport in the phloem.

Apical meristem The growing point, composed of meristematic tissue, at the tip of the root or shoot of a vascular plant.

Apnoea The stopping of breathing for brief periods, often during sleep.

Apoplast pathway A pathway for water through plants which passes through cell walls and intercellular spaces.

Arteriole A small blood vessel that subdivides to form capillaries.

Artery A blood vessel that carries blood away from the heart.

Asexual reproduction Reproduction that takes place by the process of mitosis, involving a single organism.

Association The forming of a non-chemical link between haemoglobin and oxygen.

Asthma An allergic response in which the airways become narrowed, causing difficulty in breathing.

Atom The smallest particle of an element, consisting of a core of protons and neutrons (the nucleus) surrounded by electrons.

ATP (adenosine triphosphate) Energy is stored in the molecule ATP by the reaction: $ADP + P_i \rightarrow ATP$. This energy can be made available in the cell as required by the reverse reaction, the breakdown of ATP to ADP and P_i. P_i is inorganic phosphate.

Atrioventricular node (AV node) A mass of specialised heart tissue that delays the wave of electrical excitation from the sinoatrial node for a few hundredths of a second. This allows the atria to fully contract before ventricular contraction.

Atrioventricular valve A valve in the heart between the atrium and ventricle, which closes to stop blood flowing back into the atrium from the ventricle.

Atrium (plural atria) An upper chamber of the human heart; atria are relatively thin-walled.

Autoradiograph A method of locating radioactivity by fogging of photographic film.

Ballistics A method of inserting DNA into cells by firing tungsten pellets coated with DNA from a special gun.

Base (in nucleotide) Nitrogen-containing, ring-shaped molecule that is part of the nucleotides that make up DNA and RNA.

Base pair In a DNA molecule, the pairing of two complementary bases held together by hydrogen bonds, either adenine and thymine or cytosine and guanine.

Benedict's solution A reagent made of alkaline copper sulphate, used to test for the presence of sugars.

Beta-pleated sheet A form of secondary structure in a protein in which part of the polypeptide chain forms flattened pleated areas held together by hydrogen bonds.

Bilayer A double layer of phospholipid molecules that makes up the main part of the cell surface membrane.

Bile The secretion produced by the liver. The bile salts in bile emulsify fats and so help in their digestion.

Bile duct A duct that connects the gall bladder with the duodenum.

Binary fission Asexual reproduction in which the organism splits into two.

Binding Forming a temporary bond between a substrate and the active site of an enzyme, or between a membrane protein and the substance it recognises.

Biological catalyst A protein that speeds up chemical reactions.

Biosensor A 'tool' for finding out about the body.

Biuret test A food test used to test for the presence of proteins. Biuret solution is added to a food sample, and a lilac colour results if proteins are present.

Blood vessel A tube in which blood is carried around the body.

Bolus A ball of partially digested food.

Bronchioles Small tubes branching from the bronchi in the lungs.

Bronchus (plural bronchi) One of two branches from the trachea into the lungs.

Brush border The surface of the intestinal epithelial cells in contact with the lumen, so called because of its brush-like appearance which is due to the presence of microvilli.

Budding Asexual reproduction in which a small outgrowth appears on the parent organism and forms a new organism.

Buffering The term given to the neutralising of excess hydrogen ions, by bonding to negatively charged ions or to negative charges on the surfaces of large molecules, particularly proteins.

Bundle of His A collection of nerve fibres in the heart, concerned with the beating of the heart.

Callus A mass of unspecialised plant cells.

Cambium Meristem tissue that produces xylem and phloem.

Capillary A microscopic blood vessel.

Carbohydrase A carbohydrate-digesting enzyme.

Carbohydrate A class of compounds made up of carbon, hydrogen and oxygen. Carbohydrates include sugars such as glucose and sucrose, as well as complex carbohydrates such as starch and cellulose.

Carbon–carbon bond A strong covalent bond joining two carbon atoms.

Carboxylic acid group -COOH group, found in amino acids and also in organic acids such as fatty acids.

Carcinogen A cancer-causing agent, which may be chemical, biological or physical.

Cardiac centre The region of the medulla of the brain that controls the heart rate.

Cardiac cycle The sequence of events that make up the heartbeat.

Cardiac muscle The specialised muscle found only in the heart, that is responsible for the regular contraction and relaxation of the heart.

Carotid body A group of chemoreceptor cells next to a carotid artery.

Carotid sinus A pocket in the carotid artery where there is a group of stretch receptor cells.

Carrier protein A protein that uses energy from ATP to transfer molecules of a specific type across cell surface membranes by active transport.

Casparian strip A ring of endodermal cells around the xylem and phloem of the root, that contains suberin.

Catabolic A term describing metabolic reactions that break large molecules down into smaller ones.

Catalyst A substance that speeds up the rate of a reaction by lowering the activation energy, and remains unchanged itself at the end of the reaction.

Cell The building block of which all living organisms are composed.

Cell cycle The cycle of growth and division whereby one cell becomes two.

Cell differentiation A process by which a relatively unspecialised cell undergoes a progressive change to a more specialised cell.

Cell elongation A process of growth by which new cells get longer.

Cell surface membrane (cell membrane, plasma membrane) The boundary layer of the cell, made up of a double layer of phospholipid molecules associated with other lipids and a variety of membrane proteins.

Cellulose A polysaccharide formed from glucose monomers; it has a fibrous structure and is used in plant cell walls.

Central sleep apnoea A disorder in which the person stops breathing for brief periods, often during sleep.

Centrifuge A device that spins at high speed, separating the denser components out of a suspension to form a solid pellet, while the less dense components remain suspended in the liquid supernatant.

Centriole An organelle involved in the development of the spindle fibres in mitosis and meiosis in animal cells.

Centromere The point at which the two chromatids are joined together during the early stages of cell division, and to which the spindle fibres attach.

CFTR An abbreviation for 'cystic fibrosis transmembrane regulator', the membrane channel protein for chloride ions.

Channel protein A protein or pore that spans the cell surface membrane and allows molecules of a specific type to pass through by facilitated diffusion.

Chemoreceptor A sensory receptor that detects chemical changes.

Chlorophyll A pigment molecule found in most organisms that photosynthesise.

Chloroplast A cell organelle in green plants, containing pigments including chlorophyll, in which photosynthesis occurs.

Cholesterol A complex lipid molecule used in the synthesis of hormones and cell membranes.

Chromatid Prior to cell division, each chromosome replicates and so becomes a pair of identical chromatids, held together at the centromere. Therefore a chromatid is a chromosome, but while still joined to its partner it is called a chromatid.

Chromatin Chromosomal material that can be seen in a stained undividing nucleus, when the individual chromosomes are not visible.

Chromatogram The result of a chromatography experiment; a piece of paper or a thin layer showing the origins, the solvent front and the positions of the spots after separation.

Chromatography A technique for separating substances according to their differing solubilities in a particular solvent.

Chromosome One of the thread-like structures in a nucleus, made of DNA and protein. Chromosomes become visible during cell division.

Chylomicrons Droplets resulting from the digestion of fats, containing triglycerides and phospholipids.

Chyme The soup-like mixture produced in the stomach by the churning and mixing of food combined with the action of hydrochloric acid.

Cimetidine A chemical similar in structure to histamine, used in the treatment of stomach ulcers.

Clone Genetically identical cells or individuals produced by asexual reproduction.

Coding strand The strand of the DNA molecule that is transcribed into mRNA during protein synthesis.

Codon A set of three bases in mRNA that corresponds to (codes for) a particular amino acid.

Coeliac disease A disease in which the sufferer cannot tolerate gluten.

Coenzyme A small organic molecule, which binds temporarily to an enzyme's active site and takes part in the reaction.

Cofactor A non-protein molecule required by some enzymes.

Cohesion The tendency of matter to hold itself together, as a result of attractive forces between the molecules.

Cohesion–tension theory A theory that describes how water moves up the xylem of a plant when water evaporates from the leaves.

Collagen A fibrous protein found in skin, bone, cartilage, tendons, blood vessels and teeth.

Colony (of bacteria) A visible cluster of bacterial cells that all originate from one cell.

Companion cell A specialised parenchyma cell associated with a sieve tube element in phloem tissue.

Competitive inhibition Inhibition that happens when a molecule with a shape similar to that of the substrate molecule occupies an enzyme's active site and so prevents substrate molecules from binding.

Competitive inhibitor A molecule that has a shape similar to that of a substrate molecule and can bind to an enzyme's active site, preventing the substrate molecule from binding.

Complementary bases Bases that pair in DNA. Adenine and thymine are complementary, and cytosine and guanine are complementary.

Complementary shapes Two substances that have shapes that allow them to fit together have complementary shapes.

Concentration gradient A difference in the concentration of a substance between two areas.

Condensation reaction A reaction that forms a bond and removes a molecule of water.

Connective tissue The packing tissue that fills the space around the body's internal structures. It is also present within internal structures.

Contractile protein A protein that can shorten and lengthen.

Control system A control system receives information about the changes that are occurring in the body, and sends out instructions to respond to them.

Co-ordinator The part of the brain or spinal cord that receives impulses from receptors.

Cortex Ground tissue region of a stem or root, bounded externally by the epidermis and internally by the vascular tissue region.

Countercurrent flow Two liquids flowing past each other in opposite directions to maximise the rate of exchange between them.

Creatine phosphate A molecule present in skeletal muscle that phosphorylates ADP, producing ATP for use in muscle contraction.

Crista (plural cristae) A fold of the inner membrane in a mitochondrion. Cristae increase the surface area available for ATP production.

Cuticle A waterproof layer on the surface of the epidermis of plants.

Cutting A method of plant propagation in which a piece of plant tissue is cut off the plant and encouraged to grow roots.

Cytokinesis The division of the cytoplasm following mitosis.

Cytoplasm The watery solution in a cell that is outside the membrane-bound organelles.

Cytosine One of the four bases in the nucleotides of DNA and RNA.

Daughter cell A cell produced from a parent cell by cell division.

Deletion mutation A change in the nucleotide sequence of DNA, in which a nucleotide is lost or deleted.

Demand pacemaker An artificial pacemaker that monitors the heart's activity and stimulates it to contract only when the heart rate falls below a minimum.

Denatured An enzyme is denatured when the tertiary structure of a polypeptide chain has changed and caused a change in its 3D shape.

Density The mass of a substance divided by its volume.

Deoxygenated Having low oxygen and high carbon dioxide levels.

Deoxyribose A pentose present in the nucleotides that make up DNA.

Diagnostic enzyme An enzyme used to detect a certain chemical present in body fluids.

Diaphragm The sheet of muscle that separates the thoracic cavity from the abdominal cavity.

Diaphragm muscles Muscles in the diaphragm, which contract to flatten the diaphragm.

Diastole The period of relaxation of the atria and the ventricles during the cardiac cycle.

Dicotyledon A type of flowering plant that has two cotyledons (storage leaves in the seed).

Differential centrifugation The use of a centrifuge to separate particles of different densities.

Diffusion The passive (non-energy-requiring) movement of a molecule from a region where it is at a higher concentration to a region where it is at a lower concentration.

Diffusion gradient A difference in concentration of a substance between two areas.

Digestion Breaking down large food molecules into smaller molecules that can be absorbed.

Digestive secretions (digestive juices) Secretions containing enzymes and other substances involved in digestion.

Dipeptide A molecule made up of two amino acids joined together by a peptide bond.

Dipeptidase An enzyme that hydrolyses dipeptides into amino acids.

Diploid A diploid nucleus has the full number of chromosomes in homologous pairs.

Diploid number The number of chromosomes in a diploid cell ($2n$).

Disaccharide A sugar consisting of two monosaccharides joined together by a condensation reaction.

Dissociation The breaking of the non-chemical link between oxygen and haemoglobin.

Division A method of plant propagation in which one plant is divided into several plants.

Division of labour Large multicellular organisms have many cells and they have many different types of cell. Each type of cell carries out a different function.

DNA (deoxyribonucleic acid) A macromolecule made up of nucleotides and which carries the hereditary information in the form of the sequence of the bases.

DNA ligase An enzyme that joins short pieces of DNA together during DNA replication.

DNA polymerase The enzyme that joins the nucleotides together in the replication of DNA.

Donor In genetic engineering, the organism from which the desired gene is taken.

Double circulation A system in which the heart pumps blood through the gas exchange surface in one set of blood vessels and through other body organs in a different set of blood vessels.

Down's syndrome An inherited condition in humans caused by having an extra chromosome.

Drop root Root extension similar to a pneumatophore but growing down from the branch of a tree.

Duodenum The first part of the small intestine.

Effector Part of the body that brings about a response to a stimulus.

Efferent blood vessels Blood vessels leaving a tissue or organ.

Elastic recoil The rapid return to its original size of stretched tissue as result of its own elasticity.

Electron microscope (EM) An instrument that uses electron beams and magnetic lenses to produce a magnified image of an object.

Embryo splitting Method used to clone animals, in which an early embryo is split into several embryos.

Emulsification Process by which large lipid droplets are broken down into much smaller droplets.

Emulsion test A food test used to detect fats. The sample is dissolved in alcohol, then decanted into a fresh tube. Water is added and the sample is shaken. A milky emulsion appears if fats are present.

Endocytosis Process by which a cell engulfs and ingests extracellular material; the reverse of exocytosis.

Endodermis A single layer of cells forming a sheath around the vascular region in roots. Endodermis cells have a Casparian strip around the side walls to prevent the sideways transfer of water.

Endopeptidase A protein-digesting enzyme that breaks proteins down into polypeptides.

Endoplasmic reticulum (ER) System of phospholipid membranes extending throughout most of a cell. It divides the cytoplasm into compartments. The rough endoplasmic reticulum (RER) is encrusted with ribosomes and is concerned with protein synthesis and transport. The smooth endoplasmic reticulum (SER) is concerned with such functions as steroid metabolism.

Endothelium Layer of cells lining an internal tissue.

End-point inhibition A mechanism by which metabolic pathways are regulated; the product of the pathway controls its own production by inhibiting an enzyme earlier in the pathway.

Energy system A collection of different energy pathways.

Enzyme A class of proteins that function as biological catalysts, i.e. they speed up biochemical reactions by lowering the activation energy.

Enzyme–substrate complex The temporary structure formed when a substrate molecule binds with an enzyme's active site during a reaction.

Epidermis The layer of cells at the surface.

Epiphyte A plant that normally grows on another plant rather than in soil. They are not parasitic, however, and do not use the host plant as a source of food.

Epithelial tissue (epithelium) The tissue that covers all surfaces of the body and its organs.

Equator The central part of the spindle in cell division.

Equilibrium In balance.

Eukaryote An organism with membrane-bound organelles inside its cells.

Eukaryotic cell A cell containing membrane-bound organelles.

Exchange pump A protein pump that brings potassium ions into the cell and removes sodium ions.

Exchange surface A specialised region of an organism through which molecules can pass between the environment and the organism.

Exocytosis A process by which a cell releases a substance, emptying it from vesicles at the cell surface membrane.

Exopeptidase A protein-digesting enzyme that removes amino acids from the end of a polypeptide chain.

Expiration Breathing out.

Explant A piece cut from a plant and used in tissue culture.

External intercostal muscles Intercostal muscles that contract to pull the rib cage up and out.

Extracellular digestion Digestion that takes place outside a cell.

Extracellular enzyme An enzyme that functions outside a cell.

Facilitated diffusion Movement across a cell membrane aided by a specific transport protein molecule. No energy is required.

Fatigue Extreme tiredness after exertion.

Fatty acid An organic molecule that consists of a hydrocarbon tail and a terminal carboxyl group.

Feedback control A control system in which a product regulates its own level.

Fertilisation The fusing of two gametes to form a new individual in sexual reproduction.

Fibrous proteins Proteins that are insoluble in water and usually have a structural function, such as keratin in hair.

First growth phase (G1) The first part of interphase.

Flagellum (plural flagella) A long 'whip-like' structure used for locomotion by some unicellular organisms.

Fluid mosaic model Model of the cell surface membrane, with mobile proteins scattered in a phospholipid bilayer.

Fluidity The ability to change position.

Fructose A six-carbon monosaccharide with the molecular formula $C_6H_{12}O_6$.

Galactose A six-carbon monosaccharide with the molecular formula $C_6H_{12}O_6$, which does not occur freely in nature but is a product of the digestion of lactose.

Gamete A sex cell, such as an ovum or sperm.

Gametophyte The gamete-producing form of a plant.

Ganglion (plural ganglia) A collection of the cell bodies of neurones.

Gaseous exchange The movement of gases, or dissolved gases, into and out of blood or cells.

Gastric gland A gland found in the stomach, which secretes acidic gastric juice.

Gated channels Protein channels in the cell surface membrane that can open or close in response to the binding of hormones.

Gel electrophoresis A method of separating DNA fragments by size, according to their movement in an electric field.

Gene The unit of inheritance; a length of DNA that carries a particular code.

Gene product A protein made as a result of the transcription and translation of a DNA sequence.

Gene therapy Transferring genes with a normal function into cells with faulty genes.

General formula A formula showing how many atoms of each element are present in a class of compounds.

Genetic code The code for protein synthesis in all cells, in which a triplet of bases in the DNA sequence codes for a specific amino acid.

Genetic disorder A problem in the functioning of the body caused by a faulty gene, so that the correct protein is not synthesised.

Genetic engineering Artificially changing an organism's genetic material.

Genetic markers Genes used by genetic engineers to identify recombinant DNA.

Genetically modified crop (GM crop) Crop plant that contains an altered gene.

Genomic library A collection of cloned bacteria or viruses that contains at least one copy of every DNA sequence in an organism.

Gills The gas exchange surface of a fish, where oxygen and carbon dioxide are exchanged between the blood and the surrounding water.

Globular proteins Soluble proteins with complex three-dimensional shapes. They usually have biochemical roles, for example, as enzymes.

Glucose A six-carbon monosaccharide with the molecular formula $C_6H_{12}O_6$.

Gluten A protein found in wheat, rye and some cereals.

Glycerol An organic compound which combines with fatty acids to form a lipid.

Glycogen The polysaccharide storage molecule in humans and other mammals. It is made up of many glucose monomers joined together.

Glycolipid Lipid with attached carbohydrate.

Glycoprotein Protein with attached carbohydrate.

Golgi body Stack of flattened membrane-bound sacs in which proteins are processed and packaged for export out of the cell in secretory vesicles.

Grafting A method of plant propagation in which the shoot of one plant is joined to the root of another.

Granum (plural grana) A series of stacked membranes found in chloroplasts, containing chlorophyll and other pigments.

Guanine One of the four bases in the nucleotides of DNA and RNA.

Guard cell One of a pair of cells that surround a stoma.

Gut The alimentary canal.

Haem An iron-containing molecule found in haemoglobin that allows oxygen to be transported.

Haemoglobin A molecule found in red blood cells involved in the transport of oxygen and carbon dioxide.

Halophyte Plant adapted to live in salty conditions.

Haploid A haploid nucleus has only a single set of chromosomes, one from each homologous pair.

Haploid number The number of chromosomes found in the nucleus of a haploid cell (*n*).

Hemicellulose A complex carbohydrate that is a major component of primary cell walls in plants.

Hinge cell Epidermal leaf cell that causes the leaf to roll and unroll.

Hip dysplasia A genetic disorder in dogs in which the hip joints are abnormal.

Histamine A chemical released by cells in response to some antigens. Histamine binds to receptors on other cells, leading to inflammation.

Homogenate Liquid containing cell contents, produced when cells are homogenised.

Homogeniser A blender used to break open cells.

Homologous chromosome One of a pair of chromosomes with the same sequence of genes in a diploid nucleus.

Human Genome Project (HUGO) An international programme to work out the DNA sequence of human DNA.

Hydrocarbon chain A chain of carbon atoms covalently bonded together, with each carbon also bonded to hydrogen atoms.

Hydrogen bonds Bonds that form between hydrogen atoms that are attached to oxygen or nitrogen atoms, and oxygen or nitrogen atoms elsewhere in the same molecule or an adjacent molecule.

Hydrolysis A reaction that breaks a bond, adding a molecule of water. Hydrolysis is the opposite of condensation.

Hydrophilic Having a tendency to associate with (polar) water molecules (water-loving).

Hydrophobic Having a tendency to associate with non-polar molecules (such as each other) and not with water molecules (water-hating).

Hydrostatic pressure Pressure in a fluid, such as the pressure exerted on blood by heart muscle contraction.

Hypertonic solution A solution that has a higher concentration of dissolved solutes (a lower concentration of water molecules) than another solution.

Hypha (plural hyphae) A strand of a fungal cell body.

Hypotonic solution A solution that has a lower concentration of dissolved solutes (a higher concentration of water molecules) than another solution.

Ileum The last part of the small intestine.

Induced fit hypothesis A theory of enzyme action in which the enzyme's active site only becomes complementary to the substrate after the substrate is bound to it.

Inhibition Preventing an enzyme–substrate complex from being formed, or slowing down its formation.

Inhibitor A substance that prevents or slows down the formation of an enzyme–substrate complex.

Inspiration Breathing in.

Intercellular fluid The fluid that bathes and nourishes the body cells.

Intercostal muscles The muscles between the ribs, which contract and relax to raise and lower the rib cage during breathing.

Internal intercostal muscles Intercostal muscles that contract to pull the rib cage inwards.

Internodal cutting Cutting taken from a plant stem between two nodes.

Interphase The first stage of the cell cycle.

Intracellular digestion Digestion that takes place inside a cell.

Invagination A depression in the cell surface membrane, that pushes in to form a vesicle during endocytosis.

Involuntary Without conscious control.

Iodine An element of the halogen group, a group of elements that also includes fluorine, chlorine and bromine. Iodine is used to test for starch.

Iodine test Test for starch; iodine turns a deep blue-black colour in the presence of starch.

Ion An atom or group of atoms that is positively or negatively charged.

Ionic bond A chemical bond between ions of opposite charge.

Isotonic solution Two solutions are isotonic if they have the same water potentials (the same concentrations of dissolved solutes).

Karyotype Picture showing the number, appearance and arrangement of the chromosomes of an individual.

Keratin A hard fibrous protein which is a major structural material of the skin, hair, nails, claws, feathers, hooves, scales and horns of animals.

Kilobase (kb) A unit used to measure the size of DNA fragments. 1 kilobase = 1000 bases.

Kilopascal (kPa) A unit of pressure used to measure the relative concentrations (partial pressures) of gases in mixtures.

Kinetic energy Movement energy.

Lactate (lactic acid) The end-product of anaerobic respiration in animals. Lactate builds up in vigorously exercising muscle, in which respiration is largely anaerobic.

Lacteal A branch of a lymph vessel that passes into a villus of the small intestine.

Lactose A disaccharide found in milk.

Lactose intolerant Describes a person who does not have enough lactase enzyme to digest the lactose normally present in the diet.

Latent heat of vaporisation The amount of heat that needs to be absorbed by a substance to change it into vapour. For water this is 2.2 MJ $kg^{-1} K^{-1}$.

Layering A method of plant propagation for woody plants in which growing stems are encouraged to produce roots.

Lenticel A pore in the bark of a woody plant that allows gas exchange.

Ligase An enzyme used in genetic engineering techniques to link sections of DNA together.

Light microscope An instrument in which light rays are passed through lenses to produce a magnified image of an object.

Lignin A complex carbohydrate molecule used to strengthen the xylem vessels of woody plants.

Lipase An enzyme that hydrolyses lipids.

Lipid A molecule made up of fatty acids attached to a glycerol molecule by condensation reactions.

Liposome A spherical phospholipid bilayer structure, which may contain protein.

Locating agent A chemical sprayed on a chromatogram to make the spots visible.

Lock and key mechanism A theory of enzyme action in which the enzyme's active site is complementary to the substrate.

Locus The position on a chromosome occupied by a gene.

Lumen The cavity inside a hollow structure such as the gut or blood vessels.

Lymph A fluid, derived from tissue fluid, which drains from the tissues into the lymph vessels.

Lymph nodes Groups of cells found along main lymph vessels throughout the body. They contain defence cells called lymphoctyes that respond to antigens by cloning and releasing antibodies, which enter the blood through the lymph system.

Lymph system The system that circulates lymph around the body.

Lymph vessel A vessel that helps to drain the tissue fluid and return it to the blood via the lymph system.

Macromolecule General name for a very large molecule.

Maltase An enzyme that hydrolyses maltose into glucose.

Maltose A disaccharide made up of two molecules of glucose.

Mass flow hypothesis An explanation of the movement of organic materials through the phloem vessels of a plant.

Mass transport system A system for moving large amounts of materials in an organism, such as the blood system.

Mast cell A cell involved in the immune response that produces histamine and causes inflammation.

Medulla oblongata The part of the brain that controls breathing and heart rate.

Medusa The free-swimming form of a marine organism such as a jellyfish, with a bell-shaped body.

Meiosis The type of cell division that produces the gametes (sex cells).

Meristem Region of undifferentiated plant tissue from which new cells arise.

Mesophyll The inside of a leaf, made up of loosely packed cells.

Messenger RNA (mRNA) A single-stranded molecule of RNA produced by the transcription of DNA.

Metabolism The sum total of all the chemical reactions in an organism.

Metaphase The phase of mitosis in which the chromatids line up at the equator.

Micropropagation Another name for tissue culture in plants.

Microvillus (plural microvilli) One of many tiny projections on a cell, which increase its surface area.

Mitochondrion (plural mitochondria) The organelle that is the site of most of a cell's ATP synthesis.

Mitosis Cell division in which all the chromosomes are copied and each daughter cell has the same number of chromosomes as the parent cell.

Molecular formula A representation using chemical symbols of the atoms contained in a molecule.

Molecule A group of atoms that are bonded together.

Monoglyceride A partially digested lipid.

Monomer A small molecule that joins in large numbers to form a large molecule called a polymer.

Monosaccharide A single sugar molecule (monomer) which can join together with other monosaccharides to form larger carbohydrate molecules.

Mucosa The inner layer of the gut wall.

Mucus A slimy substance secreted by a mucous membrane.

Mucus-secreting gland A gland that secretes mucus.

Multicellular Having many cells.

Murein A polymer of amino acids and carbohydrates, from which a bacterial cell wall is made.

Muscularis externa A thick layer of smooth muscle found in the gut wall.

Mutagen A substance or agent that increases the rate of gene mutation.

Mutation A change in the nucleotide sequence of an existing gene.

Mycelium The part of a fungus that consists of hyphae.

Myogenic Cardiac muscle is myogenic; it initiates contraction itself rather than being stimulated to contract by nerve impulses.

Net movement The overall movement of molecules from a high concentration to low concentration of the same molecule.

Nodal cutting Cutting taken from a stem just below a node.

Node Region of a stem where a leaf joins it.

Non-competitive inhibition Inhibition that happens when a molecule bonds to an enzyme at a position other than the active site, distorting the shape of the active site and so preventing the formation of enzyme–substrate complexes.

Non-competitive inhibitor A molecule that bonds to an enzyme at a position other than the active site, distorting the shape of the active site and so preventing the formation of enzyme–substrate complexes.

Non-polar Describes a molecule without an overall charge, that does not attract water.

Non-reducing sugar A sugar that gives a negative result with Benedict's test, but a positive result (an orange-red precipitate) if it is first hydrolysed using acid. Sucrose is an example of a non-reducing sugar.

Nuclear envelope (nuclear membrane) The double layer of membranes that surrounds the nucleus.

Nuclear transfer Method of animal cloning in which the nucleus of an adult cell is transferred into an egg cell from which the nucleus has been removed.

Nucleic acid A molecule made up of a sequence of nucleotides. DNA and RNA are nucleic acids.

Nucleotide The repeating unit in DNA and RNA, composed of a base, a sugar and a phosphate.

Nucleus An organelle containing the genetic information required to control the activities of the cell.

Oedema Tissue swelling caused by the build-up of fluid in the tissue.

Oesophagus First part of the gut, through which food passes from the mouth to the stomach.

Opercular cavity The space that surround the gills of fish.

Operculum The muscular tissue forming the movable outer covering of the gills in fish.

Optimum pH The pH at which the rate of reaction is at its maximum.

Optimum temperature The temperature at which the rate of reaction is at its maximum.

Organ A collection of groups of tissues that performs a specific function, for example, the heart.

Organ system A group of organs that all work together, for example, the cardiovascular system.

Organelle A membrane-bound structure in the cytosol of a cell, for example, mitochondrion.

Origin The point on a chromatogram where the mixture to be separated is placed.

Osmosis The passing of water from a region of higher water potential to a region of lower water potential through a partially permeable membrane.

Osteogenesis imperfecta A genetic condition in which children have brittle bones that are easily fractured.

Ovum The female gamete.

Oxygen debt The amount of oxygen required following exercise to remove the lactate produced by anaerobic respiration.

Oxygen dissociation curve A graph showing the relationship between the percentage saturation of haemoglobin with oxygen, and the partial pressure of oxygen.

Oxyhaemoglobin The complex formed when oxygen binds to haemoglobin.

Pacemaker A natural or artificial device for stimulating the heart muscle and determining the rate of its contractions.

Pancreatic duct A duct that links the pancreas with the duodenum.

Parenchyma Tissue made of parenchyma cells. Parenchyma cells are living, thin-walled cells which are the most common cell type in plants.

Parent cell A cell that divides to give rise to daughter cells.

Partial pressure A measure of the concentration of a gas, either in solution or in a mixture of gases.

Partially permeable membrane A membrane that allows some molecules to pass through but not others.

Passive process A process that does not use energy from ATP.

Pellet A solid sediment resulting when a suspension is spun in a centrifuge; it contains the denser components of the suspension.

Pentose A five-carbon sugar.

Pepsin A protease enzyme that acts in the stomach.

Peptide A molecule made by joining at least two amino acid molecules together by a condensation reaction.

Peptide bond The bond between amino acids in peptides and proteins, formed by a condensation reaction.

Percentage saturation The relative proportion of the total blood haemoglobin that is combined with oxygen.

Pericycle Tissue from the root of a plant, which is found between the phloem and the endodermis.

Peristalsis Co-ordinated waves of contraction and relaxation of the smooth muscle making up the gut wall, which propel the gut contents along the digestive tract.

Phenylketonuria A genetic disorder in which the enzyme that converts the amino acid phenylalanine to tyrosine is faulty.

Phloem A plant tissue involved in the transport of ions and organic substances.

Phosphate An inorganic group containing phosphorus and oxygen, present in many biological molecules including ATP, ADP and nucleic acids.

Phospholipid Molecule that makes up the cell membrane bilayer, consisting of glycerol, a phosphate group and two fatty acids, joined together by condensation reactions.

Photosynthesis A process carried out by green plants that converts carbon dioxide and water to carbohydrate and oxygen, using energy from sunlight.

Pinocytosis Endocytosis of liquid.

Pit A recess or cavity in a cell wall, where the secondary cell wall does not form.

Plasma The liquid part of blood, made up of water and dissolved solutes.

Plasmid A small, circular piece of DNA found in the cytoplasm of some bacteria.

Plasmodesma (plural plasmodesmata) A minute strand of cytoplasm passing through a plant cell wall, which connects the living parts of adjacent cells.

Pneumatophore An extension of the root system of some plants growing in swamp habitats. Pneumatophores grow upwards out of the water to obtain oxygen from the air.

Point mutation A change in the nucleotide sequence of DNA affecting only one or two nucleotides.

Polar molecule A molecule with charged areas, which attracts water.

Polymer A large molecule made up of many smaller molecules or monomers joined together.

Polymerase chain reaction (PCR) A method of increasing the quantity of a specific DNA fragment by reactions involving many cycles of DNA synthesis.

Polynucleotide strand A polymer of nucleotide monomers.

Polyp Immobile tube-shaped form in the life cycle of sea anemones and other animals.

Polypeptide A polymer of amino acids joined together by peptide bonds.

Polysaccharide A polymer of monosaccharides joined together by glycosidic bonds.

Polysome Several ribosomes synthesising protein on the same mRNA molecule at the same time.

Pore A gap or space in a structure.

Potometer Apparatus used to measure the uptake of water by the cut-off shoot of a plant.

Pressure receptor A cluster of sensory cells that detects changes in pressure. Pressure receptors present in the walls of the aorta and carotid arteries detect changes in blood pressure.

Primary cell wall The cell wall laid down when a cell is produced by cell division.

Primary structure The sequence of amino acids in a polypeptide chain.

Primers Short pieces of RNA used by DNA polymerase enzymes to start the synthesis of DNA.

Proboscis Tubular feeding organ of certain kinds of insect.

Product The substance produced at the end of a reaction.

Prokaryote An organism whose nucleic acid molecules are not contained inside a nuclear membrane.

Prokaryotic cell An cell in which the nucleic acid molecules are not contained inside a nuclear membrane.

Prop root Root arising from the stem of a plant above soil level, which helps to support the plant.

Prophase The first phase in mitosis, in which chromosomes contract and each becomes visible as two chromatids.

Prosthetic group A type of coenzyme that is tightly bound to an enzyme by covalent bonds.

Protease A protein-digesting enzyme.

Protein A polymer made up of amino acids. Proteins contain the elements carbon, hydrogen, oxygen, nitrogen and sometimes sulphur.

Protein pump A protein that uses energy from ATP to transfer molecules of a specific type across cell surface membranes in active transport.

Protein synthesis In protein synthesis, DNA is used as a template to make mRNA in a process called transcription. The mRNA is then used by the cell to direct the synthesis of proteins in the process of translation. Protein synthesis takes place on the ribosomes.

Proteolytic A term describing the ability of a substance (for example, an enzyme) to break down proteins and peptides to smaller peptides and amino acids.

Psychrophile A 'cold-loving' organism that can grow at 0 °C or below.

Pulmonary A term used to describe features associated with the lungs.

Pulmonary artery A blood vessel into which blood is pumped from the right ventricle of the heart, leading to the lungs.

Pulmonary vein A blood vessel in which blood from the lungs returns to the heart.

Pulse The rhythmic stretching of artery walls due to blood surges caused by the heartbeat.

Purine A nitrogenous base with a double ring structure, such as adenine or guanine. It is a component of nucleic acids.

Purkyne fibres Fibres in the walls of the ventricles of the heart, involved in the control of the heartbeat.

Pyrimidine A nitrogenous base with a single ring structure, such as thymine or adenine. It is a component of nucleic acids.

R group Amino acids have the same general formula. The group of atoms (the side chain) that is different for each amino acid is called the R group.

Rate of reaction A measure of how quickly substrate is converted to product.

Receptor A structure that detects a stimulus and converts it to another form such as a nerve impulse.

Receptor molecule A particular protein molecule within a membrane to which a specific molecule such as a hormone or antigen can bind.

Recipient In genetic engineering, the organism into which a foreign gene is inserted.

Recombinant DNA DNA formed by joining two DNA fragments from different organisms.

Red blood cells Cells in the blood that contain haemoglobin but no nucleus, used for transporting oxygen and carbon dioxide.

Reducing sugar Reducing sugars give a positive result (an orange-red precipitate) in Benedict's test. The colour change occurs because soluble copper sulphate is reduced to insoluble copper oxide. All monosaccharides are reducing sugars, and so are some disaccharides such as maltose.

Replica plating A method of transferring bacteria from one growth medium to another without changing the relative positions of the colonies.

Resolution The ability of a microscope to show two objects that are close together as separate objects.

Respiration A series of reactions in which energy is transferred from organic compounds, such as carbohydrates, to the temporary energy storage molecule ATP.

Respiratory centre The control centre in the brain that controls the rate and depth of breathing.

Respiratory surface Site at which oxygen passes into blood or cells, and carbon dioxide passes out of blood or cells.

Response A change caused by a stimulus.

Restriction endonuclease An enzyme used in genetic engineering to cut DNA molecules at specific points.

Restriction site A specific sequence in double-stranded DNA that is cut by an endonuclease enzyme.

R_f value (relative front value) A value used to identify substances on a chromatogram. It is found by dividing the distance moved by the centre of the spot by the distance moved by the solvent.

Ribonucleic acid (RNA) The single-stranded nucleic acid involved in protein synthesis.

Ribose A pentose sugar present in the nucleotides that make up RNA.

Ribosome Particle composed of RNA and protein; the site of protein synthesis.

Ringing Removing a strip of tissue including the phloem from the stem of a plant.

Root cap A thimble-like mass of cells covering and protecting the growing tip of a root.

Root hair Tubular outgrowth of epidermal cells of the root in the zone of maturation.

Root pressure The pressure built up in roots as the result of osmosis. It can cause dripping (guttation) of water from leaves and exudation from cut stumps.

Rootstock Root of a plant to which the scion (shoot) is joined during grafting.

Rough endoplasmic reticulum (RER) Endoplasmic reticulum encrusted with ribosomes, which is concerned with protein synthesis and transport.

Runner Stem that grows along the surface of the soil and forms new plants by asexual reproduction.

Saliva A secretion produced by the salivary glands, which contains amylase.

Saprophyte An organism that feeds by digesting food outside its body, and then absorbing the products of digestion.

Saturated fatty acid A fatty acid in which all the carbon atoms in the carbon chain are joined to each other by single bonds.

Scanning electron microscope Electron microscope that views the surface of a specimen, giving a three-dimensional image.

Scion Shoot of a plant which is joined to the rootstock during grafting.

Scurvy A disease characterised by general debility of the body, tenderness of the gums, bad breath, swellings under the skin and pains in the limbs. It results from a deficiency of vitamin C in the diet.

Second growth phase (G2) The third part of interphase, following the synthesis phase.

Secondary cell wall Layers added to the primary cell wall, laid down as cells mature.

Secondary structure Regular repeating structure within a polypeptide chain. There are two main types: the alpha helix and the beta-pleated sheet.

Secretion Release of a substance such as an enzyme from a cell by exocytosis.

Section Thin slice of material to be viewed under a microscope.

Sediment A solid pellet resulting when a suspension is spun in a centrifuge; it contains the denser part of the mixture.

Self-antigen Membrane proteins and glycoproteins that enable the defence system to recognise body cells.

Semi-conservative replication The process in which one strand of DNA is preserved during the replication of DNA, with a new strand being formed alongside it.

Semilunar valve A valve consisting of three pockets, found in veins and in the arteries leaving the heart.

Septum A wall between two parts of a structure.

Sequencing Working out the order of nucleotide bases in DNA.

Sex chromosome One of the X or Y chromosomes carrying the genetic information that determines whether an individual is male or female.

Sexual reproduction The production of a new individual from the fusing of two gametes.

Sieve plate Part of the end wall of a sieve tube in plant phloem. It has holes through which substances may pass as they are transported through the plant.

Sieve tube A long, slender cell with tapering ends. It is concerned with the long-distance transport of food substances in the phloem within the plant.

Simple diffusion The movement of a substance from an area where it has a higher concentration to an area where it has a lower concentration.

Sink The part of a plant that removes a particular product from circulation, usually for storage.

Sinoatrial node (SA node) A group of specialised cardiac muscle cells in the wall of the right atrium of the heart, which acts as a pacemaker.

Size markers Fragments of DNA of known size used during electrophoresis.

Small intestine Middle section of the gut, where most digestion and absorption takes place.

Smooth endoplasmic reticulum (SER) Endoplasmic reticulum that is concerned with such functions as steroid metabolism.

Smooth muscle The type of muscle that contracts to cause peristalsis in the gut and to change the diameter of blood vessels.

Solvent A substance, usually a liquid, that is used for dissolving other compounds.

Solvent front On a paper or thin-layer chromatogram, this is the point reached by the solvent at the end of the process.

Source The part of a plant that manufactures a particular product.

Specific Enzymes are specific; they catalyse only one reaction or one group of reactions.

Specific heat capacity The amount of heat required to raise the temperature of a substance by 1 K. The specific heat capacity of water is 4184 J kg^{-1} K^{-1}.

Sperm The male gamete.

Spindle An array of protein fibres present in a dividing cell, which joins the chromosomes on the equator to the poles, and is involved in separating the chromosomes during cell division.

Sporangium (plural sporangia) Structure that produces the spores in a fungus.

Sporophyte The spore-producing form of a plant.

Starch A polysaccharide composed of many glucose monomers linked together by glycosidic bonds.

Sticky end A single-stranded section of DNA left at the ends of a double-stranded DNA fragment that has been cut by an endonuclease enzyme.

Stimulus Any factor that cause a specific response.

Stoma (plural stomata) A hole in a leaf, which allows gaseous exchange with the atmosphere.

Stomach Muscular, bag-like organ where food is broken down into a soup-like mixture called chyme.

Stop codon A sequence of three nucleotides in messenger RNA that does not code for an amino acid, but signals the end of the polypeptide chain.

Storage molecule Storage molecules are usually polymers which are insoluble. Their purpose is to act as an energy store. An example of a storage molecule is starch, which can be hydrolysed to glucose. Glucose is then used as a respiratory substrate.

Storage organ An organ such as a stem or root in a perennial plant that stores food during the winter. Storage organs may be involved in asexual reproduction.

Stroma The ground substance in certain organelles, for example, a chloroplast. It contains enzymes and other chemicals.

Structural formula A representation of the atoms and bonds in a molecule that shows the order in which the atoms are connected together as well as all the bonds.

Structural molecule A molecule that forms part of the structure of a cell, such as cellulose in a plant cell wall or keratin in human hair.

Suberin A waxy chemical that acts as a waterproofer in plant cell walls.

Substrate The substance that an enzyme helps to react, in order to form the product.

Submucosa The layer in the gut wall below the mucosa.

Substitution A change in the nucleotide sequence of DNA, in which one nucleotide is replaced by another.

Sucrose A disaccharide made up of a molecule of glucose and a molecule of fructose joined together by a glycosidic bond.

Supernatant The liquid that remains above the pellet when a suspension is spun in a centrifuge.

Surface area The area of the outer covering of a cell, tissue, organ or organism.

Surface area to volume ratio The surface area of an organism divided by its volume.

Surface tension The force tending to draw liquids into the smallest possible volume, creating a 'skin' at the surface.

Symplast pathway A pathway for water through plants which passes through the cytoplasm.

Synthesis phase The second stage of interphase, when DNA is replicated.

Systemic A word meaning 'body'; the systemic circulation supplies the body systems with blood.

Systole The period of contraction of the atria and ventricles during the cardiac cycle.

Ti plasmid Tumour-inducing plasmid found in the cytoplasm of the bacterium *Agrobacterium*, used by genetic engineers to transfer DNA into plant cells.

Telophase The last phase of mitosis in which the nuclear membrane reforms around the two nuclei.

Tension A pulling force.

Terminators Modified nucleotides used in sequencing, that stop DNA synthesis.

Tertiary structure The overall 3D shape unique to a particular polypeptide chain, which is held together by hydrogen bonds, ionic bonds and sulphur bonds.

Thalassaemia A genetic disorder in which normal haemoglobin cannot be produced in red blood cells.

Thermophile A 'heat-loving' organism that can grow at temperatures above 45 °C.

Thoracic cavity The upper body space that contains the lungs and heart.

Thorax The upper part of the main body.

Thylakoid A membrane found inside chloroplasts that holds the chemicals needed for some of the reactions of photosynthesis.

Thymine One of the four bases in the nucleotides of DNA.

Tissue A group of similar cells that have a common function.

Tissue culture A method of vegetative reproduction used to clone plants.

Tissue fluid A fluid derived from blood plasma, which acts as an intermediary between blood and tissue cells.

Totipotent A cell that has the capacity to go through all the stages of development is totipotent.

Trachea The hollow tube leading from the larynx to the lungs.

Transcription The process in which the genetic code in DNA is copied to produce mRNA.

Transfer cell Specialised parenchyma cell with wall ingrowths that increase the surface area of the cell surface membrane. Transfer cells are thought to be important in the short-distance transfer of solutes.

Transfer RNA (tRNA) Small RNA molecule involved in protein synthesis.

Transgenic organism An organism that has been genetically engineered and contains a gene from a different organism.

Translation The process in which amino acids are joined together to make a polypeptide chain, using the mRNA code.

Translocation The transport of dissolved sugars and other organic solutes though a plant.

Transmission electron microscope Electron microscope that views specimens in thin sections.

Transpiration The evaporation of water vapour from the surface of a plant.

Triglyceride A lipid molecule produced by joining three fatty acids to one glycerol molecule by condensation reactions.

Triplet code A series of three bases on a strand of mRNA coding for an amino acid. The triplet code on the mRNA is complementary to the code in the DNA.

Tumour A swelling caused by the abnormal growth of cells without a useful function.

Turgid A cell that is full of water is turgid.

Turgor pressure The force exerted on the cell wall by the cell surface membrane of a plant cell due to the liquid in the cell vacuole.

Two-way chromatography A method for separating substances that have not been separated by one-way chromatography. The chromatogram is run conventionally, then it is rotated through 90° and run again, using a different solvent this time.

Ultrafiltration The movement of small molecules out through blood capillary walls as a result of hydrostatic pressure.

Ultrastructure The detailed structure of a cell, showing the organelles seen under an electron microscope.

Unicellular Having only one cell.

Unidirectional In or from one direction.

Unsaturated fatty acid A fatty acid in which some of the carbon atoms in the carbon chain are joined together by double bonds.

Uracil One of the four bases of the nucleotides of RNA.

Valve Structure found in veins and the heart that keeps blood flowing in one direction.

Variation Genetic differences between individuals of a population.

Vascular bundle A strand of plant tissue containing primary xylem and primary phloem.

Vasoconstriction Narrowing of blood vessels.

Vasodilation Widening of blood vessels.

Vector A plasmid or virus used to carry DNA from one organism into a cell of another organism.

Vegetative reproduction Asexual reproduction in a plant.

Vein A blood vessel that returns blood to the heart.

Ventilation The movement of air or water over a respiratory surface.

Ventricle A lower chamber of the human heart; ventricles are relatively thick-walled.

Venule A blood vessel that joins other venules to form veins.

Vesicles Membrane-bound pockets inside cells; vesicles contain substances such as enzymes or other secretions.

Vessels The water-conducting cells of plants, or any tubular system within an organism.

Villus (plural villi) One of the finger-like projections of the small intestine.

Volume The amount of space occupied by an object, such as a cell, tissue, organ or organism.

Water potential A measure of the ability of water molecules to move.

Water potential gradient A difference in water potential between two regions.

Xerophyte A plant adapted to living in very dry conditions.

Xylem A plant tissue mainly involved with the transport of water.

Index